KEY
A. Camp for the inmates
a. "The Small Camp"
B. Command Post Area
C. SS barracks
D. Military garages
E. Construction yard
F. Gustoff Works—the Mibau Factory
G. Buchenwald Railroad Station
H. Quarters for SS Leaders
I. German Equipment Works (DAW)
J. "Small Woods"
K. Stone quarry ramp
1. Main Gate with quarters for reporting officer
2. Political department
3. Kitchen and storehouse
4. Coal bunker
5. Laundry & bath
6. Storeroom for personal property
7. Disinfection
8. The Goethe Tree
9. Location of "horse"
10. Pathology
11. Camp for Soviet POWs

13. Crematorium
14. Movie theater
15. Brothel
16. Infir...
17. Pigs
18. Rab...
19. Pou...
20. Clea...
21. Hor...
22. Bur...
23. Wea...
24. SS...
25. Cor...
26. Adj...
27. SS Troop Staff Office
28. SS Leader Canteen
29. Main Guardhouse
30. Post Office

31. Pond for fire-fighting
32. Water tower
33. Shooting ranges

☐ Wooden blocks
☐ Stone blocks
- - - - - Chain of 58 guard posts, some of them armed with machine guns.

BLOCK 26:
SABOTAGE AT BUCHENWALD

BLOCK 26: SABOTAGE AT BUCHENWALD

|||||||||||||||||||||||||||||||||||||||| PIERRE JULITTE

TRANSLATED FROM THE FRENCH BY FRANCIS PRICE

PREFACE BY JOSEPH KESSEL

DOUBLEDAY & COMPANY, INC., GARDEN CITY, NEW YORK, 1971

This book was published in the original
French edition under the title L'ARBRE DE GOETHE
by Presses de la Cité in 1965.

Library of Congress Catalog Card Number 68–10580
Translation Copyright © 1971 by Doubleday & Company, Inc.
All Rights Reserved
Printed in the United States of America

To my interned or deported comrades
of all nationalities who died on August 24, 1944,
during the bombing of the Mibau factory.

P.J.

FOREWORD

In his book, *Der S. S. Staat,** my fellow deportee Eugen
Kogon wrote:

*The majority of the camps had their own songs which were
composed by prisoners, just for themselves. Among these songs,
there were some which became famous, such as* "The Soldiers
of the Swamp":

> As far as our eye can see
> There is only plain and marsh.
> No comforting song of bird,
> Nothing but naked oak.
> We are soldiers of the swamp,
> Marching with our shovels
> In the swamp. . . .

* A French edition of this remarkable study of the Nazi concentration
camps was published in France in 1947 under the title *L'Enfer Organise,*
and in the United States as *Theory and Practice of Hell.*

At early dawn the columns of men
Move to their work in the swamp,
We dig beneath a fevered sky
But we dream of the lands of home.
We are soldiers of the swamp,
Marching with our shovels
In the swamp. . . .

The sentries walk up and down,
But none of us may pass.
Life is the cost of flight,
And our citadel is strong.
We are soldiers of the swamp,
Marching with our shovels
In the swamp. . . .

But we never complain.
The winter one day will end
One day we will say with joy:
Our homes are free!
And then the soldiers of the swamp
Will leave their shovels where they fall
In the swamp. . . .

The story I have tried to tell is one of men who lived and fought, with fear gripping their bellies, in a swamp. They were men from every corner of Europe, men of every background and condition, who had been herded together by the Nazis and then left to rot and die. Instead, they decided to fight. And they fought, with no plan of battle other than that dictated by faith in one another—faith they had found while groping in the blackness that separated them from the world.

It is, from the first word to the last, a true story. I have, however, used fictitious names for the characters. The trials that we endured together a quarter of a century ago have made me love, rather than glorify, those who went out so courageously to battle—and understand, rather than blame, those who chose to remain behind.

PREFACE

There have been many books published on the French Resistance. And many on the concentration camps.

Too many, some people say.

I am not of this opinion. It seems to me that these two subjects provide an inexhaustible amount of material. Their interest, their importance, only increase with the passage of time. Eyewitnesses grow old and disappear. Memory sleeps. Generations come to maturity having known nothing of these torments, nothing of these exploits. And yet, the middle years of our century have been marked by their evil and their magnificence. Those who have had the good fortune to pass through this fire and hell are welcomed when they contribute their stones to the great pyramid of misery and audacity, the memory of which will surely stand the test of time.

Not all these books, certainly, are masterpieces. Far from it. But so long as the account is simple and sincere, it cannot fail to teach and move us. The focus, the facts, change in accordance with the sensitivity, humor, intelligence, and profession of the author. And, from his experience, each one of us extracts at least a new detail, a fresh view of suffering, of courage, or of horror.

Pierre Julitte's book, however, is far from being simply a collection of memories, a day-by-day chronicle. One rarely comes across a testimonial of such quality, of such intensity. And the astounding adventure it reveals to the reader has, to my knowledge, no counterpart.

The story is not confined to the Resistance or to the camps. It embraces both worlds, simultaneously; the most opposite of imaginable worlds—that of conflict, and that of passivity. They are constantly intermingled, and, in a way, they depend on each other and are supported by each other. As for the story that brings them together, it is one of the most extraordinary that one can imagine.

In the pitiful herd of humanity that peoples the concentration camp of Buchenwald—frozen, starving, beaten, doomed before their time—a few French deportees are reunited. Some of them had served in the same Resistance network. Others had shared the same profession, studied in the same schools. Their fate is the communal fate. They too bend their backs beneath the club and the whip. For them, the lack of food, the cold, illness, exhaustion, the constant fear of the gas chamber, become the primary, the obsessive preoccupation. But the horror of their situation and the determination of their executioners does not succeed completely—as it does with others—in reducing them to the status of larvae, or to the animal brutishness that would make them capable of doing anything that might help them eat a little more and suffer a little less. In the minds and hearts of the characters of this book, the spiritual fire has not been wholly extinguished. Whether this is due to the stimulus of their clandestine struggle, to their own temperaments, or to the friendship that sustains them, whatever the cause may be, beneath the ashes and the slag of physical and moral degradation, in the deepest and most secret recesses of their marrow, unknown even to themselves, a few embers smolder still.

To rekindle them, to light a new fire, may perhaps require no more than a favorable puff of wind.

Near the camp a curious factory is beginning to function. Engineers, specialists, technicians, are recruited for it from among the deportees. The most inquisitive, the best informed of these men soon begin to speculate about the nature of the work they are doing. Little by little, hypotheses take shape, isolated bits of information fall together. The factory is producing some form of secret weapon.

And then a thought that becomes an *idée fixe* takes possession of Alain, the man who is the central figure of this narrative: to sabotage, to destroy the factory.

He shares his thoughts with a few of his friends, his comrades. He enlists their support. The web grows, and cooperation, conscious or otherwise, comes from unknowns—even from a German. The impossible is conceived and will be attempted.

How will these skeletons in rags, staggering with fatigue, drained by dysentery, threatened with atrocious punishment for the slightest misdemeanor, succeed in shattering one of the most terrifying and perfectly dissimulated cogs in the Nazi war machine? It would be a betrayal of the book to reveal here the workings of the conspiracy of slaves, to uncover the risks they ran, the stratagems they used, their breathless progress toward their goal.

The single fact that is important to know before reading *Block 26* is that it does not include the smallest imagined detail, that nothing of the work derives from fiction, and that everything is true—even, so to speak, the commas.

I am well aware that the book comes to us as a novel, a form that usually presupposes a "supension of disbelief." I was the first to express surprise at this fact. But the author explained his choice. In sum, his reasons constitute a series of scruples: reservations about writing in the first person; fear of causing the action to drag by recounting every detail of the routine of days and nights; above all, the desire not to name those who, for all too apparent, too human reasons, recoiled, failed, or cracked.

To the extent that one can sense and gauge the quality of a man and a book, I became certain, after my meeting with Pierre Julitte and after reading *Block 26* that the events he has recounted, and the people who lived these events, bear the stamp of authenticity. But an impression, an intuition, no matter how strong it may be, is not sufficient in a matter of this kind.

It is for this reason that I am taking the liberty of citing an indisputable guarantor—my friend Claude de Boislambert, Grand Chancellor of the Order of the Liberation. It was he who gave me the manuscript of *Block 26.* And, in doing so, he said to me:

"Pierre Julitte served in my command, after the Liberation, when I was military governor of the Rhineland. I knew several of his comrades and his close friends at Buchenwald. I even was able to determine the fate of the astonishing German he writes about. I checked and I verified everything. And I will say this: we must believe in the unbelievable. Everything in this book happened just as he tells it."

Joseph Kessel

xii

THE CAMP

Between the sting of hunger and the frenzy of hatred,
man cannot think of the infinite.

Jean Jaurès

In working for purely material goals, we ourselves are building our prison. We are shutting ourselves up with a debased currency of our own making, one which buys nothing that makes life worthwhile.

Antoine de Saint-Exupéry, *Wind, Sand and Stars*

1.

‖‖

Snow had started to fall at the beginning of evening roll call. By now, it had wiped out the footprints along the paths, smoothed over the line of the rooftops, weighed down the branches of the pine trees beyond the electrified fence, where naked bulbs marked a line of yellow dots across the ghostly, deserted backdrop of the camp which lay crushed beneath the dark and empty sky.

A projector at the top of one of the watchtowers went on and lazily swept the night. It seemed to swallow up the shadowy patterns of the camp even as it sculpted them against the darkness. Its beam picked up a prison van that was approaching the entrance, and accompanied it as far as the gate. Snow-muffled voices momentarily broke the silence. The metallic grill clinked open, and the vehicle entered the camp.

A group of about twenty men, numb with cold, struggled

5

awkwardly with their suitcases and leaped down from the back.

Paul Genteau stretched gratefully. "This doesn't look so bad," he said.

"It can't be any worse than the prison," his neighbor replied. "At least the air is clean."

As soon as the men had been formed into a column, they were led to a building at the edge of the camp. Dazzled by the light, they squinted and shielded their eyes as they went in. The brick flooring was freshly washed and spotlessly clean. There was an odor of disinfectant everywhere. It was warm. A row of washbasins lined one entire wall. The only furniture was several long tables. An S.S. guard explained to the prisoners that they would spend the night here, and then left, locking the door behind him.

"We'll have to sleep on the ground," someone said.

Another man had turned the faucets of one of the washbasins, and remarked in surprise, "There's hot water!"

Paul Genteau opened a door and found that it led to the toilets. The other doors were barred. The windows were covered by solid shutters that he could not open.

"I wonder where we are," he said to a man he had talked with in the van.

"It looks enormous, don't you think?" the man replied. "It must be a prisoner of war camp." From the truck, they had noticed long rows of barracks, stretching off until they were finally lost from sight in the darkness.

"In any case," the other man said, "everything seems to be clean."

"That's something to be grateful for," Paul answered.

"Did you notice the little building off to the left, at the corner of the square, with a kind of square tower? That must be a chapel."

"Well, we'll see about all that tomorrow. Right now, I'm going to get cleaned up. We should try to be at least presentable when we meet our new comrades."

"Who do you think they will be?"

6

"Undoubtedly officer-prisoners. Somehow, I had imagined that we were going to be shut up in a fortress, but here we are in a camp."

"I prefer this. It's healthier, and we'll certainly have more liberty."

A few moments later everyone was busily taking advantage of the washbasins and hot water.

"Would you lend me your razor? I have no more blades."

"Would you do me a favor and trim my hair a little?"

"Hold the mirror over to the light, would you? I can't see a thing."

"God, it feels good, having hot water again."

A scent of shaving lotion and soap began to mingle with the odor of disinfectant.

Crumpled coats and trousers were taken out of the suitcases that had been returned to the men when they had left the prison in France. Their owners studied the clothes irritably and stretched them out on the tables, vainly trying to brush or pull away the creases. Those who were already washed and dressed were nibbling at hoarded provisions or smoking. In the two months in which he had known that he was going to be transferred to Germany, Paul Genteau had stinted himself on cigarettes to build up a supply. "You see," he would say to his cellmates as he sorted out items sent to him by his family, "I have to put aside everything that will keep. Anything of that kind will be a godsend to the friends we will meet over there."

Everyone settled down at last, wrapped in sweaters, lying on makeshift beds of clothing rolled up on the floor.

Genteau had difficulty getting to sleep. He was impatient to learn the details of the new existence that was being opened to him. He dreamed that he would find friends with whom, all day, every day, he could indulge himself in his favorite distraction —bridge.

The light in the barracks, which had not been turned out until two o'clock in the morning, was lit again by an S.S. guard at four o'clock. Through an interpreter, he told the men they must all be ready in thirty minutes.

At that time, they were lined up outside, in front of the building they had thought was a chapel.

Projectors were lit above the entrance to the camp, focusing on the barracks on the far side of the enormous assembly square and throwing into relief the immaculate walks that separated them. From one barracks there emerged what looked like a circus band. Clothed in crimson trousers and green vests, the musicians marched out into the square, blowing horns, beating drums and cymbals; they came to a halt near the entrance gate.

Before Paul Genteau had recovered from his astonishment, columns of men began to appear on all the paths between the barracks. Within a matter of seconds, a human sea covered the square, and its final waves were lapping at the feet of the newcomers. This mass of thirty-five thousand human beings formed itself into squares, separated by narrow passageways in which the bodies of the dead lay stark against the snow.

Genteau and his comrades, wide-eyed with disbelief, could only stare at these skeletal beings, clothed in blue rags, emaciated, exuding an odor of vermin and filth, their faces eaten away beneath a stubble of beard, their heads covered with shapeless caps or makeshift bonnets. Other men, better clothed, circled around them like snarling dogs, beating the formations into shape with bludgeons.

The new arrivals were spellbound by this nightmarish spectacle, deafened by the buzzing of thousands of indistinct murmurs. They were conscious of individual details only when they were amplified by the beams of the projectors. Here, an old man whose legs and feet were swathed in wrapping paper held together with strings. There, a man whose head was almost invisible beneath an incredibly dirty bandage. But what struck them hardest was the bone-dry thinness of all these specters. And their empty, haunted eyes.

When he was at last able to speak, Paul Genteau asked the

8

opinion of his neighbor in the line, Professor Verville, whose carefully clipped, square-cut gray beard lent him an air of infallible knowledge.

"They must be the mentally deranged," the professor said, "the depraved and the incurables of all kinds, sent here from hospitals and asylums. We always thought that the Nazi laws on euthanasia meant that they would all be killed. But it looks as if they have simply gathered them together in this camp."

"It's not possible for men to be treated this way," Paul Genteau replied, "no matter what their crimes or their faults. I wonder why we were brought here."

"We are undoubtedly just here in transit. We are going to be transferred somewhere else."

The roll call went on and on. Cold crept into the bones of the newcomers despite their warm clothing. The snow filtered into their shoes. But they were buoyed up by the feeling of their own superiority over this hideous mass. Their hands in their pockets, the collars of their coats turned up, they pounded their feet in the snow and waited impatiently for an end to this period of torture.

The loudspeakers barked, and, in a single gesture, the spectral figures lifted their caps and bonnets and then replaced them. Then, as though some invisible operator had started up a film, the formations broke up and swarmed into smaller masses in which men jostled against one another and then ran or limped away, each of them seeking his own way like a blind man in a mob. Wielding their bludgeons like machetes in the jungle, the other men opened a path for themselves through this human morass, in which, little by little, vague new groupings began to take shape.

An S.S. guard led the newcomers back to the building they had left an hour before. Smoke began to pour from the tower they had taken to be the steeple of the chapel. As they would soon learn, it was the chimney of the crematorium. At the moment, however, they were annoyed by the guard's peremptory manner.

9

Surely he must be aware that they had nothing in common with the unfortunate human refuse they had just seen.

Back in their warm, clean room, the fear of betraying their thoughts restricted any attempt at conversation. They all wore the look of men who had just taken part in a funeral and were pleased that the unpleasant task had ended. An anxiety that they might have caught colds took the place of a bereavement they did not feel. Decency forbade them to admit it, and the more charitable among them reproached themselves for having tasted, as they stood before this assemblage of mad men, dying men, the bitter, selfish pleasure of being healthy. Their flesh refused any kinship with the sufferings of the ghosts they had seen, and their impatience to be away from this accursed camp, in which they felt themselves the only members of their own species, prevented them from any display of pity. But as they rummaged in their suitcases for something to eat, a vague fear clutched at their throats and destroyed their appetites.

As warmth returned to their bodies, it dissipated their feelings of remorse. They belonged, thank God, to a world that had no connection with this camp.

Paul Genteau had recruited a team of bridge players and was discussing methods of bidding.

Off in a corner, away from the intellectuals of the group, a few young men were gossiping among themselves about their families and their jobs. They were flattered at having been placed with men of higher positions than their own. They saw in this an acknowledgment of their attainments in the Resistance, and an assurance that they would be well treated.

2.

||||||||||||||||||||||||||||||||||||||||||||||||||||||||||||||||||||||||||||||||||||||||||||||||||||||||||||||||||

The long bludgeon—a piece of heavy electric cable—whistled downward. Alain threw himself forward to escape it, but he was not fast enough. The blow caught him full across the back.

He began to run, stumbling, twisting his ankles on the uneven ground. The wooden soles, held to his feet by strips of canvas, slowed him down, and he was tempted to let the damn things fall off; but he was held back by the thought of his comrades floundering about in the mud with their feet wrapped only in paper. A stream of curses came from the *kapo** who had struck him, and he felt panic-stricken. He was out of breath, and the muscles of his legs would no longer obey him. He was going to be caught! He saw a group of men working around a cart, and ran toward them, pushed into their midst, gasping for breath, a hunted animal seeking refuge in a clump of bushes. He picked up a piece of rock from the ground and tossed it into the cart. He had already grasped a second when a blow threw him off balance. The faces of the men around him were filled with hatred. He stood motionless, looking at them, until his air of bewilderment caused them to burst into laughter. He had stumbled upon a group of the Russians, who now went back to their work, occasionally glancing malevolently at him. He bent down to pick up the rock he had dropped. The pool of mud

* There are a few words either in German or in the private language of the concentration camps, whose use the author has been unable to avoid, since no equivalents exist in other languages. A glossary of these appears at the end of this volume.

in which he was standing was stained red, and he realized he had lost one of his wooden soles. Blood was seeping through his sock, but he felt nothing; the pain that plowed a straight line across his back blocked out other suffering. He looked back at the path he had followed and saw the canvas strap of his lost sole. It would have to stay there. He could not leave the group to recover it.

The Russians jabbered among themselves, occasionally bursting into fits of laughter. The *kapo,* bludgeon raised above his head, turned suddenly in their direction, and they fled like wild boars pursued by a dog. Alain, incapable of running again, remained where he was, alone and forgotten. Then he retraced his steps and picked up the wooden sole. The end of the canvas strap that had given way was worn through. There was no hope of tacking it to the sole again. He limped over to a pile of stones and sat down heavily. Head bowed, he lifted the injured leg to rest it on his other knee and massaged his foot mechanically. He was indifferent to everything but cold, hunger, and misery.

Philippe stopped in front of him.

"Be careful," he said. "Your foot is bleeding."

Alain looked up slowly.

"Be careful. Be careful . . ."

He repeated the words several times, as if he were trying to decipher their meaning.

"I lost my fucking shoe."

"I can see that."

Philippe's voice was understanding. Another French deportee stood behind him, indifferent to what was happening. The two had set down the barrow they were carrying, a wooden gravel box with two planks nailed to its sides, as carrying poles.

Philippe turned.

"Give him your place," he ordered.

"And why should I do that?"

"Because I tell you to."

"You must be crazy."

Philippe turned to Alain. "Take his place," he said.

Alain stood up, picked up the useless wooden sole, and dropped it into the box. The other Frenchman, still standing between the carrying planks, made no move.

"All right, fuck off!" Philippe barked. "I'm the one who found this thing. Beat it!" Then, winking, at Alain: "I guess we'll have to help him along."

Alain took a step forward. The man moved off quickly, hurling obscenities over his shoulder.

"And the same to you!" Philippe called.

He bent down and lifted his end of the clumsy barrow. Alain followed suit and they walked toward a pile of broken stones surrounded by workers.

"Who's that guy?" Alain asked.

"What guy?"

"The one whose place I took."

"Oh, no one. Some fairy who was assigned to my block. He gave the clap to some Krauts. That's why he's here. I wasn't very happy dragging him around behind me. Did you see the way he acted? Drop this damn thing now and pick up your shoe. We're here."

Alain obeyed, and the workers began to shovel pieces of stone into the box.

"What are we going to do?" he asked.

"Look for a piece of wire and try to fix that dancing pump of yours."

There was a sudden clamor of voices. It came from the ramp where the Russians, just a few minutes earlier, had been loading their cart.

"Here we go again," Philippe said, "some more idiots bucking for cremation."

The rock cart was towed by a cable. Its wheels were on rails, but the rails were not properly aligned, and the cart often derailed as it moved up and down the embankment. When this happened, the loading crew, spurred on by the blows of a

13

kapo, used crowbars to set it back on its track. It was a disorderly operation, at best, and sometimes—such as now—the cart slipped backward and turned over, crushing some of the crew as it fell.

From every corner of the quarry, *kapos* came running toward the site of the accident, temporarily abandoning their *kommandos.*

The thousand of deportees laboring in the quarry stopped work. To them, the accident was a blessed interlude. Their own suffering left no room for commiseration with others. Only an old priest, arrested for hiding some English aviators who had parachuted from their disabled plane, whispered a prayer and sketched a furtive sign of the cross in the air, casting terrified glances in every direction as he did.

By now, the *kapos* were all gathered around the rock cart, shouting orders.

"Come on," Philippe murmured. "I have an idea."

The weight of the loaded barrow aggravated the pain in Alain's back, a pain that shot from his hips to the back of his neck with every step he took. Whenever his injured foot struck an uneven spot in the ground, the pain forced him to lift quickly, and his progress became a series of lurching movements.

"Come up here, in front," Philippe said. "Then you can see where you are putting your feet. No, wait a minute, it might be better if you took this wooden sole of mine."

He slipped it off, and Alain managed to work it onto his injured foot.

"That's better," Alain sighed. "If only the damned thing doesn't get infected." He glanced around, surprised at the direction Philippe was talking. "Where are we going?"

"Don't worry, you'll see in a minute."

They were walking toward a wooden shed in the center of the quarry. Just beside it, the bodies of those who had died during the day were laid out in a row. The *kapos* came here to warm themselves around a small stove, which glowed red against

14

the dark interior. Philippe peered quickly through the open door. The hut was empty.

"We'll go around to the back," he said.

He walked more slowly as they approached the line of bodies studying their feet. Alain could not take his eyes from the distorted faces, the skin stretched as taut as parchment across the cheekbones, the gaping mouths, the open, staring eyes, sunk deep in their orbits.

"There's everything we need," Philippe announced. "Just so they're not too stiff and we can get their shoes off. You take the boots from that one with the green cape. I'll get mine from the one in the striped coat. Hurry!"

A moment later, they picked up the barrow again. Now there were two pairs of galoshes lying on top of the gravel. They were covered with mud but seemed in fairly good condition. Alain stumbled like a sleepwalker, no longer even conscious of pain.

"Too bad we couldn't have taken their coats too," Philippe said. "God knows when they'll give us any. Those were old-timers here. They were outfitted like princes."

For fear that some of the Russians might see the galoshes and take them, Philippe followed a zigzag course, avoiding the groups of men who were pretending to go back to work now that the *kapos* were returning to their posts. The shovelers at the place where the barrow had been loaded were French, and when Philippe reached there he sat down on the edge of the box and pulled the galoshes on over his mudcaked stockings. Alain did the same.

"Where did you get those?" one of the deportees asked.

"In the store across the street," Philippe answered.

"Has there been a distribution?" a naïve voice inquired.

"Will you give me your old wooden soles?" asked an old man whose feet were wrapped in paper and string.

"Sure," Philippe said. He nodded to Alain and stood up again.

15

"Now, we had better take our pebbles where they're supposed to go."

With Alain following, he began picking his way on a winding path along one wall of the quarry. Approaching the road that skirted its crest, they came upon a group of deportees loading rock into a cart. The cart had a long wooden shaft from which a series of leather harnesses dangled. The men were surrounded by S.S. troops holding dogs on short leashes. When the cart was loaded, several prisoners slung the harnesses across their shoulders. One *kapo* lashed at them with his whip, cursing with every blow. The cart began to move, slowly, painfully, accompanied by a kind of chant from the men at the shaft—a repetitive, monotonous dirge. The *kapo* continued to lash at them until he was satisfied with the cadence of the chant, and then he draped the whip around his neck, turned, and rejoined the S.S. troops, that were walking along behind the cart. For a moment the laughter of the *kapos* drowned out the chant of the men.

Philippe dumped the contents of their barrow onto a pile of gravel. The bottom of the wooden box, which had been supported only by two cross strips, fell out.

"Tonight," he said, "we'll hide these planks before we take the barrow back to the tool shed. That way, no one but us will be able to use it tomorrow."

They began slowly retracing their steps. The whole excavated area of the quarry lay beneath them. The clatter of picks and the rattling of shovels mingled with the thud of rock and gravel. *Kapos* came and went. Groups of shuffling prisoners stirred up little eddies of dust, which vanished almost immediately, like those created at the bottom of a quiet pool by the passage of a fish. On the upper slopes of the quarry, men moved about their work especially slowly. They were safe up there. The S.S. and the *kapos* rarely ventured so high; when they did, their approach could be seen from afar. The Russians and the Poles reserved this privileged work site for themselves. Just the day

16

before, they had beaten to death a Frenchman who tried to join their ranks. His corpse had been added to the row of those that were carried back to the camp every evening.

Alain, following Philippe, watched the movement of Philippe's shoulders. Once again he was struck by the thought that this adult Philippe was a very different person from the friend he had known in school. They had lived almost next door to each other and had met each morning and walked to school together. They had spent their Thursday holidays and their Sundays together, sharing their pleasures and their chores. In later years, they had gone out with the same girls. They had been as closely linked as two children, and two adolescents, could be. But when their secondary studies were finished, their paths had separated. Philippe had gone on first to the École Polytechnique, and then to the architectural division of the Beaux-Arts. His association with bohemian elements there had reinforced his natural good humor. Alain had taken his degree in electrical engineering at the École Supérieure d'Électricité, and then had left for Nantes. In the ten years since then, they had met only occasionally, and too briefly to measure the changes that had taken place in each of them. It was the Small Camp that had brought them together, and again they had formed a team. Their friendship was as solid as it had ever been. But their personalities had developed and hardened, and each of them was obscurely hurt by the fact that he no longer found, in the other, an exact reflection of himself. When they were transferred to the Big Camp, they were almost relieved that they were assigned to different blocks. The pleasure they now derived from their Sunday meetings was heightened by the dissimilarity of their ways of thinking, which provided them with material for endless debates—a pastime made all the more enjoyable by the kinship of earlier years.

The empty barrow no longer weighed on Alain's shoulders and the pain in his back had abated. But his injured foot felt hot in the canvas boot, and with every step he felt he was

17

stepping on a burning coal. He was emerging gradually from his feeling of torpor and began to wonder about what he had just done.

"You don't think—"

He hesitated, and Philippe put his unformed question into words.

"—that we should not have taken the galoshes from the dead? Is that what you wanted to say?"

"Yes," Alain confessed.

"If you're going to worry about things like that, you'll never survive in this place. Listen to me. For an act to be wrong, it has to be harmful to someone. What we did wasn't harmful to anyone, and it was profitable to us. So?"

Alain did not answer. He was too exhausted to become involved in a discussion, but he could not help thinking that Philippe's theory, carried to its logical extreme, would justify cannibalism. To dine on someone who was destined for the crematorium would obviously not be harmful to the victim, but did that make it permissible? Somewhere, surely, there was a line that must not be crossed. He would have liked to know what that line was. It was all the more necessary to be sure because personal judgment could so easily become warped by cold, hunger, and fear. The problem, Alain reflected, was to keep one's body alive without killing one's self-respect.

Life was an endless march along the rim of a dangerous precipice. And the primary thing to avoid was the dizziness that came with looking down. It was enough to make certain, with every step, of the solidity of the ground just beneath your feet. And you could never permit yourself to become distracted or upset when others faltered and fell. They could not be saved. No one was strong enough to help them. At the very most, a friend might hold out a hand for a moment, to catch you as you stumbled.

18

3.

|||||||||||||||||||||||||||||||||||||||||||||||||||||||||||||||||||||||||||||||||||||||

One of the doors of the room where the new arrivals were opened abruptly, admitting a group of men who seemed to be hospital attendants or orderlies, wearing blue and white striped jackets and trousers and wooden clogs. One of them—apparently the chief, since he was wearing a black armband—asked for an interpreter. A retired major stepped forward, pleased with this opportunity to display his knowledge of German. The wearer of the armband issued his instructions. Some string, a coat hanger, a small paper bag, and a label were to be distributed to each man. Everyone was to undress, place his clothing on the hanger, put all his valuables in the little bag, then group all of this on his suitcase, tie it up, and affix a label bearing his name.

"You can say what you like," the major remarked, "but these people are well organized."

Some of the prisoners had difficulty getting their wedding rings across the swollen joints of their fingers.

"Hurry up, hurry up," the major kept repeating. "We are undoubtedly going to be taken for a medical inspection. It wouldn't do for us to keep them waiting."

"To me," Genteau said, "it looks more like they're going to steal our property."

"Of course not, young man," the major replied. "You can see for yourself that these gentlemen are hospital attendants."

The men, now naked, were pushed into the next room, where

19

a row of electric clippers dangled from cables attached to the ceiling. Everything happened very rapidly: mustache, hair, lift your arms, get up on the stool, turn around and bend over. In a few minutes, skulls and bodies were as hairless as babes.

"Did you notice," Genteau murmured to his neighbor, "where they began and where they ended? I'm glad I didn't have a mustache!"

Professor Verville, shorn of his beard, seemed even more naked than the others. His eyes, which he raised toward the ceiling as though in search of divine assistance, betrayed how deeply his spirit had been wounded.

Rageot, a former waiter, called the major "old man"; this made the major furious.

"Don't you know who I am?" he demanded.

"Oh, excuse me, Major," Rageot said jokingly. "When you had your clothes on, we could see your Legion of Honor and imagine your insignia, but now, you know—"

"When one has the honor to serve in the Resistance," the major said icily, "one owes it to himself to respect the rules of the army. Make a note of that, my friend. In France, an officer is inseparable from his rank."

"I'll make a note of it," Rageot said. "And I'll also make a note that the same officer, in Germany, is no more the owner of the hair on his ass then anyone else."

"Anarchist," the major grumbled. He glanced around, seeking support, but met with nothing but heads that were quickly turned away, eyes that were cast down. His world was crumbling beneath him.

The men were now ordered to immerse themselves one by one, in an enormous bathtub filled with creosote. The slimy liquid was black with assorted filth. One of the pseudo-orderlies was on hand to shove beneath its surface the head of anyone who hesitated to submerge himself completely.

Beneath the shower, alternately burning and icy, the men danced a kind of grotesque ballet. The creosote that patterned their skin thinned out beneath its force, streaking the water that flowed across the cement floor with milky ribbons. Since there was no soap, there was no question of washing.

Their dripping bodies were dried in a blast of air that bit into the skin. The orderlies then reappeared and sprayed them with a liquid which shot fiery arrows in the cuts opened by the clippers. The groaning, stumbling men next were herded into an underground passage and up a staircase which led into a long room containing a row of wooden counters. They were ordered to run past the counters, catching in flight a shirt, a pair of trousers, a jacket, a cap, a pair of socks and a pair of wooden soles, hurled at them by the indifferent clerks. The professor, who was painfully trying to keep up with the rest of the group, was urged on by several angry blows from the wearer of the black armband.

"I have no underwear," someone said.

No one had any.

Since the clothing tossed to them, with no regard to size, was so ridiculous, the process of getting dressed began as a kind of game. But, as soon as they were all dressed, the truth dawned on them.

Paul Genteau glanced around at his fellow prisoners. "Well," he said, "now we know. Within a month, we won't be able to tell ourselves from those ghosts we saw this morning."

An S.S. guard appeared and began shouting in German and broken French, indicating that they should line up by fives. Their names were called, and then each was issued a triangle of red cloth stamped with a black F, and another rectangle of cloth on which was printed a number. They had to remove the trousers and jackets they had just put on, to sew on their new identifications. But this at least gave them a chance to make some exchanges and adapt the size of the clothing more closely to the size of the man.

The major lifted his shoulders resignedly. "Would it be possible

for us to take a few of the things from our suitcases?" he asked
the wearer of the black armband, very politely.

The only reply was an obscene gesture.

"By fives!" the S.S. guard screamed again.

Shivering, dragging the awkward wooden soles in the slushy,
dirty snow, the group departed for the Small Camp.

4.

||||||||||||||||||||||||||||||||||||||||||||||||||||||||||||||||||||||||||||||||||||||||||||||||

The light of dawn was picking at the snow-shrouded gloom
of the quarry.

Alain met Philippe at the tool shed. No one had been tempted
by the seemingly useless barrow. They took it and went to get
the hidden planks which formed its bottom.

"It was high time we had some galoshes," Philippe said. "Look
at those poor guys with their wooden soles. How is your foot
getting along?"

"All right," Alain replied. "It hurts a little, but it doesn't
seem to be getting infected. But my back feels like a mass of
pulp."

"What's wrong with your back?"

"Didn't I tell you? A *kapo* hit me across the back with his
stick. It was while I was getting away from him that I lost that
wooden sole."

"Yesterday was really a good day for you!"

"Yes. It's a damned good thing I met you when I did."

About noon, they found an old piece of cord and made
two long slings out of it. Whenever the barrow was empty, they

put these around their necks and slipped the carrying poles into the loops at the ends. In this way, they could walk with their hands in their pockets and warm their stiffened fingers.

"You see," Philippe said, "little by little, things will work out."

But the snow had begun to fall again, and Alain reflected that this would not help anything work out. It filtered through the collar of his jacket and the opening of his loosely fastened shirt until, half-melted, it reached his naked skin. Then little icy drops ran down to the line of his belt, chilling his stomach and abdomen.

The evening roll call on the wind-swept square promised to be a gay affair.

5.

Each day, as they carried their makeshift barrow from one end of the quarry to another, Philippe and Alain exchanged whatever scraps of information they had picked up about the camp. There were a great many *kommando* groups who worked outdoors but not in the quarry. They were erecting some kind of earthworks. The work exhausted the unfortunate men assigned to it within a matter of weeks. Some of them had very bad reputations, and the S.S. troops who guarded them were always accompanied by dogs.

Each week, some of the deportees were sent off to secondary camps in a "transport" group. Some of these deportees came back, in bad condition. Those who spent time in the salt mines were covered with ulcerous sores and died very shortly, after atrocious suffering.

It was the general opinion that a man was better off remaining in the camp than getting into one of the transport groups, no matter which group it was. The name of one of the groups—Dora—was pronounced only in whispers, as though it were an evocation of Hell. No one, however, really knew anything about Dora, since no deportee had ever returned from it. The few men claimed that the reason for this was simple: There were no survivors at Dora.

It was also true that, in some of the *kommandos* of the camp itself, the work was light and was done indoors. This was the case with the *kommando* assigned to making and repairing socks and the one assigned to tailoring. The work of these deportees consisted solely of darning, sewing, and mending. They spent their days sitting indoors, sheltered from the harshness of the weather. It was even claimed that they were served a supplementary ration of soup at noon and that they were counted for the evening roll call in their shops instead of being forced to stand for hours in the cold. But the total complement of these indoor *kommando* groups was very small. It was clear to everyone that these groups were reserved for certain privileged individuals who benefited from protection in high places. The fact that a deputy to the French National Assembly was employed in the *kommando* for socks was cited as proof of this. But one of his fellow deputies worked in the quarry, although they had belonged to the same political party and had arrived at the camp at the same time.

It was not the S.S. that regulated these assignments. The best assignments were controlled by some German Communist internees—the senior *kapos*. Philippe and Alain knew them only by sight and, obviously, had no chance of obtaining any prefer-

24

ential treatment. Since neither of them spoke German, they also had no hope of being assigned to one of the offices.

There were rumors about the opening of a factory adjoining the camp, where some of the deportees would be employed. The two men tried to determine whether there was any basis for these stories, but the information they managed to collect was contradictory. They had almost given up hope of learning the truth when Philippe met a certain Desbrosse, who claimed to be an employee of the *Arbeitsstatistik,* the bureau in charge of manpower. It seemed that, in him, Philippe and Alain had at last found someone on whom they could rely. He assured them that the factory was almost completed and that some of the deportees were going to be selected to work in it. They would be chosen from among those who had stated, when they were questioned on arrival at the camp, that they were electricians, mechanics, or engineers.

Philippe was almost sure that he had mentioned only his architectural background.

"You would have done better to say you were an engineer, even if it isn't true," Desbrosse remarked. "But there must be something that can be done about it. I'll see what I can find out."

Philippe offered him a cigarette and made an appointment to meet him the following Sunday. When he went for the appointment, with Alain, Desbrosse was waiting for them in front of his block of barracks.

"I found out what you wanted to know," he said. "There are several men who are working on the recruiting for the factory. They go over the records of all the deportees in the camp and then set up lists of specialists, category by category. One of them is a close friend of mine. If I ask him to, he'll certainly agree to do something for you. He just has to correct your record and then put your number on the list of engineers. But a favor like that should be worth something, don't you think so?"

Desbrosse pocketed the half-empty package of Gauloises that Philippe held out to him.

"You can count on me," he said.

He had already turned to go when Alain called him back.

"Will you remember my friend's number?" he asked.

"I'll write it down," Desbrosse said. He extracted a tiny stump of pencil from the hem in the sleeve of his jacket and sucked on it for a moment before writing Philippe's number on the cigarette pack.

"While you're at it," Alain said, "write mine down too and ask your friend to make sure I'm on the list of engineers. I should be; I'm a graduate of the École Supérieure d'Électricité."

"Do you have some cigarettes?" Desbrosse demanded.

"He doesn't get any packages," Philippe interrupted. "He's in the 'Night and Fog' category. You should help him get into the factory. He's an officer in the Free French Army, one of the first who followed General de Gaulle to London in 1940."

Desbrosse examined Alain suspiciously.

"Then what are you doing here?" he asked. "How come you're not in a prisoner of war camp?"

"I was arrested while I was on a mission in France," Alain said.

"What's your rank?"

"Squadron commander."

"What?"

Alain laughed. "Major, if you prefer that."

"How old are you?"

"Thirty-three."

"And you're already a major?" Desbrosse was clearly incredulous.

"That's what I said."

"Well, I guess a man gets ahead fast in the Free French Army. What did you do there? Or perhaps you'd rather not tell me. But don't worry; I won't repeat it to anyone."

"Oh, you can repeat it," Alain said. "The Gestapo already knows. At first, I was on General de Gaulle's staff—"

"Do you know him personally?"

"You can't be on the staff of a general without knowing him."

26

"Have you talked to him often?"

"Of course."

"When did you see him for the last time?"

"A year ago. Just before I left on my last mission."

"Then you were a spy?"

"When a man is working in his own country and for his own country, he doesn't call himself a spy," Alain said. "Besides, my job was primarily organization, not getting and sending back information."

Desbrosse's attitude seemed to have changed completely. "But in that case," he said, "you're a big wheel."

Alain began to laugh again. "Not here, in any case. I was assigned to the quarry."

"I can understand why you want to work somewhere else," Desbrosse said. "But why hasn't someone taken care of you before this?"

"Who do you suppose would have done it?"

"The senior *kapos*—"

"You don't think for a minute that they know anything about me, do you? To them, I'm a French deportee like all the others."

"That's true, I guess. They don't know who you are. Do you speak German?"

"No," Alain said, "but I do very well in English."

"That won't do any good here. But I'm going to see what I can do for you." He turned to Philippe, and said, "Thanks for the cigarettes. Both of you should come back to see me next Sunday, and I'll let you know what I can find out."

Philippe and Alain were at the meeting place at the appointed time.

"It's all settled," Desbrosse told them. "You are both on the list of engineers. The first batch of men for the factory is going to be selected very soon. If you can get me a few more cigarettes, I'll see to it that you're on it."

Philippe had no more. "As soon as I get some," he said, "I

promise you I'll bring you a whole pack. Tell your friend that. He can certainly extend me a little credit."

A few days later, Philippe received a package containing two packs of cigarettes. Carrying the one the block chief had not appropriated, he ran over to Desbrosse's barracks between the nightly roll call and curfew. When he could not find him, he asked another French deportee about him.

"Oh, yes!" the man said. "Desbrosse, that rat who cadged cigarettes from everyone. Well, you got here too late. He left for Dora."

"But why was he sent on one of the transports when he worked for the *Arbeitsstatistik?*" Philippe asked.

"He said he worked there, but it wasn't true. It was a trick he used to trap suckers. What he didn't talk about so often was that he was always going to see the senior *kapos.* If you want my opinion, Desbrosse was one of their informers. He must have played one of his tricks on them and they got rid of him."

As soon as they met the next morning, Philippe told Alain what he had learned.

They wondered if Desbrosse really got the information he had given them about the factory from the senior *kapos,* or whether this too was simply a part of the lies he had spread to obtain cigarettes.

That day, the barrow seemed heavier, the wind icier, the hunger more unbearable.

Night after night, Alain stole nails from the cots in his barracks. When he had enough of them, he and Philippe secured two cleats inside the wooden case of the barrow. Before taking it to be refilled, they used these to raise the bottom, reducing its capacity to almost nothing, without anything being apparent from outside. Carrying it back empty, they replaced the bottom in its normal position.

28

6.

||||||||||||||||||||||||||||||||||||||||||||||||||||||||||||||||||||||||||||||||||||||||||||||||||||||||

The Small Camp was separated from the Big Camp by a barbed-wire fence which was broken up in several places by points controlled by German internees. These Germans profited from their posts by engaging in all kinds of illicit dealings, the least important of which involved allowing the deportees to go from one camp to the other in exchange for a small bribe.

Thousands of human derelicts, judged unfit for work of any kind, lived, or rather died, in the Small Camp, in horrifying conditions. Men with one arm or one leg, men worn out with age, or incurably ill, made up the swarming population of this twentieth-century Court of Miracles. During the day, they were forced to remain outside the wooden, windowless barracks, in which they were piled one on top of another at night. The more robust among them walked around in little groups or leaned against the foundations of the buildings to shelter themselves from the wind. Those whose legs would no longer carry them simply sat on the ground in the filthy snow, their empty eyes staring at the approach of death.

On their arrival, newcomers were put in quarantine in the Small Camp. According to the S.S. command, it was for reasons of hygiene that they were not sent directly to the work blocks of the Big Camp. In the event that they were germ carriers, they might have caused the outbreak of an epidemic there. In the Small Camp, obviously, this was of no importance. Erysipelas and scarlet fever claimed innumerable lives every day, dysentery ravaged the empty bellies, and if the number of the tubercular was not large it was because their illness killed them in a matter of weeks.

At the end of the period of quarantine, deportees fit for work were transferred to the Big Camp.

In the harsh, gray light, Paul Genteau and his comrades contemplated their companions. They found them even more horrible than those they had seen a few hours earlier at the roll call, under the brutal light of the projectors. They dared not become separated from one another, and huddled together like a flock of poultry sheltering from the weather.

A shrunken old man came over to them, dragging one leg, his body painfully twisted.

"You are French," he murmured hoarsely. Then he introduced himself: Colonel de Balteuil.

The major drew himself to attention, took off his cap and gave his own name.

"I had the honor to serve under you at Metz, Colonel." Then, almost as though they were meeting casually on the street, he added, "What are you doing here?"

Genteau was annoyed by the major's manner. It's clear enough, he thought. The colonel is preparing to die, just like all the others. He could not help speaking the thought aloud to the man standing next to him, a strapping fellow bursting with health. It was difficult for Genteau to conceive that this man too might become a shattered wreck like those around them. All that he knew of him was that his name was Geoffrin, and that he had been research director at the Natural History Museum in Paris. His head, resembling that of a Roman emperor, had impressed Genteau, and during their journey from the prison he had struck up short conversations with him two or three times. Geoffrin was not distant, but neither was he talkative. In comparison with many of his comrades, who swung like a weathervane from optimism to pessimism, he gave a comforting impression of physical and moral solidity, and his natural authority was not altered in the least by the rags he wore.

"Come with me," Geoffrin now said to Genteau. "We're not going to learn anything by staying here with this flock of frightened sheep. Let's try to find out where we are."

The Frenchmen in the area were easily identifiable by the letter F printed on the red triangles sewn to their coats, and Geoffrin approached those he saw. But in spite of his easygoing manner and an apparently innate ability to lead the conversation along his own lines, he did not succeed in learning anything of great importance. The camp was called Buchenwald. It was a Hell from which there was no possibility of escape. It was questionable whether it was better to be in the Big Camp than in the Small Camp, because the prisoners in the Big Camp, even though they were better housed, were forced to work. But this was of little importance, since no one could choose his camp. Every man fit for work was either transferred to the Big Camp, at the end of the quarantine period, or sent to other camps that were dependencies of Buchenwald. Some of these were good, but some of them were bad. . . .

"This is all very vague," Geoffrin concluded as he and Genteau walked back toward the other members of their group. "Either everyone we question is an imbecile, which is hard to believe, or else we've gotten ourselves into a fine kettle of fish."

They sat down on the wooden steps of one of the barracks, in the narrow space which the constant passage of feet had cleared of snow.

A wheelbarrow, laden with fleshless, naked corpses, and pushed by men almost as skeletal as their burden, passed on its way to the crematorium. Geoffrin and Genteau stood up and removed their caps. They realized at once that they were the only ones to do so. The men who had been in this camp longer than they had, lived in too close an intimacy with death for it still to warrant, in their eyes, a salute. Professor Verville had sketched

31

the sign of the cross in the air and was promptly attacked by a group of aged Russians, who were too weak to do him any harm, and by a man wearing an armband, who cursed at him in German and struck him several times.

"Well, well," Geoffrin said as he sat down again.

A man, whose elegant bearing stood out in marked contrast to the general degradation, walked toward them. He was wearing no hat, and his hair was long and carefully combed. His face was freshly shaven, and although his jacket was made of the same striped material as that of the majority of the deportees, it had clearly been cut for him. It had the easy nonchalance of a blazer. There was a pocket on the breast, and it was almost a surprise not to see the border of a fine white handkerchief. His gray trousers were immaculate and sharply creased. Between the areas of fresh mud that stained them, the black leather of his shoes was shining.

"My old friend," he said, as he came up to Geoffrin.

"Alstein!" Geoffrin stood up quickly.

"I saw your name on the list of arrivals, just a few minutes ago and quite by chance. I am glad to see you again, although I would have preferred a meeting under other conditions. And this Verville who arrived with you, is that the professor? I know him. I might even say that he honors me with his friendship. Where is he?"

His words were tinged with a scarcely discernible Germanic accent. He took Geoffrin's arm, and they went off in search of Professor Verville.

Rageot was sucking at the stem of an empty pipe, which was one of the few things he had managed to save after his arrival at the camp. During the immersion in the creosote bath, he had succeeded in slipping it to one of his friends. In exchange for a pair of gilded cuff links he had hidden in his mouth, he had obtained from one of the German gatekeepers a kind of yellowish sawdust which had the vague odor of tobacco.

After the evening roll call, which had been held in the barracks, he had invited a few comrades to come and have a smoke outside. Sitting in the darkness, with their feet against a pile of snow, they passed the pipe around, and each man, in his turn, inhaled reverently. Suddenly, the door of the barracks opened and a man was hurled from the top of the steps, landing with a heavy thud almost at their feet. As he was trying to get up, he was beaten back to the ground by a little group of men who had come racing out of the building. They seized him by the arms and legs, lifted him high in the air, and then, on a sharp note of command from one of their number, allowed him to fall again. They repeated this operation two or three times, always holding the man so that his back and head were first to strike the ground. They made no sound, and neither did their victim. The only thing to be heard was the command of their leader, followed by a dull thud. A thin ray of light coming from around a corner of the building announced the approach of a *lagerschutz*—a camp policeman recruited from among the internees—carrying a flashlight. Before he had reached a point from which he could see them, the men were back inside the building and had closed the door behind them. The flashlight beam paused for an instant on the jerking body stretched in the dirty snow, then swept across the group of smokers, who were still too stunned to think of flight. The *lagerschutz* continued on his round, as if nothing had happened. The door opened enough to reveal a crack of light, silhouetting the heads of two or three men who peered into the darkness before running back down the steps and leaning over the dying figure. Two men seized him by the thighs and lifted him up vertically, his legs waving in the air. They lifted aside his arms, which were hanging inert, and finished the work they had begun by pounding his head against the ground,

33

as a workman does with a tamper to level the earth. Then they dropped the body and went back into the barracks.

The pipe had gone out. Rageot thrust it into his pocket and went back into the building, followed by his friends. None of them had said a word.

The corpse was picked up in the morning and took its place in the roll call with the others who had died in the night. The count was complete. It was of little importance whether it was a count of the living or of the dead.

Genteau attempted to learn the reasons for the murder.

"It's something that's just between the Russians," he was told evasively. It was clear to him that this was a subject to be avoided.

He later discovered that there was a large group of Soviet prisoners of war in the camp. They were feared and respected by their compatriots, on whom they impressed a kind of private moral order which condoned theft, and assassination of deportees of other nationalities, but which demanded a solidarity among Russians imposed by the most brutal methods. They punished harshly or "physically eliminated" all who did not respect their law.

An old man with whom Genteau was talking one day said to him, "They make up a sort of congregation of Knights Templar—Russian and Communist Templars, of course. In the primitive world of this camp, they represent the only collectivity governed by the principles of a moral philosophy, debatable from the point of view of its outward manifestations, but whose spiritual sources are nonetheless undeniable. In the confusion of laws of right and laws of might to which we are subjected, these Russian soldiers hold an important place. Their unity and discipline assure their compatriots advantages which, without them, the German internees would never permit them to obtain."

7.

||||||||||||||||||||||||||||||||||||||||||||||||||||||||||||||||||||||||||||||||||||||||||||||||||||

The news of the arrival of a small group of French Resistance members had spread slowly. When it reached Alain, he decided to visit the Small Camp on the following Sunday. Philippe had given him a cigarette, and he put half of it aside to bribe the gatekeeper.

It was easy enough to pick out the latest arrivals. They were marked by faces that were less emaciated than those of the older inhabitants, and by the relatively new wooden soles on their feet. But twenty men are not easy to find, among thousands, and Alain wandered about aimlessly for a long time. The first newcomers he saw were not French; the initials on the red triangles they wore bore witness to that. He found a man who had arrived at the Small Camp with his own group and asked whether it was true that some other Frenchmen had recently arrived. The other man knew nothing about it. And, for that matter, what difference did it make? Alain was on the point of conceding that he was right. In a crowded railway station, does a sensible man try to find friends swallowed up in a crowd that will soon be scattered by departing trains? Here, the trains had their own detours, long or short, but they all seemed to have the same destination—the crematorium. Although Alain went on with his search, it had lost its meaning. It had been scarcely six weeks since he himself had left the Small Camp, but he had already forgotten its horror. The search now obliged him to look at so many of the wretched, so many of the dying, that he wondered how he had been able to live among them. He had almost decided to abandon his quest when he noticed a silhouette that seemed vaguely familiar. The man had his back turned to him. He was wearing a cap of the familiar striped material, and he held his head slightly inclined toward his right shoulder, as though he were observing the movement of his right hand. Elbows glued against his body, his left hand in his pocket, the right seemed to be moving in rhythm to whatever he was saying; palm turned upward, the thumb and index finger forming an open V and the others curled back. His trousers were too short, leaving his ankles naked. He was walking slowly, talking with another man who was also obviously a newcomer to the camp. Alain caught up with them, passed them, and then turned around. As he had thought, they were both Frenchmen. He tried to dig from memory the features of the one he had first noticed—the long, rather angular nose; the eyes set deep in an intelligent face, underlined by a well-drawn chin. He was certain he had seen this man before.

Mentally obliterating the shapeless garments, he clothed him in a military uniform. That brought back nothing. He imagined the nose bridged with glasses, and instantly remembered. Beyond a shadow of a doubt, it was Paul Genteau, his classmate and friend at the École Supérieure d'Électricité. The name had come back to Alain almost simultaneously with the memory of the face, although he had not thought of Genteau since they had completed their studies.

He walked up to him, holding out his hand.

"You don't recognize me?" he said. "Alain Fevrier."

"Oh! Excuse me—"

"I look like hell, is that what you mean?"

"No," Genteau replied, when he had recovered from his surprise, "it was just that I didn't expect to find you here. Have you been in the Small Camp long? I hadn't seen you before."

Alain was abruptly conscious of the extent of his physical deterioration. "I'm in the Big Camp," he said.

Genteau considered this for a moment. "Where do you work?" he said at last.

"In the quarry."

"Is it as bad as they say?"

"Yes, but I've worked out a pretty good deal."

Somehow, the spark of student friendship had not rekindled. "This is Geoffrin," Genteau said awkwardly, "the research director at the Natural History Museum."

The three men began walking together. Alain did not dare ask his companions the reasons for their arrest, and they did not bring up the subject. The conversation bogged down in commonplace observations about the life of the camp and its inmates. Alain explained the meaning of the colors of the cloth triangles that marked the categories of German internees. The "reds" were political prisoners, most of them Communists. The "greens" were common law criminals. The "blacks" covered a wide range of antisocial types considered detrimental to the war effort. The "purples" were conscientious objectors. And lastly, the "pinks" were homosexuals.

"What surprises me," Geoffrin said, "is that, aside from the roll calls, when they show up for a few minutes, we never see the S.S."

"Do you really miss them?" Alain said jokingly.

"No, of course not, but is it the same way in the Big Camp?"

"In the camp itself, yes. Only the *kommandos* that work outside have S.S. guards. The whole administration of the camp is run by German Communist internees, and they wear black armbands."

Geoffrin nodded. "At first we thought that they were all in mourning."

"If so," Alain said grimly, "it must be for their victims."

The conversation seemed on the point of dying altogether, and rather than let this happen Alain allowed himself to be carried away by his natural tendency toward didactics.

"The *Lagerälteste* and his assistants have supreme authority

37

in the camp," he said. "They are directly responsible to the S.S. command, and there are two distinct departments within the camp, responsible to them—the administrative department and the labor department. The first includes branches such as the *Arbeitsstatistik,* responsible for all assignments, supply, kitchens, clothing, the interior police and firemen, the block chiefs and their assistants, the *stubendienst.* The second includes all the *kapos,* who are the chiefs of the *kommando* groups."

"The way we are treated by these so-called comrades is unbelievable," Geoffrin burst out.

"What do you expect?" Alain said. "They are just human beings, after all; or perhaps I should say they are just Germans, after all. They might have been in the S.S. themselves—"

"No," Genteau interrupted. "That they could not have been. Their ideology made it impossible."

"On the contrary," Alain said, "it predisposed them to think of concentration camps as a normal instrument of government. Don't forget that the camps first flourished in Russia. Do you think that it was difficult to recruit guards for them? Stalinism and Hitlerism are identical in their views on one point—the choice of the means of pressure."

"Very well," Genteau said. "I'll accept your point of view about that. But it does not explain the systematic use of brutality."

"Genteau," Alain said mildly, "would you accept appointment to an administrative post in the camp?"

"Certainly not."

"Good. Then that's all there is to it."

"What do you mean?"

"To accept such a job, you would automatically have to subscribe to the system."

"What system?"

"The idea of physical punishment as the only means of command. To subscribe to that—well, to subscribe to that, you would have to have a taste for brutality. From there, it is only a step to the confusion of duty and pleasure. Add to that the fact that

38

the camp officials make up a caste whose members are elected by other members, and you must recognize that the system inevitably evolves in the direction of increasing brutality."

"That's exactly what's so disagreeable," Geoffrin intervened. "On the day of our arrival, I had a long discussion with a German friend—Alstein—about the possibility of some improvement in our lots. There doesn't seem to be much hope of it, unless a man is willing to accept this moral degradation."

"Your friend Alstein seems to have come out of it rather well," Genteau put in.

Geoffrin nodded. "Yes, but he is probably the only one who has succeeded at it without assuming any administrative or command post. He is a doctor's secretary. In fact, he has hopes of getting me into the laboratory where he works."

"In any case," Alain said, "the S.S. must think it's a huge joke when they watch the way the Communists treat us."

A long file of deportees was approaching one of the entrances to the Small Camp, walking two by two, each pair carrying a large can.

"I had better get back to my own building," Alain said. "It's time for the ration. I'll see you soon!"

8.

From the moment he passed through the fence separating the two camps, Alain was no longer concerned with anything but the ration. For fear of arriving too late he almost ran, and was completely out of breath when he reached his building. The soup barrels were not yet there, but the deportees' mess tins were already gone and everyone was standing in line, waiting. Once again, Alain began pondering the problem of assuring himself a portion that might actually contain some nourishment. There were always several barrels, and their contents were not of uniform consistency. On the top, there was nothing but water. The solid elements were down below. And the *stubendienst* did not all serve in the same way. Some of them plunged the ladle to the bottom of the can every time, thereby favoring the first to be served. Others simply skimmed the surface with the ladle. Chance alone decided what anyone received. Alain knew this, but he could not believe that there was not a magic formula which would resolve this game of chance in his favor. It was a thought that held an almost hypnotic power.

There was a sudden commotion around him now. The men who carried the cans had entered the building.

Alain became aware of the reality around him. He shook off the nightmare of food and sat down on the end of a bench left free by the rush toward the cans. He was suddenly conscious of the condition to which he had been lowered by the life of the camp. The problems of importance now were such things as a covering for his feet or the content of his ration. They invaded his mind as weeds invade an abandoned garden, and choked off any other form of thought. Misery left room for nothing but a search for remedies. He tried desperately to think of something that might lift him above this brutish level. Escape? There was no question of it. Even if he were to believe—and this was absurd—that he could evade the watchfulness of a *kommando* chief and break through the electrified fence, where would he go, clothed in rags, betrayed by the cut of his hair, without strength, without any reserve of food, in the middle of a deserted forest in which the dogs could track him with no difficulty. For that matter, there had never been a successful escape, and the Germans themselves were convinced of the vanity of any attempt.

The progress of military operations offered no better ground for abstract thought. News of the war reached the camp only in the form of rumors. These were so distorted by repetition that they always reflected extremes which could lead to a belief in the imminent collapse of Germany on one day and of the Allies on the next. The gulf between an excessive optimism and an excessive pessimism was too broad for exhausted minds and nerves to bridge. Since it was not possible to know anything of the war, the course of wisdom lay in attempting to forget it. And also to forget one's family, since, here too there was nothing that could be done. The deportees in the "Sea Spray" category had the right to send and to receive a single postcard each month. They could also receive packages. Alain belonged to the "Night and Fog" category and had no right either to mail or to packages. He regretted the packages keenly, although those men allowed them often received them half-empty. So that when he observed the anguish of those whose monthly message had gone astray, he was almost relieved that he had expected nothing. All the cards, whether sent or received, had to be written in German, and those that arrived were a form of torture only slightly less cruel than those that did not arrive. In the attempt to escape the vigilance of the censors, they were written in sibylline terms, and more often than not the prisoners who received them were faced with enigmas they could not resolve. By the time they had been subjected to endless interpretation, the few poor words they contained, clumsily translated at both origin and destination, assumed terrifying meanings. They gave rise to uncertainties that could never be forgotten or put aside. They stimulated desires that could never be satisfied, fears that could never be calmed, and hopes that would always remain uncertain.

The months Alain had spent in prison had revived in him a religious faith first awakened by the dangers of war. By opening a limitless field to his meditations, it had made the image of death less frightful and the time of waiting more bearable. But the constant tumult of the camp made meditation impossible, and death approached by paths too terrible for it to be considered as a consummation. It, too, was something that must be forgotten, even though it was everywhere and its shadow lay across every horizon.

Moral escape was no more possible than physical escape. The wise thing to do was to jettison family, humanity, the war and the future, and to reject a past which had become a measure of present horror. And then, adrift in a flimsy shell of solitude, it was necessary to do battle with the present, hand to hand, moment by moment.

In this confrontation, men and events lost their relative dimensions. Alain had been made aware of this in the Small Camp that very morning. In the confusion of the multitude, every man was alone. The conversation with Paul Genteau and Geoffrin had begun without any degree of warmth, and it had ended with a vague *au revoir*. Each of them had left the others to their voids and returned to his own. Basically, Alain thought, I would have done just as well not to go to the Small Camp. I should have smoked the half-cigarette I used to bribe my way in.

He stood up, watching one of the men who had finished devouring his soup. He followed him to the washrooms. When the man had rinsed out his mess tin, Alain seized it without saying a word and went to stand in line with those who were still waiting to receive their ration.

During the afternoon, Alain succeeded in finding a place near the stove. In spite of the noise around him, he went to sleep, his face buried in his arm.

It was night when he awoke. The electric bulbs, hanging by wires from the ceiling, gave off a yellowish light. Sitting across from him, two Russians were playing chess. They had traced out a board on the tabletop with chalk, and for their chessmen they were using little cubes of wood marked in pencil with Cyrillic characters.

Alain stood up and stretched. According to the clock above the door of the mess hall, it was five o'clock. It would be another hour before roll call. The air in the barracks stank. Outside, it was cold. When he glanced around him, Alain saw that there was no one here he knew. He was suddenly, overwhelmingly depressed, and decided to go off in search of Philippe.

He found him, smoking a butt in the relative privacy of the toilets.

Through a sort of tacit agreement, they had long since given up any discussion of their families or their past life; Alain, because it was contrary to the system of moral hygiene he had established for himself; Philippe, because he felt no need to talk about such things. Since the monotony of their daily existence offered little food for conversation, there was not much left to them.

Alain seized the opportunity provided by his visit to the Small Camp and told Philippe the story of his meeting with Genteau.

"I wasn't particularly close to him," he said. "In a single school year, you don't have much chance to know anyone unless you are living together, which we weren't. You know the names of the people you work with on experiments, and that's about all."

He explained, at some length, that he had remembered Paul Genteau not only because he was one of the best mathematicians in the class, but because he had had an extraordinary gift for practical jokes.

"Not idiot jokes," he specified, "but elaborately worked-out plans in which he involved his victim for days, sometimes for weeks. And it wasn't always the other students; sometimes it was the professors."

He was about to embark on an account of one of these hoaxes when Philippe, who was not at all interested in the personality of Genteau, suggested that they go back into the mess hall. They had shared the last puffs of the cigarette butt, and now it contained only a few shreds of tobacco, which Philippe stored carefully in his pocket.

"You seem very depressed today," Philippe remarked.

"I am," Alain confessed. "I feel like a blind man locked up in

43

a zoo—as incapable of defending myself as I am of making friends with the animals. Ever since I got here, I've been trying to see things clearly, to find the key, the combination that would see me through. You've been doing the same thing, but neither one of us is getting anywhere."

"Why don't you look at it another way?" Philippe said. "Say that we haven't *yet* gotten anywhere."

Alain shook his head. "It's trying to fight against something when you can't see what you're doing that I can't stand," he said. "If only there were something we could do to avoid the constant risk of being sent to Dora."

"Dora," Philippe said thoughtfully. "From what I know of the Germans, if they gave such a pretty name to a camp it must be one hell of a spot."

Alain brought the conversation back to the search for some practical way to improve their immediate condition. But they both knew how powerless they were.

"The only thing we can do," Philippe said, "the only objective we can set for ourselves, is to try to hang on until we are liberated. Set your mind to that; just put it in neutral."

"It already is," Alain said. "It has to be."

"Except when it's a matter of solving the problems that come up every day."

"Yes, I know; applying the principle that any act that isn't harmful to anyone can't be wrong. To tell you the truth, I find your principle a little too abstract."

"Are you still worried about the way we got our galoshes?"

"No," Alain lied. "I was talking in general terms."

They found a place on a bench in the mess hall.

Philippe at once set to work to defend his point of view. More than half of the French deportees were not members of the Resistance. Among the Russians, the proportion of common law criminals or of men rounded up indiscriminately by the Germans was even higher. That situation did not create a very high moral climate.

44

"Under such circumstances," Philippe argued, "we have to have some kind of manageable touchstone with which to judge their actions and our own. But I'm perfectly willing to admit that there are other criteria for judging ours."

To Philippe, however, the value of such criteria was restricted by the conditions in the camp. No one could play at being St. Martin without first having a cloak to share, and in the anarchy that surrounded them no one could do anything useful for the collectivity.

Alain conceded that he was right, but something deep inside him persisted in its revolt against this submission to circumstances. "Nevertheless," he said stubbornly, "we must retain the strength for some actions that are entirely our own."

"How do you expect us to carry out some daily good deed?" Philippe demanded. "We need all the time we have just to defend ourselves."

Alain reared back like a parade horse. As a child, nothing had irritated him more than the constant talk of doing a good deed each day. It had seemed to him an illustration of the most distorted of morals, a kind of bigotry for the use of children.

"It's not only against others that we must defend ourselves," he said, "it's against ourselves. Once a good deed is accomplished, its author thinks he can call it quits. He thinks he has bought the right to be lazy, selfish, and deceitful, just like the old maid who goes to early mass every morning and thinks that, for the rest of the day, she can do anything she pleases."

Philippe had known Alain's point of view for twenty years, and it amused him to hear Alain use the words of an adult to elaborate the same arguments he had advanced as a child.

To Alain's way of thinking, a good deed performed as a kind of duty possessed no more spiritual value than an obligatory morning mass; it was not a freely given offering, but the purchase of an inexpensive moral repose. For that matter, the good deed often consisted of giving away candy you didn't like, and receiving in exchange a delicious caramel. And in winter, the foot-

45

warmer beneath the cushioned prayer stool of the pew pervaded the skirts of bigots with its pleasant warmth.

"You see," Alain concluded, "a system of morals can't be translated into rules of procedure. Rules and regulations are dead things. Morals are living things. They are actions in an unending war we wage against ourselves, a war in which there can be no peace. It's the piece of candy you like best that should be given to a friend, and if you go to the early mass you should leave the foot-warmer at home."

"Do you realize," Philippe observed, "that what you are saying constitutes a defense of self-mortification?"

Alain shook his head. Pursuing the theme of his initial comparison, he went on to say that there was no war without wounded and dead, but that did not mean that the aim of war was the creation of victims.

"Its aim is victory, and the victims are only its instrument. Without sacrifice, or without mortification, if you prefer, there can be no meritorious action; but mortification is not sufficient to create the meritorious action."

Philippe replied that starving, exhausted, and beaten men could not be expected to possess any great aptitude for sacrifice.

"I think we have to look deeper than that to find the motive for their behavior," Alain said. "The truth is that hunger, fatigue, and the constant fear of punishment have made us lose our taste for what we always expect from sacrifice—moral satisfaction. That's the caramel we receive in exchange for the piece of candy we don't like. I was convinced that everyone, or at least all normal human beings, possessed a taste for that particular caramel. But that isn't true. Its attraction depends not only on the man but on the circumstances."

He had suddenly realized that perhaps he was wrong in setting himself up as an arbiter of the daily good deed and the early mass.

"Reduced to that form," he said, "morals are a little bit like military regulations. They don't make heroes, but they can make

46

a victorious army from a troop of more or less courage̲
Besides, it isn't because there are always cheats that the rules
the game are worthless. You just have to play it honestly."

"In any case," Philippe interrupted, "we have no candy to
give away, and we don't have to force ourselves to get up for
the early mass. We can't offer any sacrifice, because everything
we have to offer is already demanded from us."

"That didn't prevent you from helping me when I lost my
shoe the other day," Alain said. "That was certainly a gratuitous
action."

"It didn't cost me anything. It would be more praiseworthy to
share my ration with you, and I don't do that."

"That would be suicide. But when you receive a package, I
profit from it. Just a few minutes ago, you shared the last of
your cigarette with me."

After a moment's silence, in which he seemed to be asking
Philippe's pardon for having nothing to offer him, Alain told him
that on the preceding Wednesday, when the normal ration of
soup had been replaced by potatoes cooked in their skins, he
had forced himself to peel them slowly.

"And what did you do with the skins?" Philippe asked. "Keep
them for dessert?"

"No, I didn't eat them at all. And I promised myself that I
would do the same thing every time we had potatoes."

"Why?"

"To convince myself that I am not completely done for yet,
that I can still will myself to do a thing. It's a test I put myself to.
If the day comes when I can no longer prevent myself from
eating my potatoes in their skins, I will tell you. It will mean
I'm ready for the crematorium."

Philippe smiled. "I did the same thing," he said. "I peeled my
potatoes too. I wasn't sure then why I was doing it, but you've
just explained it to me. The man sitting next to me helped me,
though. He ate the skins as fast as I put them down on the table."

||||||||||||||||||||||||||||||||||||||||||||||||||||||||||||||||||||||||||||||||||||||||||||||||||

Charlie was a quiet young man who did not seem unduly disturbed by the life of the camp. When one of his comrades professed astonishment at this, he had answered, with a smile: "I had two brothers. One of them was killed in forty, and the other was shot a month before I was arrested. So I would be wrong to complain about my own fate. I'm twenty-three years old, I'm still living, and I'm going to make very sure that my parents still have one son." He used his knowledge of German to gain small advantages. When the block leader had something to say to the French prisoners, it was Charlie he called on to interpret for him. In exchange for this service, Charlie received a ration of good, thick soup from the barrel the block chief appropriated every day for himself and his assistants.

Every Sunday afternoon Charlie went down to the infirmary and gave a French lesson to a man named Jakob, a German internee who worked there. He was paid for this with a slice of the white bread reserved for patients and a bowl of vegetable soup. From time to time, he also received a slip which exempted him from work the next day, on the pretext that he had to appear for a medical checkup. But, in spite of all of his efforts, Charlie was still a member of one of the *kommandos* assigned to the quarry.

When a convoy for Dora had to be made up, it was in the quarry *kommandos* that the *Arbeitsstatistik* found the necessary men. The appearance of the recruiting team spread terror among

the deportees, and they scattered in every direction. But the S.
troops gathered them together again with bludgeons and, if necessary, with guns. They herded them into a corner of the quarry
and noted down the numbers of the healthiest among them. The
next day, these men were sent away and nothing more was ever
heard of them.

Charlie's size, his good health, and his nationality made him a
prime target for these roundups. His escape from them, until
now, had been little short of a miracle. Once, when he was on
the point of being taken, he had used a jagged piece of stone
to cut a long gash in his leg and then had limped painfully
over to the S.S., displaying the bleeding wound. He was greeted
with a laugh that echoed from one end of the quarry to the
other. For an instant, he had thought they saw through his ruse
and that he was lost. But this was not the case. The chief of the
Arbeitsstatistik was a homosexual for whom the sight of blood
brought on an hysterical orgasm of pleasure. On a similar occasion, Charlie had managed to hide the red triangle with its
telltale F and had mingled with the *kapos* in the quarry, carrying
on a conversation and apparently so unconcerned that no one
paid any attention to him. He could not, however, hide from
himself the fact that sooner or later he would be taken, unless
he succeeded in changing his *kommando*.

For a long time, he had been asking his French pupil, Jakob,
to help him. Charlie was certain that a man could not hold a
post as fruitful in all kinds of advantages as Jakob's without
having influential friends.

As soon as Charlie had swallowed his soup one Sunday, he
hastened over to the infirmary. The Sunday before, Jakob had
held out some hope that he might be able to get Charlie a post
as an interpreter. It would be a real sinecure.

As soon as Charlie arrived at the infirmary, he learned that
the *kapo* in charge of the canteen had already filled the post.
By way of consolation, Jakob now offered him the hope of
transfer to a small *kommando* which supposedly was an excellent

49

. It worked outdoors but carried out tasks far less painful and dangerous than those in the quarry. Ernst, its *kapo,* was a good fellow who did not bully his men. The most important thing was to get along with him, and Jakob had not hidden the fact that the best way to accomplish this was to offer him trifling gifts.

Ernst arrived just as they were finishing the lesson. He was large and fat, and his little, piglike eyes glittered maliciously in the round expanse of his face. His number had only three figures. Charlie noted this evidence of seniority in the camp and was astonished that a man who held it did not occupy a higher post.

Jakob brought a bowl of soup for his guest, and said, "I wanted to introduce you to my comrade. He is giving me lessons. Couldn't you take him into your *kommando?"*

The *kapo* stopped eating, wiped his mouth with the back of his hand, and looked up at Charlie, whom he had ignored until this moment.

"But he's a Frenchman."

Charlie was aware that Ernst's tone of voice could not have held more disgust if he had been a worm that had fallen into his soup.

"A Frenchman who speaks German," Charlie hastened to put in, "and can even speak it goddamned well, as you can see. If you take me on, I give you my word that you won't have to put up with any crap from me."

The *kapo* burst out laughing. "All right, all right, I understand."

He turned to Jakob, and said, "Does your professor teach you French the same way he speaks German? If so, it must be pretty funny."

"I also know how to express myself in academic German," Charlie intervened. "If you want me to, I can recite Schiller for you."

"No, no," Ernst said. "Don't bother with that. But tell me if you get packages from home. That's much more interesting."

"Yes, I do."

"Chocolate and cigarettes?"

"Yes."

"In that case, we might be able to make a deal. Show me what you have and I'll take you."

"When?"

"I'll take you when I have seen your cigarettes and your chocolate."

"But I won't have any until I get my next package."

"So neither will I. I'll be waiting. You can wait too. And don't forget that I'll have to get the authorization of the *Arbeitsstatistik* to have you transferred."

There was nothing further to discuss.

"What block are you in?" Charlie asked.

"In block 40. Now get out of here. Jakob and I have serious thing to talk about and you understand German a little too well."

On his way back to his own building, Charlie stopped at the block of the S.S. Institute of Hygiene. There, he talked to Alstein, questioning him about the degree of trust he might place in Ernst.

10.

||||||||||||||||||||||||||||||||||||||||||||||||||||||||||||||||||||||||||||||||||||||||||||||||||||

Carrying their mess tins, Paul Genteau and Geoffrin found places at a table. They rummaged in their pockets for their spoons and began to eat in silence. A Frenchman, seated across from them, spoke up cheerfully.

t's good, isn't it! It's too bad that we only have it like this
y other Sunday."

He was talking about the porridge, which today was made of
white flour and slightly sweetened. Compared to the everyday
ration, in which a few bits of potato or rutabaga floated in
lukewarm water, this was a gourmet's delight.

"Have you been here for a long time?" Genteau asked.

"I'm one of the first Frenchmen who arrived at Buchenwald,"
the man said, "and now I think I've been here longer than any
of the others. The few who were here before me are all dead,
as far as I know, or have been sent to Dora, which comes down
to the same thing. I've been here since May of last year, believe
it or not."

"And you've never left the Small Camp?"

"Oh, yes. I worked in the quarry and in the *kommandos* that
were doing the earthworks, for a year. But I was so sick at the
beginning of summer that I was admitted to the infirmary. I
wonder now how I survived. The patients there are supposed to
receive a special ration, but the orderlies use it for their black
market deals. They do the same thing with the medicines. There
was nothing left for us. A Czech doctor took a liking to me, and
when I was a little better he arranged it so that I was not sent
back to the Big Camp. It's no paradise here, but at least you
don't work. And that way, you can hang on to what strength
you have."

"Then you never succeeded in getting a good assignment?"

"What do you mean by a good assignment?"

"I don't know anything about them myself. But I was told
that some of the *kommandos* work indoors."

"Some do, that's true, but to be assigned to them you have to
have friends somewhere or be a specialist. And I don't fit in,
either way. So I'm just as happy staying right here. But you
may have better luck than I did."

"What makes you think that?"

"Because a factory is going to be opened very near here and

52

the workers will have to come from this camp, because there's no other source of manpower within ten kilometers."

"What kind of factory?"

"That I don't know, but what difference does it make? A factory is a factory, with a roof and walls. That's what's important. You'll realize it after you've worked outdoors awhile."

Another Frenchman had sat down next to them.

"Do you really believe it?" he asked, "this story about the factory?"

The first man nodded vigorously. "Of course I do."

"You make me laugh."

"I saw it being built."

"You don't even know what you saw being built."

"I tell you I saw the factory being built."

"It's not a factory. It's a new camp. They're going to move the men from the Big Camp into it, and then we'll move into their old places."

"Who told you that?"

"A guy in block 63 who knows everything. He even told me that it was going to happen very soon. The electric fences and the watchtowers have already been installed all around the buildings. So you see—"

"We're obviously not talking about the same buildings. The factory buildings are on the left, beyond the station, as you go away from the camp. They're not barracks. They're big, empty halls, with cement floors."

"The place you're talking about isn't a factory, it's an airport that's being built."

"An airport? You're crazy. The ground is on a slope."

"The halls you're talking about may be hangars. But I know that it's an airport. Everyone in the Small Camp who could stand on his feet made four trips to the quarry every day, for weeks, hauling the stones that were used for the runway."

"Not only men in the Small Camp. All the *kommandos* worked at moving stones, mine included. As if I didn't remember that! A three-kilometer detour on the way back, every night, with a load of rocks on your shoulders, and not a small load either. There were some dead men after that."

"In that case, you'd certainly remember. The ground was covered with stones, the whole length of the road. Everyone said it was for an airport."

"Yes, but it was on that stone foundation that the factory buildings were put up. I saw them being built. My *kommando* was working in the S.S. garages, just across from them. We were putting in a drainage system."

"You just didn't understand what you saw, that's all. I don't know where the new buildings are that my friend told me about, but what I do know is that they are for a new camp, to take the place of the Big Camp. The Small Camp will either be done away with or rebuilt. That much is certain."

Genteau stood up and winked at Geoffrin, indicating that he should follow him.

"None of that was very clear," he said. "Does this factory really exist, yes or no? It would certainly be interesting to know. If it does exist, it can't be more than a few hundred meters from the camp. This is at least the tenth time I've heard talk about it, but I don't know any more than I did before. It's damned annoying."

"It's not surprising that no one in the Small Camp knows anything," Geoffrin said. "The men who are here never leave the camp. We'll have to ask someone from the Big Camp."

"I should have asked Alain Fevrier about it."

"When Alstein comes to see me again, I'll find out what he knows."

11.

Rageot, the man who had managed to save his pipe, had made an excursion into the Big Camp. He was not too sure of himself at first and wandered about discreetly, his hands in his pockets, trying to listen to the conversation of the groups of men that cluttered the walks on a Sunday.

"I'm going to see what's going on over there," he had stated before he left. "I want to know what's in store for us when the quarantine is over, and I can't find out from the stupid bastards in the Small Camp. There are bound to be clues to getting along. The whole thing is to find out what they are."

After talking with several Frenchmen, however, Rageot still had learned nothing. He decided to go into one of the buildings and examine the triangles on the jackets, looking for an F.

"Who are you looking for?" someone behind him asked.

He turned around. "It may be you I'm looking for."

"Me?"

"Yes, someone with eyes and a head who can tell me something about what the hell goes on in this fucking camp. I've been here for twenty days, in quarantine, in block 61. What's going to happen when they let me out?"

The other man laughed mirthlessly. "That, my friend, isn't easy to say."

"How long have you been here?"

"Three months."

"And what have you done?"

arrested?"

give a damn about that. I mean since you got out
une."

I'm in a construction *kommando*—leveling the ground, digging
ditches, that kind of thing."

"Is it bad?"

"Look at me. Do I look like someone in a good *kommando?*"

"What's wrong with it?"

"Everything. Twelve hours a day—and that's not counting the
roll calls—out in the snow and the rain, digging ditches, with
dogs behind you every minute and the S.S. itching to let them
loose. Take a look at this."

He pulled up one of his trouser legs. An arc-shaped wound
was oozing pus and blood in the fleshy part of the calf.

"See what I mean? And that happened because I stopped
working for less than a minute."

"You should have it taken care of," Rageot said, and the
other man laughed again.

"You think they take care of a dog bite? I can see that you're
new here."

"Do you think you'll have to stay in the same *kommando?*"

"That's not up to me."

"Who decides, then?"

"I don't know. Nobody knows."

Rageot scratched his head thoughtfully. "What did you do before the war?"

"Mechanic. Automobiles. I was picked up because I did a little
body snatching of parts from the Krauts' cars. How about you?"

"I'm a waiter. I was caught trying to pick up parachuted arms."

"The Resistance?"

"Yes. But tell me, there are some people who say that mechanics
are going to work in a factory. Do you know anything about
that?"

"Sure. Nobody talks about anything else. There's a factory,
all right, but it's not for us. I know about it. For the past two

56

weeks, my *kommando* has been digging the drainage ditches for it."

"And?"

"I can tell you this. We're not the ones who'll be working there."

"What makes you so sure?"

"Simple. At one end of each hall, there's a big room with latrines and showers. Showers! Do you think they would have installed showers for us? They're for Germans. Or maybe for volunteer workers. But not for us."

"But I heard that the factory's surrounded by a fence just like the one around the camp."

"That's true."

"Then maybe it's going to be another camp."

"Not a chance. The buildings are factory buildings. But that's where you've missed the point. The fence and the watchtowers—there are watchtowers too—are a German trick. When the Allied planes see them, they'll think it's a camp. So, no danger of bombing. The Krauts are no fools. They want to be able to manufacture anything they like in there, and they don't want to be disturbed."

Rageot went back to the Small Camp. He knew now that there really was a factory, and he still thought it possible that the deportees would furnish the manpower for it.

The next day he was taken to the labor office with the other men who had been brought in at the same time as he, and when he was asked his profession he stated, without hesitation, that he was a mechanic, a toolmaker.

12.

|||||||||||||||||||||||||||||||||||||||||||||||||||||||||||||||||||||||||||||||||||||||||||||||||||||||||||

A man from the *lagerschutz* came into the barracks. He went directly to the corner occupied by the block chief, which was partially enclosed by a wooden partition, low enough so that the block chief could survey the room, even when he was sitting down. The two men talked for a moment, smoking, and then the block chief shouted an order for silence and called out a number, in German. It took a moment or two for Alain to realize the number was his. His body was bathed in a cold sweat as he walked to the block chief's corner. He had no idea what had happened or was going to happen to him. He was immensely relieved to learn that the *lagerschutz,* a Luxemburger who spoke French, was going to take him to the *kapo* of the canteen, a German Communist internee who was in charge of supplies for the camp. He had been pointed out to Alain once, and Alain had seen him several times since, always ostentatiously dressed, wearing black boots with a dazzling shine and followed by a thoroughbred Doberman, as plump and healthy in appearance as his master. The canteen *kapo* was one of the most privileged individuals in the camp, and he wanted to be sure that everyone knew it. Alain could only wonder what he wanted. The *lagerschutz* knew nothing, but his manner indicated clearly that the invitation should be considered a signal honor.

The canteen did not deserve the name. Nothing was sold or served, it was simply a warehouse for provisions. To protect the contents from pilferage, the building had no windows. What day-

58

light there was came through narrow slits in the walls, heavily barred and too high to be reached. The single door was as massive as the gate of a prison, so a smaller door had been cut into it, and this in turn was provided with a square peephole. The *lagerschutz* pulled on a weight that hung on a chain beside the door. A bell rang somewhere inside the building, followed by the barking of dogs. After a moment, the peephole opened. The *lagerschutz* spoke a few words. The head on the other side nodded, and the peephole was closed again.

"You don't just walk into the canteen," the *lagerschutz* told Alain, as if to reassure him. "He's going to make sure that they really sent for you. You can imagine that they have to be careful, with all the stuff that's inside here. What a temptation for thieves!"

They waited for some time before the door opened. Alain went inside, but the *lagerschutz* was brusquely turned away. The dogs went on barking, racing up and down behind the screen that held them back. The darkness was broken only by the yellowish light of a few naked bulbs. Alain's guide led him down a long path between piles of what seemed to be sacks of flour. He opened a door, and they entered an office that would have done credit to a prosperous commercial enterprise. Metal filing cabinets lined the walls, there was a rug on the floor, and lamps shed clear light on tables covered with files and account books. It was as though Alain had been transported into a normal world, a world of civilized men, concerned with such things as comfort and efficiency. The contrast between this and what he had seen for the past months was so brutal that he unconsciously slowed his pace, as if to prolong the pleasure. He could not help thinking how agreeable it would be to work here, and for a moment he was overcome by the hope that the *kapo* had sent for him to propose this.

He was directed into an adjoining room that was even larger than the office. It resembled both a beer hall and the living room of some newly rich bourgeois, a collector of everything that was most hideous in the "decorative arts." A half-dozen men were seated round a large table littered with glasses and bottles. The air was heavy with the odor of cigars. The *kapo* of the canteen stood up and walked over toward Alain, his hand outstretched. He spoke to him in precise English but with a heavy American accent.

"Welcome, comrade," he said. "I know that you don't speak German but that you do speak English. If it's agreeable to you, we will use that language. My guests understand it, more or less. I happen to know it because I lived for eight years in the United States, and we have all been here together for so long that I have taught it to them. It may be useful to them someday. We have to make the best of circumstances, and our confinement at least offers us the leisure to study and learn, don't you agree? That, in fact, is why I asked you to come here. But let me introduce you to my colleagues."

As the introductions went on, Alain heard one German name after another, each of them followed by the title of the *kapo* in question. The man would then get to his feet and bow slightly before extending his hand.

When the introductions were over, Alain sat down at the table, still overcome with astonishment. During the first World War, when he was still a small child, an American officer billeted in a nearby chateau had taken him one day, in his short pants, with no jacket and wearing espadrilles, to a reception given by the general staff. In his rags in this gathering of the grand *kapos*, he remembered his feelings of that earlier day.

He was surrounded by the lords of Buchenwald. They were obviously healthy, and neatly dressed. But the most noticeable thing about them was their hair. With the exception of these camp dignitaries, all the deportees were forced to submit to the clippers approximately every two months. On one occasion the clippers would shave on either side of a median line, and on the next along this line itself, so that the deportees wore either a crest of hair extending from the forehead to the back of the neck

60

or a shaved band between two shaggy zones. Alain had often thought that this was among the more refined of the many affronts to the dignity of the deportees, depriving them, even more effectively than the rags they wore, of the aspect of a normal human being. The shining, carefully tended hair of his host and of the guests was one of the symbols of their power and privilege. One of these new Samsons, who was bald, and thereby deprived of the possibility of publicly displaying his rank, had chosen to grow a thick, black beard, with no thought to the grotesque contrast between the lower part of his face and his naked, gleaming skull.

Like all the German political prisoners, the senior *kapos* wore a red triangle on their jackets. Alain noted that most of the numbers had only three figures; their owners must have arrived at the camp when it was first opened, or only shortly thereafter. The common herd of deportees considered such numbers a mark of infamy, but these men wore them as though they were decorations, neat and proper, larger than the required size. Their right sleeves were decorated with the black armband, and on the back of their jackets the cross of red paint was replaced with carefully sewn vermilion cloth. This cross was intended to make escape difficult, by calling attention to the man who wore it, but they had made of it an insignia of their supremacy.

Alain's attention was so completely absorbed by the appearance of the men around him that he almost failed to hear the opening remarks of the *kapo* of the canteen:

"We have learned that you were a member of General de Gaulle's staff, and that, at the time of your arrest, you held an important position in the French Resistance. That's why I asked you to come here. We all hope that you will agree to explain your leader's goals to us. We are not asking you to betray any secrets. We hope you might give us a picture of the Free French movement and the way it has developed."

"I'll tell you whatever I can," Alain said, "but I must confess that you've taken me by surprise. To be complete, the kind of

61

summary you're asking for requires preparation. If you'll give me a few minutes to get my thoughts in order . . ."

The *kapo* nodded agreeably. "Of course, of course. Here, have a glass of beer, and help yourself to those cigarettes. In Germany today, no matter where you are, you would find it hard to get things like that. But perhaps you would prefer a cigar?"

The beer was delicious, and as Alain inhaled deeply on a Turkish cigarette he made a swift mental calculation of the advantages he might secure for himself if he could appropriate the cigarette butts piled in the ashtray nearest him. Under the influence of alcohol, his mind leaped ahead, and as he worked out the summary, he also studied the possibility of transferring some of the butts into his pocket. Of course, he told himself, it's probably not very good manners, but under the circumstances the rules of hospitality can certainly be relaxed a little.

He took another swallow of beer and felt that he was now ready to begin his little lecture. He stood up, not with the idea of lending any greater importance to his words but because a standing position gave him a pretext for pulling the ashtray over, so that it was directly in front of him.

The other men had ceased talking as soon as he stood up.

"Anyone who wants to understand General de Gaulle's goals," he began, "should bear in mind the situation that existed on June 8, 1940, when he made his first appeal . . ."

For an hour after that, carried away by his subject and by the rapt attention of his audience, he forgot his condition. He was consumed with the desire to communicate the faith that stirred inside him. He paused only occasionally, to allow the *kapo* of the canteen to translate into German a phrase whose meaning might have escaped the other guests. Four cigarette butts and two half-consumed cigars, to say nothing of one entire cigarette, found their way into his pocket, without incident. But his strength could not stand up too long to the tension imposed on him by talking to the *kapos* and trying to steal the butts at the same time, and moreover, in the course of a year spent in prison and in this

62

camp, water had been his only drink, and he was slightly intoxicated from the beer. He realized suddenly that he was bathed in sweat. Spots danced before his eyes, and he knew that he was on the point of fainting.

He just had time to say, "I must ask your permission to rest for a moment," before he collapsed into his chair. He managed, with great difficulty, to keep his eyes open, but he could not succeed in focusing them.

Even though his cheeks were covered with the stubble of a week-old beard, his pallor did not escape his hosts. In the confusion that followed, he had a vague impression of someone putting a glass into his hand. He had strength enough to carry it to his mouth. The tiny sip of liquid burned his throat but restored his clarity of mind and vision in an instant.

"What do you think of that liqueur?" the *kapo* of the canteen asked. "We distill it right here in the building, from a base of fermented sugar."

Sugar that was intended for the deportees, Alain thought, and took another sip.

"I supply it to the S.S.," the *kapo* added proudly. "We must all apologize to you for having asked you to do something beyond your strength. Fritz will bring you something to eat; that will make you feel better."

The German internee who had admitted Alain to the building and had since been playing the role of butler brought him an enormous plate of kidney beans, topped with sausages and slices of white bread.

"Take your time," one of the *kapos* said. "You can go on with your talk when you are feeling better."

Alain forced himself to swallow the food without undue haste, and when he had washed down the last of it with a glass of beer he felt that he had never before eaten so splendid a feast. Euphoria swept over him. It was absolutely necessary that his lecture be too lengthy to finish today and sufficiently interesting to warrant a second invitation.

He stood up to speak again, and this time he concentrated on his subject and ignored his collection of cigarette butts.

He left an hour later, after having been invited to return the following week. Night had fallen, icy cold and foggy. Even though it was Sunday, the crematorium was functioning at full blast, and the sky above the chimney was streaked with red. The thick, black smoke it vomited out was quickly scattered by the wind, spreading across the square and pervading every corner of it with an atrocious stench. Alain's feeling of triumph gave way to remorse and disgust. A moment before, he had been thinking of himself as an officer in the Free French Forces, upheld by his faith and secure in the power it conferred on him. Now, abruptly returned to the level of an anonymous deportee, he had the impression he had been trapped by comfort—food, drink, cigarettes. The character he had portrayed was ridiculous— so sure of his mission, so proud of sacrificing himself to it. The stench of the crematorium smoke brought him brutally face to face with reality. He was nothing but a miserable carcass. An ill-tempered whim on the part of a *kapo* far less powerful than those whose guest he had been could send him, tomorrow, to feed that nauseating smoke. For a time, he had given in to the illusion of being a man. But he was living in a world where he was nothing, where *kapos* with pomaded hair ate and drank their fill and fattened their dogs on the rations of the deportees. It was for the *kapos* that he had outlined his feelings, spoken of ideals. Deep inside themselves, they must have laughed. He saw himself as he really was, dressed in striped and filthy rags. A jacket, a pair of pants, a shirt without buttons, not even an undershirt or a pair of shorts. In place of a hat, an old cap whose visor had been torn off. And his head, with that crest of hair between the two shaven expanses. In such a disguise, he should never have spoken as he had to these sleek and self-satisfied men. His words had lost their meaning the instant they

64

left his mouth; in any case, they could never have been understood by his audience.

As he crossed the square, he drew his shoulders back, holding his arms tight against his body, trying to protect himself from the cold, clenching his fists in his pockets. He was sick with anger at himself and hatred for these privileged *kapos* who had seduced him with a display of intellectual interest in General de Gaulle. What they wanted, simply, was a moment's distraction. And when he had seen the luxury in which they lived, and compared it with the misery of the camp, he had been dazzled. He should have thrown in their faces the scorn and contempt he felt for the life they had carved out of the flesh of the deportees. Perhaps, under the first impact of shock, they would have understood. As it was, he had actually talked to them as though he hoped to make them share his faith in France! But they were monsters, nothing more, and impervious to faith of any kind. That was what he should have told them. They would have had him killed. No doubt of that. But at least there would be some purpose to his death. Instead, he had allowed himself to be contaminated by them. He had drunk their beer, eaten their beans, their bread, and their sausages, smoked their cigarettes. He had become their debtor, had even hoped and planned to go deeper in their debt by maneuvering for another invitation on the following Sunday. And this time, it was not in order to convince them of the grandeur of France. It was useless to hide it from himself; it was the comfort, the food, and the drink that attracted him. Well, he would not go. But for that matter, a great many things could happen before the week was out. He could be sent to Dora. He might even be dead. But he thrust aside the thought of that.

He had been walking in circles, as if in an attempt to exhaust his anger. Suddenly, the projectors above the entrance gate went on, illuminating the enormous, muddy square where the tens of thousands of men in the camp were assembled well before dawn every morning and every night, to stand for hours at rigid attention while they were counted, block by block, each block neatly aligned, twenty men to a row. The lights brought Alain back to reality. He began running toward his own barracks, afraid of being late. In the central street of the camp, he passed the band, on its way to take up its position for the roll call. When the *kommandos* left for their work areas in the morning, this collection of noisemakers was stationed near the gate to play melodies from Viennese operettas as they passed.

His fellow prisoners were swarming out of the barracks as he arrived, and Alain was swallowed up in the tumultuous mass, shoved back and forth by men intent on evading the bludgeon of the block chief. Fear of the bludgeon swept all other thoughts from Alain's mind. Usually he made a point of choosing his neighbors in the formation—a prudent policy, since if there was some disorder in the ranks the guilty party was not the only one punished. Also, conversation with friends made the long hours of standing in the square somewhat less unbearable. But none of the Frenchmen in his block were anywhere near him now, and it was too late to find them.

He stood through the roll call that night without being able to exchange a word with anyone.

13.

||||||||||||||||||||||||||||||||||||||||||||||||||||||||||||||||||||||||||||||||||||||||||||||||

When roll call was over, the men were marched away from the square in columns, which broke up as soon as they reached the central street between the barracks. Alain hurried over to join some French friends before they were lost in the rapidly dissolving mass of humanity. He knew from experience that bands of Russian and German criminals habitually used the confusion of these few minutes to attack and rob prisoners who, because of their nationality, might be expected to receive packages from their families, and he had no desire to be left alone. Deportees of the same nationality generally grouped together in self-defense when they were attacked, but they could never count on any help beyond that of their own compatriots. One night, when Alain had gone to the assistance of a solitary Dutchman attacked by a gang of Russians, some Germans who were also present had stood idly by. He had come out of the ensuing fight with a split eyebrow and a leg bearing the mark of a heavy boot. The thought that he had inflicted more serious wounds on his adversaries had been no consolation.

Charlie was among the group of Frenchmen Alain joined, and they walked back toward their block together.

"What's new with you?" Alain asked.

"My friend," Charlie answered happily, "I've met the *kapo* of a *kommando* that suits me to a T, a tiny little *kommando* where all they do is twiddle their thumbs. He says he'll take me into it if I can pay him off well enough. He wants cigarettes and chocolate. I told him that I usually get some in my packages and that he'd have a share if he signs me on. But this character isn't satisfied with promises. He wants to be paid, cash on the line. If it's going to work, I'll have to get a package very soon."

Alain was afraid that Charlie was being victimized, just as Philippe had been by Desbrosse.

"This *kapo*," he said, "sounds to me like one of those little crooks who take advantage of people like you. You give him your chocolate and cigarettes. He shares it with a clerk in the *Arbeitsstatistik* who makes up one ticket to transfer you to his *kommando,* and then, two days later, makes up another one to send you to Dora. That way, the place in his *kommando* is free again, for another generous donor."

"Do you think I'm stupid enough to fall for a stunt as old as that?" Charlie protested. "Obviously, the *kapo* shares the bribes he's asking for with someone in the *Arbeitsstatistik;* if he didn't do that, he wouldn't be able to choose his own slaves. But I've done some research on him, and he's all right. Alstein—a German I knew in France before the war—explained the whole situation to me. This *kapo* is a philosopher. He could have become a big shot with long hair, but he is lazy, he has no ambition, and he's wary of the things that go on in the upper echelons. He prefers to lead a simple life as the chief of a little group made up of hand-picked men as unambitious as he is and as eager to remain in that quiet *kommando* as he is eager to keep them, so that he can smoke their cigarettes and eat their food. The bad part is that, for the moment, I don't have either cigarettes or food."

"What about the job as interpreter?" Alain said. "Isn't there anything doing there? Last week, you were hoping for that."

"That got fouled up. There was a place, but the *kapo* of the canteen arranged for it to be given to a Czech Communist he knew before the war—a guy, needless to say, who speaks no language at all except his own."

Mention of the *kapo* of the canteen reminded Alain of his experience that afternoon. He searched through his pocket and carefully extracted the butts and the whole cigarette he had managed to steal. The cigarette was a little twisted, but still presentable.

"Here," he said to Charlie. "You still have time to find your philosopher friend and make a down payment."

Charlie stared at the objects Alain had put in his hand.

"Where did you get this?" he demanded.

"If your benefactor asks you," Alain said, "tell him that it was given to you by a friend of the *kapo* of the canteen. That will make him think you have friends in higher places than his. Good luck."

Alain went into his building, hoping that Charlie might succeed in getting away from the quarry *kommando*. Perhaps, after all, he would go back to the canteen the following Sunday.

He managed to find a place between two men on a narrow

bench and sat down to await the opening of the dormitory, his forearms on the table, his head between his hands.

He was dozing and had not noticed that one of his neighbors had left, when Charlie sat down in the empty place and put a hand on his shoulder.

"It's done," he said. "Your trick worked. The *kapo* is taking me into his *kommando* without even waiting for the *Arbeitsstatistik* to transfer me. I wish you could have seen his face when I told him that I got the tobacco from a friend of the *kapo* of the canteen. That was a great idea."

Their conversation was interrupted by an order for silence from the block leader. He had addressed himself to "Charlie and the other Frenchmen," because he knew Charlie's name. Alain was only a number to him.

Charlie was ordered to ask this number why he had been sent for that afternoon by the *kapo* of the canteen.

"Tell him that he's a friend of mine," Alain said.

Charlie was dumbfounded, but he translated what he had been told. The block leader sent Charlie away, invited Alain to sit down on his bed, and offered him a cigarette. Since conversation between them was impossible, they smoked in silence, neither of them certain of what attitude to assume.

Alain ostentatiously dropped a long butt on the floor, crushed it beneath his heel, nodded good night to the block chief, and went back to join Charlie. Together, they went over to the toilets. In spite of the stench, there were always a great many men here. The confusion of sound gave a certain degree of privacy to any conversation. Moreover, it was the only corner of the building where smoking was permitted.

Alain told Charlie the story of his visit to the *kapo* of the canteen. As he spoke, he found himself thinking of what Philippe had said: "For an action to be wrong, it has to be harmful to someone." He had done no harm to anyone by spending the afternoon in the company of men for whom he had nothing but contempt, and he had been able to help Charlie. He decided he would go back to the canteen the following Sunday.

14.

||||||||||||||||||||||||||||||||||||||||||||||||||||||||||||||||||||||||||||||||||||||||||||

"I was looking for you all afternoon yesterday," Philippe said when he and Alain met at the quarry tool shed. "Where were you?"

"I was hauled off to the canteen by a *lagerschutz,* to give a lecture to the senior *kapos* about General de Gaulle, the Free French Forces, and the Resistance."

"Well, well, so Desbrosse really was one of their spies."

"No doubt about it. He's the only one who could have told them about me."

"Tell me all about it. Don't keep me in suspense."

"They're a bunch of filthy pigs."

"No doubt about that, but did you at least manage to get something from them?"

Alain was on the point of telling him about the cigarette and the butts. But since he had given them to Charlie instead of sharing them with Philippe, he decided against it.

"They served me kidney beans, sausages, white bread, and beer," he said. "But it all had to be eaten right there."

"That's not what I meant. Are the senior *kapos* going to pull some strings for you?"

Alain realized then that it had never occurred to him to exploit to his own advantage the interest of these men.

"I have to go back again next Sunday," he said. "Yesterday, I was taken by surprise."

Philippe nodded. "And you let yourself get carried away by your subject. Knowing you as I do, I could have predicted that."

Alain had to admit that Philippe was right: He had allowed himself to be carried away by his subject. He had filched a few cigarette butts, but he had not for a moment considered the real advantages he could have derived from the situation.

"It's really stupid," Philippe said irritably.

"No, you don't understand."

"I understand that you missed a rare opportunity."

"Perhaps, but primarily an opportunity to become disgusted with myself. Can't you see, I don't want to owe anything to those men."

But, deep inside himself, he was not certain that was true.

15.

|||||||||||||||||||||||||||||||||||||||||||||||||||||||||||||||||||||||||||||||||||||||||||||||||||||

That Sunday, the morning roll call was later than usual. It always was when a public hanging was scheduled. Daylight was a necessity if the scene of the execution was to be properly lit.

The prisoners were lined up in the huge central square and then left to wait. The orchestra played waltzes, punctuated with the clash of cymbals. The Frenchmen in each block had managed to keep together. In an effort to distract their thoughts from what was about to happen, they forced themselves to talk to their neighbors. But the conversation soon lagged and died.

After a seemingly endless silence, it was Charlie who at last spoke up. He told a story he had heard from a deportee transferred from another camp about one of the prisoners there. Overcome by despair, he had decided to commit suicide, but every one of his attempts failed. When he hanged himself, he was discovered before he was dead. When he threw himself into the reservoir, he had been fished out, but the man who saved him had contracted pneumonia and died. There was a temporary break-down in the current when he threw himself on the electrified fence of the camp. An S.S. guard in one of the watchtowers had assumed that this was an escape attempt and sprayed the entire area with a submachine gun. The would-be suicide had not been hit, but three other deportees were fatally wounded. His comrades had tried everything to dissuade the man from continuing with enterprises that resulted only in the deaths of men who wanted to go on living. Charlie told all of this with an air of complete veracity and kept his audience breathless with suspense. It seemed that, in the end, one of his friends had taken pity on the desperate man. He assured him that, if he really had made up his mind that he wanted to be done with this life, he had only to find himself a place in the first row at roll call and kick the S.S. guard in the ass when he walked past. "You'll see," he had told him. "You won't miss this time." The suggestion had been put to the test that very night.

"Well," Charlie said, "you'll never guess what happened. When he was kicked, the S.S. turned around, looking very sheepish, and all he had said was: "What's the matter? Have we already lost the war?"

The men who were near enough to hear Charlie were grateful to him for trying to make them forget, for a few minutes, what they had been brought here to see. But their laughter was hollow and short-lived.

One after another, the musicians of the orchestra ceased play-ing. The big drum went on alone for a moment, as if it were sounding a death knell. The battery of loudspeakers above the gate bellowed a command for attention. The murmuring of thousands of voices died away instantly. *"Mützen . . . ab!"*

72

At this command, the deportees brought their head coverings down against their right legs. A few bursts of nervous laughter greeted the passage of the S.S. guards. Charlie's little story was making the rounds.

The condemned men had been led into the square, just to the left of the entrance to the camp. There were three lines of five men each, standing behind a crudely constructed wooden crossbeam from which dangled five nooses. A little block of wood had been placed between the lips of each of the men, like the bit of a horse's bridle, and secured by a wire around the back of their necks. Their hands were tied behind their backs.

A contingent of S.S. guards ordered the first row of five to a position under the wooden crossbeam. Some deportees, drafted into service as executioners, slipped the nooses around the necks of the victims. A moment later, the steps on which they were standing were pulled away and the bodies swung out into the void, slowly twisting and turning.

The silence of death hung over the square, broken only by the coughing of the ill and the hysterical laughter of some young Russians, excited beyond control by the involuntary writhing and jerking of the hanged men. Death was slow in coming, giving to those waiting clear view of what their own agony would be.

When at last there was no more movement, the cords were released. The inert bodies collapsed into the mud like broken toys and were pulled aside. The operation was repeated for the second row of the condemned, and then for the third.

It was all done. The loudspeakers blared their pitiless command: *"Mützen . . . auf!"* But horror had paralyzed so many of the deportees that, instead of a single slapping sound from thousands of headgear, there was only a prolonged rustling. The enraged barking of the S.S. duty officer, magnified by the loudspeakers, was like a clap of thunder. The men came to with a start, awakened from their nightmare. When the command was repeated, the headgear was replaced in a single movement, with a single sound.

After the midday ration, Alain walked over to the canteen building.

Ever since the preceding Sunday, he had been trying to analyze his reasons for returning. It had not been easy. The thought of eating a plateful of beans and sausages distorts human judgment. To simplify the problem, he had resolved to refuse any food, drink, or tobacco that might be offered. With that out of the way, there remained nothing more for him to do but to balance the utility his visit might have against the damage to his self-respect. He was, after all, an officer in the Free French Forces, and he had been profoundly humiliated by appearing in front of these men in his present condition. And it was not he, Alain Fevrier, they had sent for, it was a French officer who came from London and had known General de Gaulle. Thus, it was actually General de Gaulle and the whole of the Free French Forces that had been insulted. But this was another aspect of the matter that did not hold up under any detailed study. Alain had a sudden vision of an engraved calling card, reading "The *kapo* of the Canteen," and written out beneath this, "and the other senior *kapos* request the honor of your presence, as an officer representing the Free French Forces, at . . . etc." At the corner of the card, there was the inevitable R.S.V.P. His rage collapsed like a spent balloon. He must not forget that he was in a concentration camp. One thing, however, remained certain: The senior *kapos* were detestable creatures. He had the feeling of dirtying himself by having anything to do with them, simply because any relationship with them might appear to be approval of their actions. And to receive something from them was to go far beyond this tacit approval. It was the

74

equivalent of becoming their accomplice, since anything they had to give was the fruit of theft and corruption.

On the other hand, Alain had not forgotten that it was his visit to the canteen that enabled Charlie to escape from the quarry *kommando*. But it was also worth remembering that the senior *kapos* had had nothing to do with this. It was because he had filched some cigarette butts and one entire cigarette from them that he had been able to help Charlie.

In all of this, there remained the fact that the power of the senior *kapos* could be put to good use. This was certainly worth trying, not for any selfish purpose but for humanitarian ends, in the general interest. The display they made of their privileges bore witness to their vanity. It was this vanity Alain must play on if he hoped to succeed. But to succeed in what? He did not yet know. It would depend on the circumstances, on the turn the conversation might take, the occasions that presented themselves. It was impossible to draw up a definite plan at this point. Alain's resolve stiffened. He would go back to the canteen, and he would do whatever seemed necessary to attain a goal of which he was still uncertain.

In the final analysis, acceptance of their food, drink, and tobacco formed a part of doing whatever was necessary. That was a point on which it was relatively easy to set his mind at rest.

When Alain reentered the smoke-filled room in which the senior *kapos* gathered, he found that it had lost a good deal of its impressiveness. He felt completely at ease. As far as the *kapos* themselves were concerned, he had rid himself of all his complexes.

He had prepared his lecture to be as brief as possible. He wanted to avail himself of whatever time might be required to lead the conversation into an area more favorable to his plans.

When he had finished, the *kapo* of the canteen thanked him and suggested that his colleagues might like to ask some questions. They did so, one after another, with an intelligence Alain had not expected. Almost all of them expressed themselves quite easily in English. Fritz, the servant, had brought Alain a plate containing fried potatoes, an enormous portion of sausage, and an abundant supply of bread. He answered their questions as he ate, and commented on topics they began to discuss among themselves.

When the conversation showed signs of losing impetus, Alain, controlling his voice and making an effort to seem natural, said:

"It has been a pleasure for me to outline the origins, the methods, and the goals of the French Resistance to men of your merit."

"We are all the more grateful to you," the *kapo* of the canteen replied, "because we Communists will be called on to occupy positions on the highest level in the Germany of tomorrow. We are not very numerous any longer, but the trials we have been through have tempered and matured the survivors. They have also given them time for careful thought. If you think about it, you will realize that there are practically no German Communists at liberty today, except for those who fled abroad. They will have no right to speak; they will never be pardoned for having abandoned the struggle. It is we who will have the glorious duty of bringing Lenin's doctrine to our country when it is freed from Nazism, and of restoring to our compatriots the meaning of socialism and personal dignity, which Hitler has abolished."

Alain could not prevent himself from glancing around the table at the litter of plates, glasses of beer, packages of cigarettes, and boxes of cigars. His look clearly betrayed his surprise at these words, because the *kapo* began speaking again at once.

"Don't assume, because of the conditions we have achieved here," he said, "that we have forgotten the principles of our party. You should know what this camp was like when we came here."

He went on to explain that, on the very spot where he was standing, there had been nothing but forest. The first prisoners

76

had slept in tents, on the ground like animals, in a clearing the S.S. and the Hitler Youth from Wiemar had surrounded with barbed wire, and where they had constructed a barracks for their guards.

The city that had become Buchenwald, as well as the road that led to it, its streets, its sewers, its water supply system, its wooden barracks and its concrete buildings, had all been built by German internees. It was finished before any of the foreign deportees were brought here.

"The *kapos*," he continued, "were selected by the S.S. from among the common law criminals, the 'greens.' We, the political prisoners, the 'reds,' were forced to live by their law for years. Since the *kapos* were incapable of organizing anything, they attempted to maintain their position with the S.S. by showing that they could be more cruel than the S.S. itself. If the work in any area did not progress at the required cadence, one man in every ten was taken out each night to receive fifty blows to the kidneys with a heavy staff. And this man was always one of us, because we were held responsible for everything that did not go according to plan."

The Communists had realized that they must do something, or else they would all perish, down to the last man. They had attempted to convince the S.S. that the efficiency of the work would improve if the positions of authority were taken away from the common law criminals and given to them. But the S.S. had refused even to listen.

"So," the *kapo* of the canteen explained, "we staked everything on one throw of the dice. One night we cut the throats of all the 'greens' who had been assigned posts by the S.S., from the *Lagerälteste* to the most insignificant block chiefs—and not forgetting the *kapos,* the chief of the *Arbeitsstatistik* or the *lagerschutz*. Next morning, every one of the dead men had been replaced in his job by a Communist. We were still in the majority, and when roll call was held we reported every prisoner in the camp present. Not one single 'green' dared to challenge us. They all knew that the slightest move in that direction would be the end of them."

The new *Lagerälteste,* chosen by the rebels, had gone to report to the S.S. duty officer, who, as usual, was waiting in the guardroom to be informed that everything was ready for the roll call. He had explained to him that all the "green" officials were dead and had handed him a list of their suggested replacements—all Communists. He had also assured the officer that, if the list was approved, the camp would be administered to the satisfaction of the S.S.

The camp commandant had arrived almost immediately, and the doors to the guardroom had closed behind him and the leader of the revolt.

At this point in his story, the *kapo* could not help laughing.

"With every minute that passed," he said, "we got more scared. You can imagine how easy it would have been for the S.S. to liquidate all the leaders; we had pointed them out when we handed over the list of candidates for the different posts. Well, they did nothing about it. They appointed them. I must say though that they have never had occasion to regret it, because since we took over the administration from the 'greens,' everything has gone along very well. So well, in fact, that the S.S. themselves have replaced with Communists the common law criminals who occupied positions of authority in the other big concentration camps."*

* This account of the seizure of power by the German Communists does not correspond to the truth, but the senior *kapos* made a great point of establishing it as legend. In fact, the German Communist internees infiltrated the administration of the camp only by degrees. The discipline, the sense of secrecy, and the tactical skill learned during their years in a militant underground movement assured them, in the long run, of total victory over the "greens."

It should be added that, however deplorable the manner in which the German Communists administered the Buchenwald camp may have been, their presence in positions of authority was far preferable for the deportees to that of the common law prisoners. To be convinced of this, it was sufficient to be sent, as the author was, to a camp such as Dora, which was administered by the "greens."

In spite of himself, Alain could not help establishing a mental parallel between certain ministers of the Vichy government and the Communist governors of Buchenwald. Each of them, in his fashion, gloried in the confidence shown him by the Nazis, and neglected nothing to preserve and exploit it to his own ends.

The *kapo* of the canteen was clearly reveling in his own importance as he continued with his story:

"Compared with what it was before," he said, "the camp has become a sanitarium. And that, you must understand, is the result of our work. I'm sure you will agree it entitles us to certain rights. But for that matter, even if we were to give up the few privileges we allow ourselves, the situation of the tens of thousands of our comrades would not be improved to any noticeable extent. By subjecting ourselves to the common regime, we would be endangering our own lives without benefiting anyone else—and our lives are indispensable to the Germany and the world of tomorrow. If the food and drink we have were to be divided among even ten thousand of the others, what would it give to each of them?"

This statement reminded Alain of something he had read, in 1936, in a French newspaper of the Far Right: The income of the famous "two hundred families," if it were divided among all the French people, would amount to no more than a few francs for each of them every year.

He was aware of the first stirrings of an even more violent rage than what he had experienced when he left the canteen building on the preceding Sunday. He struggled desperately to conceal it; these *kapos* were intelligent. They had understood everything he had told them. The discussion that had followed his lecture was proof of that. And they had been capable of calmly taking a frightful risk in order to win control of the administration of the camp. But they had made use of it only to carry out the will of the S.S. They had never used their authority to establish a rule of law and justice in the camp, to apply here the principles of the social and moral philosophy they claimed to adhere to. Almost without transition, they had passed from the status of slave to that of beneficiary. Shamelessly, even ostentatiously, they enjoyed the privileges of their position in the feudal system of the camp, and they had proven themselves as iniquitous, as brutal, and murderous as their former masters, the common law prisoners. The block chiefs reserved the best of the ration to themselves and plundered the packages sent by the families of the men under their command. The *kapos* of the good *kommandos* admitted only deportees who could supply them with tobacco. Corruption was the rule, from top to bottom of the administrative ladder set up by the senior *kapos* with the complicity of the S.S. guards, who were regularly furnished with liquor made in the canteen from the sugar intended for the Sunday ration of the deportees. The lesser officials, to whom these *kapos* had delegated the actual carrying out of their functions, appropriated their own share of the profits directly from the common herd of the camp inmates, and after they had been counted twice each day no one gave another thought to these peasants. Some of the "greens" had even managed to secure a new hold on the lower echelons of the camp hierarchy. They were efficient and easily satisfied butchers, and therefore useful. Several of them had been appointed *kapos* of the quarry *kommandos*.

The indignation that seethed in Alain was so powerful that it had not escaped the men around him. They were all staring at him, and a grim silence had fallen in the room. He had to do something to turn their attention away from the emotion that he felt they could read in his face.

"I hope you will forgive my reactions," he said, "but what you have just told me throws a new light on the camp, an entirely new light, to me. I won't deny to you that many of the things that happen here have revolted me. I am not referring only to the hangings. I am thinking of the brutalities that are constantly committed by some of the internees against others.

80

What you have told me makes it clear that, far from considering such acts normal, you deplore them too, even though you cannot suppress them."

"You have understood us perfectly," one of the *kapos* cut in. "You mustn't lose sight of the fact that the population of the camp is stubborn and would be hard to manage if the use of threats was abandoned entirely. But threats would lose all effectiveness if they did not sometimes lead to punishment. The whole problem lies in making it as infrequent as possible and, when it is necessary to employ it, to apply it with justice, but strictly.

"Take the case of the Russians. The Gestapo treats their country more harshly than France. The penalty for resistance is not deportation but death. That is why most of the Soviet citizens here are the kind of men they are, even more detestable than the 'greens.' They deserted communism to serve the Nazis. But, after having betrayed their own country, they wanted to cheat the masters they had sold out to. It isn't the struggle for the liberty of their people and the triumph of the proletariat that brought them here, but robbery and extortion. In spite of their rottenness, we have succeeded in limiting their extortionist activities—no one will ever make them vanish completely—by enlisting the support of the best of their compatriots and, particularly, of the Soviet prisoners of war who have been brought here as a disciplinary measure. We grouped all of them in one block. They are men whose spirits have been molded by Communist doctrine. We have granted them some appreciable advantages. They are not sent away in the transport, and they are assigned to good *kommandos*. Their food rations are higher than those of the other deportees. But, on the other hand, we have required them to insure the behavior of their compatriots. And they handle this very well, you have to admit that. We close our eyes to the methods they are forced to employ: they are the only ones that work."

"As it happens," Alain said, "I wanted to suggest that you might do something about the Frenchmen."

He had just that moment realized what advantage might be gained from the relationship he had established with the senior *kapos*. But the *kapo* of the canteen interrupted him at once.

"There's no point in talking to us about that," he said. "We will never grant any advantage to the French. After the Russians, they are the worst troublemakers in the camp. They are undisciplined, and they have a taste for comfort which makes them unbearable and unsuitable for any form of collective life."

It was Alain's turn to interrupt. "You didn't let me speak," he said, "or rather, you are mistaken about the meaning of what I said. It was what you just told me about the Russians and about the role of the prisoners of war in their community that prompted me. I am not asking you for anything. I am offering to rid you of the problems caused you by the French. You say that they cannot adapt to a collective life. As for me, I think that since they are the only Latin members of the basically Germanic and Slav population of the camp, there exists, between them and their German, Russian, Polish, and Czech comrades, a lack of understanding which fosters latent hostility. Gather them together in blocks where they will be among themselves, and I will answer for their discipline and their good behavior."

"And, in return, you would want to be named chief of one of these blocks?"

"Not at all. On the contrary, if you agree to regroup the Frenchmen in the camp, I'll give you my word to ask for nothing."

"That is too bad for you, comrade, because we like you, and we were prepared to do something to better your personal situation. As a matter of fact, we were talking about that when you arrived."

"I'm deeply touched by that," Alain said, "and I thank you for it."

82

He was suddenly rediscovering the feelings he had had as he parachuted into France at night, to carry out a mission. He had been wondering what impulse had forced him to volunteer, when he could easily have remained in London. In spite of the bombings, life had been pleasant there, and he had always known what awaited him the moment he set foot on the Gestapo's hunting ground.

Once again, he had burned his bridges behind him. He was both proud and furious with himself.

"You will certainly understand," he went on, "that, now that I know what the whole camp owes you, I should like to do whatever I can to help in your work, but certainly without asking anything for myself. I have not been through what you have, and there could be no reason why I should enjoy any particular consideration."

The irony of his words was a product of his anger with himself. For a moment, he was afraid that it must be obvious to the Germans, so he continued hurriedly: "The regrouping of the French would make everyone's existence here easier; that of the men who are now in the blocks with them and are annoyed by them; your own, because, as I told you, I will be responsible for their discipline and their good behavior; and last of all, their own, because they will be grateful to be with their own people again."

The *kapo* of the canteen held a brief discussion, in German, with his colleagues. "All right," he agreed. "Just to please you, we have decided to try it. I will speak to the *Lagerälteste* about it. But I feel sorry for the block chief who will be in charge of the French!"

After that, Alain thought it best to say good night. One of the senior *kapos* left the building with him.

In the main square, he paused, studied Alain's face in the gathering dark, clapped him on the shoulder, and said, very slowly, in French, with a thick Teutonic accent: "You're a stupid bastard. But you'll go to work in the factory just the same."

Before Alain had had the time to recover from his surprise, the *kapo* had disappeared into the darkness.

16.

IIIIIIIIIIIIIIIIIIIIIIIIIIIIIIIIIIIIIIIIIIIIIIIIIIIIIIIIIIIIIIIIIIIIIIIIIIIIIIIIIIIIIIIIIIIIIIIIIIIIIII

Alain had succeeded in finding a place next to Charlie for the roll call.

"How do you like it in your new *kommando?*" he asked.

"I couldn't like it better. There are only about fifty of us—mostly Germans, a few Croats, and three Czechs. I'm the only Frenchman."

"No Russians?"

"No, no Russians. The *kapo* wants a crew in which all speak the same language."

"And is the *kapo* still all right?"

"Sure. I got a package yesterday, and I kept my promise to him. I took it to him, in block 40, before taking anything out of it. He was very reasonable about what he took. All in all, it's working out very well. This *kommando* is a different thing entirely from the quarry."

"What do you do?"

"The first two days of the week, we worked in the railroad station in Weimar. They drove us there in a truck. We loaded frieght cars."

"Then you must have seen some civilians."

"Yes, a few, from a distance."

84

"How did they behave toward you?"

"They acted as if we didn't exist."

"But didn't the German internees try to talk to them?"

Charlie shook his head. "No. But there was a crew of French workers right near us, some of the voluntary workers in this country. They were interested in us, or at least, they were interested in me. I attracted their attention by swearing under my breath, in French. I have the feeling that I could strike up a conversation with some of them if I saw them again. It's forbidden, of course, but with a little time you can accomplish almost anything. Unfortunately, I don't know when we'll be going back to Weimar. We're working in the factory now."

"At last—"

"At last, what?"

"At last, someone who may be able to give me some information. Does this factory really exist?"

"I'll say it does!"

"Where is it?"

"When you come to the end of the Avenue of Triumph, you come out between two low buildings which someone told me are the guardhouse and the S.S. post office."

"Where the statue of the Hitler eagle is, in the middle of the road?"

"Yes. We have to take off our hats every time we pass that eagle. Just beyond that, the road angles off slightly to the right, and then the factory is just behind the railroad siding."

"But that means it's practically next door to us!"

"About half a kilometer from here."

Alain could scarcely contain his astonishment at the fact that a building so close at hand could have been the subject of so many fables.

"What sort of factory does it look like?" he asked.

"It looks like any other factory. Huge rectangular buildings, one right next to the other, with staggered roofs. Inside—"

"Have you been inside?"

"We work on the inside. In the building where we are, there are rows of benches and lots of machines."

"What kind of machines?"

Charlie lifted his shoulders. "I don't know anything about that kind of thing. Little, individual machines. They must be what they call machine tools."

"Who works them?"

"Most of them aren't being used, but it's the deportees who will be using them."

"Are you sure of that?"

"Absolutely. There are some who seem to be specialists who are already at work."

"Who tells them what to do?"

"German civilians."

"And what are they doing?"

"I don't know anything about that."

"What about your *kommando;* what does it do?"

"Everything and nothing. One team sweeps out the place, another is painting water mains. My own is putting up partitions for what will be some little rooms inside the main building."

"Do you think it would be worth the trouble to try to get an assignment to work in this factory?"

"Worth the trouble? Think about it for a minute—working indoors, in peace and quiet, without a *kapo* on your back: it's next door to Paradise. If I were in your place, I would ask the senior *kapos* to transfer me there immediately."

Alain sighed. "I can't ask the senior *kapos* for anything," he said.

"What are you talking about?" Charlie demanded. "Didn't you spend the afternoon with them?"

"Yes. But I won't ask them for anything for myself."

"What do you mean by that?"

"I made them a promise not to. But I did ask them to do something for all of us. And they promised me that they would."

"For all of us?"

"For the French. We will be all together, just the Frenchmen, in our own blocks."

"What's the point in that?"

"It will permit us to organize, to defend ourselves, to form a national group, instead of remaining just a collection of individual victims."

Charlie let out a low, whistling sound. "Do you have something in the back of your mind?" he asked.

"No, nothing at all, except what I've told you. And even that is still confused in my own mind. But I've had enough of living with people whose language we don't understand and who don't understand ours. It's because of that that everyone considers everyone else a savage. Among Frenchmen, at least we could argue about a thing before getting into a fight about it."

"I see what you mean. And it's for that reason that you gave your word not to ask the senior *kapos* for anything for yourself? Well, my friend, take it from me, you've missed your chance."

"How so?"

"Because they will never regroup us."

"Why not? They practically promised me they would."

"It would be against all the principles of the camp. This place is governed by the law of depersonalization. Everything is geared to that end. The deportee, reduced to a number, is constantly juggled around with other numbers. He isn't supposed to have a single friend. He isn't supposed to be able to trust anyone. In the face of the authority of the *kapos* and the block chiefs, he is always supposed to be an isolated number, a frightened and isolated number. It's a whole philosophy of command. It's not 'divide and conquer,' it's 'reduce to nothing and conquer.'"

"Then you think I behaved like an idiot?"

"Let's say like an idealist. Here, unfortunately, that's almost the same thing."

Alain sought desperately to cling to an idea which, only a moment before, had seemed a certainty and now a naïve dream.

"But in your *kommando*—" he began.

"In my *kommando,* we are bound together by our own interest in staying there and in making it possible for the *kapo* to get along without bothering us. It's a tacit agreement that holds us together."

"But you manage to respect that agreement because you all speak the same language. The same kind of arrangement could be worked out in a French block. We would relieve the block chief of any worry about discipline. In exchange, he wouldn't bother us."

"Go right on talking. To relieve him of any worry about discipline, you would have to assure discipline yourself. The bludgeon you want to take away from him, you would have to hold yourself. And use it. If the *kapos* keep the promise they made, I wish you good luck. To listen to you, anyone would think you don't know our compatriots."

Alain was annoyed. "They're certainly worth as much as the Germans, Czechs, and Yugoslavs in your *kommando,*" he said irritably.

"Not at all," Charlie retorted calmly. "The members of my *kommando* are hand-picked by the *kapo.* There are no parasites, and no troublemakers. If you could pick and choose among the Frenchmen—"

"There's no need to pick and choose. You're not going to try and make me believe that you need a bludgeon to maintain order among Frenchmen. All that will be needed is for some of us to set an example and explain to the others that it's in their own best interests to behave like civilized human beings—"

"Huh," Charlie grunted, "civilized human beings with empty bellies—"

"Empty or not, it's the same thing."

"I hope you're right. But in the meantime, you'd be smart to try and get out of the quarry and into the factory."

"Don't think I don't want to."

"After the roll call, I'll go to see that German I told you about, Alstein. Perhaps he'll be able to do something for you.

He's an ex-diplomat. My father has known him for a long time and used to tell me he's an astonishing person, a Renaissance character misplaced in the twentieth century, reacting to Nazi brutality as his predecessors did to the harshness of the Middle Ages. He is cultured, Catholic, capable of sacrificing everything for an idea, but gifted with a sense of intrigue and a degree of intelligence—to say nothing of a native shrewdness—which always makes it possible for him to get along, no matter what the situation."

"That's a pretty ambiguous account."

"The man himself is ambiguous. He is a German, but he has French friends. He's a Catholic, but he's one of the more important figures in a camp dominated by Communists. And yet he betrays neither his compatriots nor his faith. Your idea of a French block may interest him."

"How does it happen that he's done nothing for you?"

"He's tried, many times. But for Alstein really to be able to set me up somewhere, either I would have to be an important person myself or I would have to be a specialist in something or other. Unfortunately, I'm neither."

17.

Alain had found a place on one of the benches in the mess hall. With his elbows on the table, half asleep, he was attempting to analyze the reasons behind his request to the senior *kapos* to regroup the Frenchmen in the camp. Now that he had given it some thought, he was not far from sharing the opinion of

Charlie, who believed neither in the regrouping nor in its possible benefits. It occurred to Alain that this was yet another occasion on which his imagination had led him into a blind alley, to the detriment of his own best interests.

The dormitory was just beyond the mess hall. Alain would have liked to be able to go and stretch out, but no one was allowed there before the block chief gave the order. The battle that would have to be fought then, to obtain a cover and a place where he might get some rest, already frightened him.

The interior of the dormitory consisted of a series of raised levels that formed narrow alleys running the length of the room. The levels were divided by supporting beams into rectangular compartments, each of them roughly the size of a single sleeping mat. Four such compartments were set side by side between each two alleys. The sleeping mats were made of a rough cloth, woven from strips of paper and torn in innumerable places. Their padding, of wood fiber, was now no more than dust. It came out through all the holes of its envelope, and at the slightest movement it would sift through the gaps in the flooring and spread a fine powder across the level beneath.

Threadbare coverings, soiled by the excrements of the dysenterics, the oozing sores of the wounded, and the urine of the incontinent, were piled at the entrance to the dormitory.

Each night, the same scene took place. The first men in the dormitory seized several of the coverings and hid them beneath their bodies on the sleeping mats. By the time the last men arrived, the stock was exhausted, and they were forced to fight if they wanted one. The block chief and the *stubendienst* intervened, lashing about indiscriminately with their bludgeons until the battling groups were at last broken up and everyone had sought his own place to sleep, with or without a cover. The population of the block was twice that for which it had been built, so two men were now assigned to each of the rectangular floor spaces. If, by chance, a man found himself alone on his sleeping mat during the winter, he would begin groping in the

90

obscurity of the neighboring compartments, looking for two comrades who would agree to take him in. Then he would insert himself between them, his head next to their feet, hoping to profit from the feeble warmth of their bodies. If he had had the good luck to get one of the coverings, he was always welcome: if not, he rarely found a place. Turned away everywhere with blows and kicks, he was forced to resign himself to shivering alone all night or to lying in wait until someone went to the toilets. If he then succeeded in locating the man's place, he could hope to slip into it without attracting the attention of the second occupant of the mat. When the original occupant returned, everything depended on the relationship of the opposing forces. Either things were worked out peacefully or another battle began. Fear of the block chief usually imposed a solution.

Alain wondered if he would get to the door of the dormitory in time to get a cover and if he would succeed in finding a place in one of the upper compartments of the central bay. These, to his way of thinking, were the least of the assorted evils of the building. They were sheltered from the bludgeons of the block chief and his assistants and were not exposed to the drippings of urine from the ill. Moreover, there was little risk of being trampled by those who were forced to make the trip to the toilets during the night. Finally, they were some distance from the windows on either side of the dormitory, which were always left open, and therefore were safe from the icy air, the blasts of snow and rain which often reached into the lower levels of the lateral bays.

In a block inhabited solely by Frenchmen, Alain was thinking, it would be possible to do away with these daily battles by assigning a permanent compartment to each man and by organizing the distribution of the covers. Everyone would find such a system to his advantage, except those who were allotted places near the windows; but perhaps these could be chosen from among the strongest men and they could be given supplementary coverings. As it was, it was always the weakest who were relegated to the worst places. A fair system, which took into consideration the infirmities of some of the prisoners, might be substituted for the rule of force.

The opening of the dormitory door put an end to Alain's musings. He took part in the general rush almost indifferently and barely succeeded in snatching up one end of a cover. A German held the other end. Alain would have liked to explain that they could share it for the night and then go with him directly to the central bay. He tried to make himself understood with gestures, but another German shoved him roughly away. He gave up this particular battle, made his way to the upper-level compartments, and found a vacant place next to a Pole who was seated on two covers. Between them, they managed to turn away a series of assailants who became less and less vigorous, less and less resolute as the struggle went on.

Alain took off his galoshes and the coat of thin striped cloth. He laid this out across his body, with the collar at his feet, and put his legs through the sleeves. Then he replaced the galoshes on his feet and stretched out. He pulled the muddy bottom of his coat up to his shoulders and then tugged on the cover he was sharing with his neighbor. For that night, his battle was won. He was sound asleep before the battle had ended on the lower levels. He heard nothing of the running back and forth and the cries of pain brought on by the intervention of the block chief, pursuing those who had not yet found a place to stay.

Reveille took him by surprise. He had the feeling that he had only just gone to sleep. He pulled his legs from the coat, slipped the galoshes back on his feet and began the journey down, exchanging blows and curses with the men emerging from the compartments on the lower levels. In the midst of this crush, he managed to take off his jacket and shirt as he crossed the mess hall, and arrived at the entrance to the block stripped to the waist. A cold draft howled through the open door and swept into the washrooms. Here, under the surveillance of a *stubendienst,* the deportees performed their morning toilet around a big, circular basin. Water spouted, horizontally at first, from the summit of a column at the center of the basin. As it fell, the trajectory of its slender sprays assumed the form of the ribs of an umbrella. Alain held his clothing clutched against his chest, concerned only with avoiding the *stubendienst's* bludgeon. There was no question of forcing his way to the basin to wash: there were too many men there already, and the temperature did not make it an alluring prospect. Moreover, with no soap, these threads of water allowed nothing more than a pretense at cleanliness. The object was to get back and get dressed as quickly as possible and without having been hit by the bludgeon. Along one wall, there was a metal tube which sprayed water into a filthy basin intended for rinsing out the mess tins. Alain dipped a hand furtively into the greasy slime and then rubbed it across his chest. The trace of moisture on his skin was sufficient to convince the *stubendienst* that he had washed.

Fighting against the late-comers being herded into the washroom by the block chief, he regained the relative sanctuary of the mess hall, sat down at a table, and put on his clothes. The distribution of the morning ration was about to begin, as always, in an atmosphere of noise and disorder. The starving men were counted, recounted, and forced to move from one table to another until there were equal groups around each table.

Each group, of five or seven according to the day, received one loaf of bread. When it was brought, every hand at the table tried to grab it. The member of the group who got it waited for the knife to be brought and then made the distribution. The bread was eccentrically shaped, with portions at the center higher than those at the ends. The squaring of the circle and the trisection of the arc presented fewer problems than the sharing

93

of this loaf. Everyone was convinced that he had been cheated and cast greedy eyes on the other portions, which were always larger than his.

Suddenly there would be an uproar of angry voices. One slice was missing. It had been stolen, brazenly, in full view of everyone. Jealousy and hunger took possession of the still half-sleeping prisoners. In an instant they were upon one of their number. A collective hysteria had located its victim. It had been necessary only for someone to point him out. All the scattered hatreds in the room converged on him like bees swarming toward a branch. His ration was torn from his hands, and he was buried in an avalanche of blows. It was useless to protest. It was not justice that was gratified, but the spirit of revolt. Since it could not be brought to bear on those who had caused it, it vented its wrath on him.

Holding a mess tin in his hand, Alain stood on line to receive a dipperful of a lukewarm, yellowish liquid whose only relationship to coffee was the word itself. Grease from the bottom of the tin floated to the surface of the liquid in little rainbow-colored clouds, but he swallowed it at a single gulp. He nibbled slowly at his bread, holding it in his fist for fear of having it stolen in some new scrimmage. He would have nothing else to eat until tonight.

Plunged into his own thoughts, he did not move quickly enough to avoid the bludgeon when the column began to form to move out for roll call. The bodies of those who had died in the night, stiff as poles or curled up like infants in the womb, were deposited on the hard soil of the walk. One man was missing. The *stubendienst* searched the dormitory and discovered him, already deep in coma. They dragged him out and left him with the other corpses.

That morning, Alain was acutely aware of everything that happened in this everyday routine, but only because he was thinking that it might be different in a block where there were only Frenchmen.

94

This thought furnished the basic topic of his conversation in the quarry with Philippe. They struggled to maintain the hopes for a regrouping of their compatriots by sketching out plans of organization, but they had tacitly agreed to mention the subject to no one.

18.

|||||||||||||||||||||||||||||||||||||||||||||||||||||||||||||||||||||||||||||||||||||||||||||||||||||||

The camp floundered in the depths of the interminable winter of Buchenwald, a winter that lasted six months.

The piercing wind stirred whirlpools of snow in the beam of the projectors as they cut the darkness of the square. The flakes seemed to be fleeing in disorder before an invisible enemy, seeking a place of refuge where they might melt and escape their tormentor. But everything they encountered was so icy, and the fine crystals of which they were composed were so fragile, that their mad flight went on until a gust of wind crushed them against the side of a building, or until they came to rest on a face and mingled with the tears of the prisoners. They drew endless veils across the shafts of light and streaked the night with a confusion of arabesques in which the line of the horizon was lost.

The formation of motionless and frozen men, standing elbow to elbow in their paper-thin garments, pitched and tossed like a reflection caught in the moving web of the projector's beams. On the frozen earth, hard and resonant as a shelf of stone, the storm whipped at a tide of powdery snow whose waves broke against naked ankles emerging from the canvas uppers of galoshes. The cold crushed the men's feet like the spikes of a torturer's boot and then climbed to their famished bellies to join the pain that permeated their ears, their throats, their noses, leaving their heads empty and their hearts laboring in their chests. The fog of their breathing condensed on their lips, and the skin split beneath it. Paralyzed hands were hidden in the sleeves of crossed forearms to protect the ribs from the knives planted there by the wind. To escape the snowy projectiles that had taken them for a target, eyes were tightly closed. Fragments of snowflakes ridged the brows and clustered on the lids before finally melting.

No one spoke. It was enough to try not to die.

Immobility numbed the muscles, and the cramps it caused merged with the bite of the cold.

Here and there, a prisoner would rub his nose to prevent it from freezing and change the position of a hat that was too small to shelter both ears at the same time. For a moment, the milky fluttering of the snow would be disturbed, and then he resumed his scarecrow stance.

From time to time, a body would collapse, carrying with it in its fall all those who stood in front of it, as if they were a row of dominoes. Or it might simply drop where it had stood, a miserable pile of rags spiked with the points of elbows and knees, like a marionette whose string has broken. The dead and the dying alike were passed from hand to hand, dragged along the ground to their final destination beside the building. The feeble warmth of the body welded its clothing to the ice, and before it could be carried away later the rags had to be torn away. Urged by the bludgeon of the *stubendienst,* a prisoner who had been standing in the last line would be sent to occupy the empty place in the ranks.

All notion of time was gone. The skull was as hollow, as echoing, as a bell. Had this torture been going on for one minute, ten minutes, an hour? It was better not to wonder. Because, day after day, morning and night, less frightful or more, but always beyond the limits by which pain can be measured, it would be repeated, until the cold of death took possession of a prey which would be stolen from it shortly by the flames of the crematorium.

Periodically, during the roll call, there were moments of respite from torture. The deportees were not required to stand at attention while the S.S., in the warmth of the guardhouse, went through countless additions and subtractions before coming to the conclusion that they had been mistaken in their count. In these periods, the formations simply fell apart. With the original rectangle of each block as its center, a kind of nebula was formed, with the outer elements struggling to find a path that would lead them to the warmth of the center. The system, under attack from every angle, began to rotate slowly around its source. The friction of one body against another and the protection they offered each other brought warmth to frozen arms and legs. Overburdened lungs exhaled a fetid stench from one mouth to another, but this was drowned in a mingling of the bitter odors of filthy clothing and flesh that had not seen soap in months. And woe to the individual whose legs gave way beneath him. The human carrousel, incapable of halting, crushed him beneath a slow and inexorable trampling of wooden soles carrying the weight of men pressed hard against their neighbors and seeking, with every step, to recover a constantly interrupted rhythm.

The barkings of the loudspeakers shattered the nebula. The bludgeons flailed again, the deportees resumed their formation to be recounted and stood at attention for another eternity, waiting until they could again find protection, in the accumulation of their bodies, against the bite of the cold. Or perhaps, after a final salute, they might at last be taken back to their blocks, their racked and exhausted legs feebly attempting to maintain the required cadence.

When they were again inside the barracks, the warmth sank fiery needles into frozen hands and feet. Swollen chilblains burst, cracked lips bled. The mess hall filled with men whose lurching, disordered movements obeyed no law but that of pain. Moans of agony punctuated the arguments that erupted in the line of prisoners waiting to receive their dipperful of liquid sop. With the morning slice of black bread, which was made largely of sawdust and accompanied, according to the day of the week, by a slender round of sausage, a pat of margarine the size of a little finger or a spoonful of watery cheese, this thin gruel constituted an entire day's nourishment.

The first swallow of the hot liquid was too much for some of the men; its reaction on the secretions of their stomachs was beyond their strength to control. If their mess tins had not been turned over, their neighbors battled among themselves for them.

In the Small Camp, where there were no projectors, the roll calls took place in the barracks during the winter months. The brevity of the day made it impossible for them to be held outdoors.

The deportees were lined up, in five rows, in front of the raised floorings that ran, like shelves, along the wooden walls. Approximately ten feet wide, with a vertical space of less than two feet between them, these shelves were the sleeping areas. At night, in these rabbit warrens, bodies swarmed and mingled together like a horde of larvae, groping for a shred of rotting cover, gasping for air in the asphyxiating atmosphere. On the upper level, the only one on which it was possible to breathe, the condensation that formed on the roof in cold weather rained

98

icy particles on the sleepers, periodically jerking them awake as they slapped at their faces in fear and pain.

When packages arrived, the block chief distributed them after the roll call, shouting out the number of the addressee in German.

When Paul Genteau's number was called for the first time, he fought his way through the men around him, his heart pounding against his ribs, as deeply moved by the message from home represented by this box as by the hope of appeasing his hunger.

The block chief tore apart the already broken package, emptied it, set aside what he wanted for himself, and pushed the remains toward Genteau. Genteau gathered the plundered treasure into his arms as if it had been the body of his wife, because he had recognized her handwriting on the address.

He had taken only a few steps toward the corner to which he habitually retreated when a band of young Russians fell on him from the upper level of the sleeping shelves. They were holding outspread rags of coverings between them, like the wings of bats, and he was borne down beneath their weight and almost suffocated by the cloth. Before he succeeded in freeing himself, his attackers had vanished into the rows of shelves like scavengers retreating to their lairs. He had lost all the provisions so lovingly hoarded. In his clenched fist, there remained only a little scrap of brown paper bearing his wife's first name, all that was left of the address of the sender. He thrust it into his pocket, and when everyone else was alseep he pressed it against his lips.

When he was awakened next morning, he was holding a shapeless ball which he threw into the purifying fire of the stove, as though to protect the beloved name from contamination.

At the next distribution of packages, he noticed that whenever a number was called four or five men moved forward together. The addressee had arranged to be protected by friends, with whom he would share whatever the block chief deigned to leave him.

19.

|||||||||||||||||||||||||||||||||||||||||||||||||||||||||||||||||||||||||||||||||||||||||||||||||||

From the outside, the block of the S.S. Institute of Hygiene, and the block occupied by the human guinea pigs, could be distinguished from the other blocks in the camp by little more than the barbed wire fence that surrounded and isolated them. All the deportees regarded these blocks with horror. They knew that anyone assigned to the guinea-pig block was subjected to mysterious experiments the results of which were always fatal. This reputation extended to the Institute of Hygiene. Mistakenly so, since no crime was committed here. The Institute of Hygiene contained a laboratory for the preparation of antityphus vaccine, and some of the deportees worked there under the orders of Dr. Ding. This doctor directed both the laboratory and the experiments carried out on the human guinea pigs; this fact alone was sufficient for the terror inspired by the guinea-pig block to be reflected also on the Institute of Hygiene.

A door had been cut into the fence behind the Institute of Hygiene. Charlie pressed on an electric button, and a Russian deportee came to open the door. His striped uniform was new and immaculate, and his appearance of good health contrasted sharply with that of the poor devils who were shuffling about in the streets. Alain followed Charlie to a little staircase which led beneath the principal building of the block. The basement room into which they emerged was ventilated through air holes in the rear wall of the building. The lighting, sharp and clear, came from bulbs strung along the low ceiling. The walls were white and stark.

The first face Alain was conscious of was Geoffrin's. His forearms crossed on the table in front of him, he was listening attentively to the man who sat opposite. He glanced over at Alain. For a second or two, he seemed not to have recognized him, and then he waved a hand in a gesture of welcome. The man he was talking to turned around and then stood up to greet Charlie. It was Herbert Alstein.

When the introductions had been made, Alstein turned to Alain. "I am delighted to make your acquaintance. Our friend Charlie has already told me a good deal about you. I know that it is because of you that he was able to better his own condition and that you hope now to be able to better the condition of all the Frenchmen in the camp by obtaining their regrouping. You have—indeed, you have had ever since I first heard this—all my best wishes in your efforts. I see that you already know Monsieur Geoffrin. To say that it gave me pleasure to find him here would be the blackest form of humor, but in our common distress his presence has brought me the pleasure of being able to share again our memories of other days. But I have left you standing. Forgive me."

Alstein expressed himself in punctilious French, uttering each phrase as though he were carrying on a drawing-room conversation.

He walked to another table, and Alain understood from his gestures that he was asking the men sitting around it, very politely, if he might borrow the two unoccupied stools. As he carried them back, it occurred to Alain that it had been months since he had heard the word "Monsieur."

When they sat down again, Alstein carefully arranged the crease in his trousers and then picked up the thread of his conversation.

"We had been discussing your father," he said to Charlie, "and those wonderful conversations about contemporary French

101

literature we used to have in your beautiful apartment in Paris. To me, the Quai Voltaire will always remain the ideal location for a city dwelling. The windows, opening out on a view of the Louvre and the Tuileries Gardens—beauty and history, harmoniously intertwined. And your parents had the rare ability to furnish their home in such a manner that it was not until evening that the grace and style of the objects and the splendor of the paintings turned the eye from the view."

Alstein turned to Alain. "And you, cher monsieur, where do you live?"

The question surprised Alain, but he felt he could provide an answer that would be appreciated by Alstein. In Nantes, he had occupied the top floor of an eighteenth-century mansion, built by a slave trader, on the Place de la Petite Hollande. He remembered the elegant wrought-iron balustrade of the staircase and described the arabesques of the shadows it cast on the old stone walls. He told of the parquet floors, of their precious woods from Africa. The building, like all those built on the swamps along the Erdre, rested on mahogany pilings, which had been rotting every since the land reclamation programs had brought them above the level of the water.

"Then it was in Nantes that you were arrested?" Alstein said.

Alain realized that the first question had been only the beginning of a formal interrogation. He answered readily but felt relieved when the conversation turned to the situation in France, the Resistance, and General de Gaulle. In these matters, he considered himself on safe ground, and his answers reflected his assurance. Alstein, however, was not to be deflected from his inquest. The questions he asked were aimed at assuring himself that Alain was not bluffing when he mentioned the officials he had met in London or in France. On several occasions Alain sought to bring Geoffrin into the conversation, hoping for his support. But their work had always been in different spheres, and neither before the war nor in the Resistance had

102

they known the same people. There was a visible lessening of the interest Alstein had originally shown in Alain.

Charlie attempted to bring the discussion around to the purpose of their visit by asking Geoffrin what *kommando* he had been assigned to. It was Alstein who answered.

"Our friend has not yet been released from quarantine," he said, "and I have not yet despaired of getting him assigned here, to the Institute of Hygiene. His scientific qualifications should make that possible. Unfortunately, at the moment, Dr. Ding feels that he has a large enough staff. I have been trying to impress on him how rare it is to have a biologist of Monsieur Geoffrin's ability in the camp." He turned again to Alain, and added, "But wasn't there something you wanted to ask me about your assignment?"

Alain stated that he was an electrical engineer and had hoped to learn something of his chances of being employed in the factory. If they were not good, might there, perhaps, be some way of improving them?

Alstein wrote down Alain's number and promised to see what he could learn. His tone was cold, and Alain's hopes plummeted. Alstein's reply seemed to him to be merely a polite expression of indifference. Alain thanked him in advance for anything he might be able to do and went on to say, as he got up to leave with Charlie and Geoffrin, that he was grateful to Alstein for the most pleasant afternoon he had spent since his arrival in the camp.

Alstein, the perfect host, accompanied his guests to the barbed-wire fence surrounding the block. They walked together for a moment, silently. Alain was enormously depressed, and overwhelmed by a feeling that he had been deceived. Even though he knew very well that he was wrong, he could not avoid being slightly angry with Charlie because of his friend's attitude. Since he didn't want to say anything he knew he would regret later, he left Charlie and walked with Geoffrin toward the Small Camp.

"A curious man, this Alstein," he said. "I would like to know him better. Who is he, exactly?"

"He's a difficult man to define," Geoffrin replied. "I don't imagine that under any circumstances he could separate himself from that distinction of attitude, of movement and speech that you must have noticed. He comes from a Rhenish family, well-to-do and very Catholic. I met his mother once, and she is without doubt a great lady. Also, he studied in Germany and then in England. I think it was at Oxford that he cast aside the brutality normal to Germanic students and came to understand that the behavior of a gentleman must remain independent of the conditions in which he finds himself. The Weimar Republic sent him to Paris as an attaché of the German embassy there, and I am certain that he would have had a very successful career in the diplomatic service if it had not been for Hitler's coming to power. But he had had just enough time to fall in love with France when the Nazi rabble took over the German diplomatic corps. It was at that time that I knew him, and I could see at firsthand his dilemma. His background, his culture, and his tastes all contributed to the pleasure he derived from his position and the advantages it afforded him; but his convictions made it impossible for him to collaborate with men such as these. So, rather than return home, he resigned from his post and stayed on in Paris, without a *sou*. He barely made a living, in a publishing company. When it became certain there was going to be a war, his patriotism drove him back to Germany. Because of his love for France, however, he stubbornly refused to accept the positions in France for which his knowledge of our language and his contacts made him the obvious choice. It was this that eventually brought him here. He told me, confidentially, that the German Communists who rule the camp hate him. His contempt for everything vulgar and brutal, and his Catholicism—of which he is inordinately proud—are unbearable to them. But his record of anti-Naziism forces them to accept him. He must have demonstrated an extraordinary skill in the kind of tactics required here, or he would never have obtained a position as secretary to Dr. Ding."

Although he did not say so, Alain thought it likely that the senior *kapos* had had no qualified Communist available for the job, and that, even if they had, they might have preferred not to take the risk of seeing one of their number associated with Dr. Ding. It was not simply by chance that the chief of the human guinea-pig block was a "green," while all the other block chiefs were "reds."

"Alstein enjoys exceptional privileges," Geoffrin went on. "He is not subject to the normal brutalities of the camp, and he is exempt from all physical work. He sleeps between sheets, bathes in hot water, and lives among well-educated men. And in addition to this, he wears his hair as he pleases and even manages to be well dressed. You know better than I that, in this camp, that constitutes a symbol of power. He told me that his ambition was to use that power to help those French deportees who deserve help."

This was exactly what Alain had feared. What, he wondered, was Alstein's criterion? The depression he had felt after their conversation suggested that it might be based on the possibility of a return for his services, after the liberation. If such were the case, he did not, Alain thought, have much to hope for from Alstein.

When Alain returned to his block, it had begun to snow again. The flakes accumulated on his shoulders and slipped into his collar. The icy humidity penetrated swiftly. In a little while, in the square for roll call, it would pierce to the bone, and all night long he would shiver uncontrollably in his soaking garments.

Charlie saw him come in and led him at once to the toilets. He had stopped by to see his *kapo,* in block 40, and had obtained an empty cement sack, made of heavy kraft paper. He began separating the layers of the paper and sharing them with Alain. They made a kind of chasuble of them and slipped it between their shirts, their jackets, down into their pants. But the paper was still visible at the collar, and if the block chief noticed it they were certain to be bludgeoned. They decided to wear it directly over their skin, so that it would be hidden by the shirt.

"It scratches," Charlie said.

"So much the better," Alain replied. "That stirs up the circulation." He smiled, and added, "And you have given me the best part, the inner lining of the bag. The chalk there is being transformed into a mustard plaster. It's wonderful."

His ill temper with Charlie had almost vanished. He expressed what remained of it in an imitation of Alstein's voice: "Monsieur, your father would be legitimately proud if he knew the extent of his son's abilities and altruism. Thanks be to him for having given birth to so gifted and generous a human."

"Papa," Charlie replied, "is better off knowing nothing of the shit pot into which we have fallen. And I really am sorry about Alstein. He was not as cordial as I had hoped, but don't jump to premature conclusions from this first meeting. He isn't the type of man who gets carried away easily and promises the moon to anyone who comes along. If he thinks you deserve it, he will do everything he can to help you. And he can do a good deal."

"Then let's hope he thinks I deserve it," Alain sighed.

He was profoundly discouraged.

He was even more discouraged, three days later, when he met Genteau at the quarry and learned from him that, when their period of quarantine ended, Geoffrin had been sent to Dora. Not only, he thought, does Herbert Alstein reserve his help for a select few, but that help is apparently of little use.

His paper chasuble had grown soft and pliant from contact with his skin. The welcome warmth it brought him kept him that night from telling Charlie about Geoffrin's departure.

106

20.

|||||||||||||||||||||||||||||||||||||||||||||||||||||||||||||||||||||||||||||||||||||||||||||||

Genteau had been assigned to Philippe's block, and they had immediately become friends. At the same time, Rageot had made his first appearance in Alain's block. He was wearing a leather crash helmet whose large flaps joined beneath his chin and gave his head the appearance of a football. On either side of the helmet, there was a kind of semicircular ear, formed from the vertical seams. The opening out into it for the face revealed an oval dominated by a pointed nose and two constantly alert eyes.

"It's Mickey Mouse," Charlie said as soon as he saw Rageot.

Rageot did, in fact, resemble the cartoon character, and thenceforth he was known as Mickey. Small and wiry, he had an exceptional talent for avoiding quarrels and disarming any potential aggressor with a grin. On the day after his arrival in the block, he went to work in the factory.

"You see," he said, laughing, "my scheme worked. I told them I was a mechanic-toolmaker and they took me on, just like that. Now, I hope you can explain to me what this profession is all about, because my own ideas are pretty vague. In the café where I worked, I had a customer who came in for an apéritif every night. He was very proud of being a mechanic-toolmaker. And that's what I remembered. But we never used to talk about his job. His real passion was horses. And on that subject, he knew what he was talking about. He used to leave his bets with me to give to the bookmaker, and whenever I could add something of my own, I did. He didn't mind. There were times when

107

I doubled my tips for the whole week just by gambling a few francs."

He was an inexhaustible store of memories, and anyone listening to him would have assumed he had met only pleasant, amusing people in the course of an existence tailored to his measure, rich in happy chances and profitable adventures. Deportation had in no way altered his natural resilience. He had made a pair of dice from cubes of dried bread and happily accepted wagers from anyone naïve enough to play with him. He knew how to lose a cigarette he had won only a moment before, and since he habitually cheated, the game contributed to his livelihood.

"You understand," he said to Alain one day, in his cracked voice, "if there are people dumb enough to get rooked, they'll manage to do it one way or another. So why not by me? Besides, I only take on the ones who can lose without it doing them any harm. I never play for anyone's ration. But if he receives a package, there's no harm in sharing it with him a little. Don't you agree?"

Alain did not agree. Mickey's sense of moral values clashed with his own, but he did not tell him so, because he could not help feeling a certain admiration for this little man who knew how to laugh and to make the best of everything.

He was shocked by Mickey's assignment to the factory. It had come about so rapidly, while he, in all the months in the quarry, had had the feeling of struggling, like a fly in a jar, without being able to get out.

"How did you manage to get signed on there?" he asked. "You're not going to make me believe that all you had to do was tell them you were a toolmaker."

"I had a bit of luck," Mickey answered modestly.

He went on to explain that he had had the help of a *lagerschutz,* a Luxemburger who had run a black market business in cigarettes between Belgium and France before he was arrested.

"It was this same guy who kept me supplied in 1941,"

Mickey said. "You can imagine that, in my café, I had plenty of customers for him. That little business of his was doing pretty well, and I introduced him to a girl friend of mine who helped him squander the profits. He had quite a thing for her. When we saw each other here, the first thing he did was ask me about her. I told him that she had been heartbroken ever since he got picked up. A real little widow, faithful in every way, that's what she had become. Wasn't that better than telling him the truth?"

The conscience of the *lagerschutz's* protégé was not entirely at peace, however.

"Of course," he confessed, "I felt sort of funny using a cop to pull strings for me, but what could I do about it? *C'est la guerre.* And besides, he isn't a real cop. . . ."

Obviously, Mickey knew nothing of mechanical matters. On his first day in the factory, he had found another French deportee who actually was a mechanic but had been enrolled, by mistake, as an electrician.

"I told so many lies to the German foreman's interpreter that, in the end, I became the electrician. Installing wall plugs— it doesn't take a genius to do that."

He was already planning to set himself up as an electrical repairman after his return to France.

"Figure it out for yourself how much work there'll be. Nothing has been repaired since the beginning of the war. Then, good-bye to serving lemonade. I'll make a real place for myself. I have a buddy who's in the black market. He makes money by the bushel, and I'm sure he'll advance me the money to get started. It'll be fun, changing professions, just like that, as a result of all this. You're an electrical engineer, you should give me lessons."

21.

"Put this thing down a minute," Alain said.

Philippe dropped his end of the barrow. "What's the matter?" he asked.

"I don't know. But I just can't put one foot in front of the other, and I'm shivering all over."

"Do you have a fever?"

"I think so. I can almost feel it climbing."

"Do you have any pain?"

"No, but I'm having trouble breathing."

"Quick, let's get moving."

A *kapo* was moving toward them. They picked up the barrow and started off again.

The afternoon was an endless nightmare to Alain. He staggered and stumbled. His legs refused to obey. His ears filled with an incessant buzzing.

During the roll call that night, he could feel the blood pounding in his temples. The effort required to remain standing made him nauseous. The beam of the projectors lit a fire in his skull.

He made up his mind to go to the infirmary.

"My friend," Charlie told him, "you don't know what goes on over there. You'll begin by waiting for an hour or more, stark naked, in a draft that would kill off a Hercules. And don't think that after all that you'll be taken care of. A bunch of ignorant employees decide what's to be done with you. They don't know any more about medicine than I do, but as bullies they're outstanding. If they don't think you look sick enough, they'll throw you out. If they do, they'll give you a slip exempting you from work tomorrow, and they may or may not authorize you to come to the real sick call, the morning one, where there are doctors. But I can tell you, to get that, you either have to have one foot in the grave or else some very good luck."

Alain persisted in his intention.

"All right," Charlie said, "if you insist on going to the infirmary, tell whoever examines you that you have dysentery. They give out some kind of coal tablets to anyone with colic. You can bring them back to me. I need some."

A horde of wounded men, of skeletal figures coughing out their lungs, of wretched old men propping each other up, milled about the entrance to the infirmary. Some, unable to walk, were carried by their comrades.

Alain took his place in the ragged column.

From time to time, a *lagerschutz* appeared in the door and allowed another batch of men to enter. Through the windows of the room to which they were taken, Alain could see them taking off their clothes. Their fleshless bodies already resembled those that went by in wheelbarrows to the crematorium. Enormous boils erupted on the backs and arms of some. Others, with infinite care, tried to remove the rags that were stuck to open sores. Their jacket or coat across their shoulders, their shirt folded into a bundle and clutched against their chest, they waited their turn to be subjected to the first of the sorting-out processes. The injured were herded through one door to the left, the ill through another door to the right. And periodically, from the two ends of the building, men would emerge and put on their clothes in the frigid night.

Alain was at last admitted to the vast shed. In spite of the open windows, the stench was suffocating. He undressed and waited. When his turn came, he tried to indicate that he had a fever by feeling his own pulse, pointing at his chest, and coughing.

111

The German employee cursed at him and shoved him toward the exit door. Alain resisted as best he could and began shouting, "I'm ill! I'm ill!" In the end, he was thrust into the next room. Some of the deportees were already lined up in there, standing with their backs to the wall and their trousers lowered. A length of string hung down between their buttocks, and then looped up to a nail in the wooden partition. Their clothing was laid out at their feet, with the jacket folded so that the triangle and the number were visible. Alain was summoned by a man seated behind a little table, a Frenchman in charge of this consultation room.

"I'm French," Alain announced.

"Then give me your number, stick one of those thermometers up your ass, and try to have enough fever. If you don't, you'll be told to go to hell. The Kraut is in a foul mood tonight."

Alain realized then that there was a thermometer attached to each of the lengths of string. Those that were not in use had been replaced in glasses filled with an opaque liquid. He had scarcely had time to make use of one of them when another employee came in, a German this time, who clearly considered himself important. He glanced briefly at the thermometer of the first of the deportees in line, and while he was shaking it out before returning it to its glass he said something Alain did not understand. Then he went on to the second man in line. After having examined his thermometer, he laughed, and without another word clenched his fist and punched the man full in the face. The emaciated figure collapsed and remained stretched on the ground, dazed, his face streaming blood, not daring to get up. Only when the German kicked him in the ribs did he at last reach out for his clothing and stagger toward the door, hobbled by his pants, which he had not had time to pull up.

The German examined Alain's thermometer and spat out a few words. He did not strike him, but it was obvious that his decision was not favorable.

As soon as he had left the room, the Frenchman got up from

his table. He was holding some little rectangles of paper in his hand. He handed these out to those of the deportees who had been judged ill enough to return the following morning. In some cases, he filled a glass with a liquid contained in a large apothecary jar provided with a faucet, and made the man drink it. The same glass served for all.

"Nothing for you," he said, as he passed in front of Alain.

"But I hadn't had the thermometer long enough," Alain said. "I know very well I have a fever."

"What do you expect me to do?"

"I'm going to put the thermometer back and wait until the Kraut comes back."

"Oh no you don't. If he recognizes you, he'll clobber both of us."

Alain was growing desperate. "But if I go to the quarry tomorrow, I'll be dead tomorrow night. I'm telling you, I've got a fever that would kill a horse."

"All I'm here for," the man said, "is to fill out the papers."

"But just the same," Alain persisted, "you could at least try to do something for another Frenchman. We have to take enough from all the others; the least we can do is help each other out."

"Sure. But if I stick my nose into it and gave a slip to all the Frenchmen who come here, they'd find out about it fast, and I wouldn't be here much longer myself. I've already had quite enough of the quarry, thank you."

Alain realized that he was pounding his head against a stone wall. Charlie had been right, he thought, in attempting to dissuade him from coming to the infirmary. That suddenly reminded him that Charlie had asked him to get some of the coal tablets. He announced resignedly that he was also suffering from dysentery.

"You should have said that sooner," the Frenchman said. "If you've got the shits, you're entitled to a day of rest, no more, but at least you're that much to the good."

113

He filled the glass from another apothecary jar and handed it to Alain. "Here, swallow this. It will dry up your guts."

Alain meekly swallowed whatever it was the glass contained. The Frenchman had gone back to his table and filled out a slip.

"Good luck," he said as he held it out. By this time, a new group of ailing men had come in. They must have been *habitués,* because they went directly over to the wall and lined up, with their clothing at their feet, their number clearly visible. A moment later each of them had a length of string dangling from his rump.

Alain left the building and put his clothing on outside, shivering in the rising wind. When he returned to his block, he found Charlie and told him the story of his visit to the infirmary.

"And there you are," he concluded. "I got nothing at all for my own illness, but I did get a day of rest for yours. And as a bonus I was given a glass of some kind of medicine."

Charlie nodded. "That's it, all right—the logic of the camp."

"I'm sorry I couldn't bring you the coal tablets."

"Don't worry about it. Tomorrow, I'll try to make a fire during the rest period, and I'll put aside some cinders I can chew on. They'll probably be as effective as the tablets, although I imagine they contain some kind of purifying agent. And don't feel sorry for yourself because you missed the soup. It was nothing but dirty water. There weren't even the usual scraps of rutabaga in it. I hope at least you didn't catch cold at the infirmary."

"No, I think I was lucky. Tomorrow, I'll sleep all day, and I'll be better after that."

"Sleep all day? Where?"

"In the dormitory."

"It's easy to see that this is your first so-called 'day of rest.' You'll find that you'll have a choice between the block fatigue duty and walking around outside."

"What fatigue duty?"

114

"Cleaning out the building, washing the latrines, carrying anything that has to be carried. If you want to try to get out of it, there's only one way: Don't go back to the block after roll call, and that means staying outside, because there's no place where you'll find shelter. As for going into the dormitory, forget about it. It's forbidden."

Alain's look was so desperate that Charlie felt called on to comfort him.

"Still," he said, "it's not as bad as working in the quarry. It's not so cold if you stay between the barracks. And if there are enough men left behind in the block, the work will be done in a hurry, and after that you can rest. If you're really lucky, you might even escape the fatigue duty entirely. The main thing is to stay out of sight of the *stubendienst* when there is something to be done."

After a monumental struggle, Charlie secured possession of a cover and a reasonably well-sheltered sleeping compartment. He dragged Alain into it with him, and all through the rest of the night, he could feel his friend's body shivering against his own.

22.

The sound of reveille wrenched Alain from a sleep peopled by nightmares. The return to reality was a laborious process, with every movement paid for in pain. He finally managed to rid himself of the coat he had pulled up over his legs, and Charlie helped him climb down from the compartment and make his way to the mess hall.

The idea of taking off his shirt and jacket and exposing himself to the blast of air in the washrooms terrified him. But there was no way of avoiding it. The cold, striking against his naked flesh, was like the lash of a whip. He fought his way through the men surrounding the basin and held his head under the threads of icy water spouting from the column. They ran down across his shoulders and back and splashed onto his chest, cutting his breath short. He caught at the rim of the basin with both hands to support himself. He was unable to straighten up, but at the same time he was conscious of a profound sense of well-being. He would have remained there indefinitely if one of the men waiting behind him had not pulled him back. Ignoring the crush around him, he gathered up the clothing he had let drop in the liquid mud that covered the ground. He felt light-headed, empty, as he might have after sexual release. When he had put on his clothes again, he found a place on a bench in the mess hall. He was no longer in pain. I must be dying, he thought. But even that was no longer of any importance. He felt well again, and that was all that mattered.

The bread was shared out, and he received his portion. As he bit into it, he realized that he was not hungry. Mechanically, he slipped the bread into his shirt. It was the only place where he could keep it. He had not received the slender round of sausage which constituted the remainder of the morning meal. What difference did that make? It was not worth it to him to fight for a round of sausage.

The block chief called up some of the deportees by number and handed them slips of paper. Alain thought vaguely that there seemed to be a good many of them today. Charlie motioned to him, and he followed him silently outside for the roll call.

"You're in luck," Charlie said. "There are at least twelve men, in addition to the sick ones, who aren't going to work this morning. They must be leaving in a transport. But they undoubtedly won't be called until this afternoon."

"But what do you mean when you say I'm in luck?"

116

"Because they will have to stay in the block. That means there will be plenty of men for the fatigue duties, and you may be able to get out of it. There are several Frenchmen among them. Try to arrange something with them."

Instead of reporting to the area where his *kommando* formed after the morning roll call, Alain started back toward his barracks. The walk was obstructed by a portable fence of barbed wire and wood, and a pair of *lagerschutzs,* bludgeons in hand, prevented anyone from entering. He showed them the slip he had received the night before in the infirmary and was directed to a corner of the big square where hundreds of deportees were already gathered—all those who had been exempted from work that day, either because they were ill or because they were scheduled to leave in a transport. One by one, as the slips they carried were checked and registered, they were passed through an endless series of barriers.

While this was going on on one side of the square, the columns of *kommandos* were passing through the camp gates on the other. When the last of them had gone, leaving the abandoned bodies of the dead behind, groups of *lagerschutz* began scouring the square for any deportees trying to escape from work. In the glaring light of the projectors, they were like little figures playing at cops and robbers. But the robbers, when they were caught, did not receive a symbolic tap on the shoulder. They were bludgeoned to the ground, their number was taken, and for the next two weeks they would be assigned to what was called the "shit *kommando,*" the harshest of the camp's disciplinary *kommandos.* The men assigned to it spent their day trotting back and forth between the S.S. vegetable garden and a gigantic sewage ditch, emptying the pails that they carried in the garden and then refilling them from the ditch. If their work was too slow to suit his mood, the *kapo* kicked or pushed them into the ditch. It was exhausting, revolting work, and its value as a punitive measure was increased because the members of the shit *kom-*

mando gave off such a stench that no one could tolerate their presence afterward.

Hiding in the predawn darkness of the street, Alain watched the formation of the fatigue teams through the windows of his building. He did not go in until he saw the block chief and the *stubendienst* sit down around a table. They cut themselves thick slices of bread, spread them lavishly with margarine, and then chewed peacefully. Alain slipped into a corner of the mess hall, trying not to attract their attention. No one said anything to him. Straddling the end of one of the benches, with his back propped against the wall, he fell asleep immediately, in spite of the cold.

The day was hours old when he awoke. Two Frenchmen, seated just a little distance down the bench from him, were talking together.

"This transport to Schönebeck isn't a bad deal," one of them said.

"You really think so?"

"Yes, I knew a guy who was sent there and later brought back here."

"What did he say about it?"

"They work in a factory."

"As workmen?"

"No. Manual labor, odd jobs. But it's heated, and they're guarded by German civilians who don't carry bludgeons."

"What about the food?"

"Better than it is here, I'm told."

"We'll be getting new clothes before we leave."

"What? What kind of clothes?"

"Striped uniforms."

"That means they'll take away my coat."

"I suppose they will, because everything is striped. But the clothing is all new."

Alain had been following the conversation absentmindedly. It

118

seemed to him that what he had just heard should interest him. But it remained formless in his mind. He felt that it could not really concern him, but at the same time he knew that he should make an effort to take advantage of the situation. He turned to look at the man who had mentioned losing his coat. He was wearing a three-quarter-length jacket of thick blue cloth, with a sheepskin collar. He had thrust his hands deep into the vertical openings of pockets on either side of the chest. He must be good and warm, Alain thought, and the idea he had been looking for suddenly came to him. He shook himself awake, thinking how best to enter the conversation.

"Are you sure," he said, "that they're going to give you new clothes?"

"Absolutely. Everyone who leaves here in a transport is given a brand new striped uniform."

Alain turned to the other man. "In that case," he said, "you don't care about your coat?"

"It isn't that I don't care about it. I just don't like them taking it away from me."

"Of course not," Alain agreed, "but they'll take it just the same."

"Yes, they will, the bastards."

"Since that's what's going to happen anyway, let's make an exchange. I'll give you my striped coat, and you give me your jacket. You won't lose anything, and I'll gain from it."

"And if I accept, what can you give me besides that old rag of yours?"

"I don't have anything else."

"Then go to hell. Your idea of an exchange isn't bad, though. I can easily find someone who will give me something."

Alain raised his arm to argue, and as he did so he felt the slice of bread against his ribs.

"Wait a minute," he said. "I can give you my bread ration from this morning."

"Let me see it."

119

Alain took the bread from its hiding place.

"It's a deal. Give it to me."

Each of them ripped out the stitching of his number, and they exchanged garments.

The short jacket was in good condition and completely padded on the inside. It was incredibly heavy and felt very warm.

"How did you ever manage to get a thing like this?" he asked.

"Oh, it was easy. One day, when the block chief went to pick up some clothing at the supply room, I was in the building because I was sick. He took me with him, to carry things. So I kept the best one for myself. That was fair enough, wasn't it? It's so heavily quilted that it even deadens a blow from a bludgeon, and—look, I'll show you—there are fastenings at the wrists so the air can't get into the sleeves. It probably belonged to some Russian big shot who got himself caught. And the fur collar can be turned up, too. There's a flap to hold it closed. That protects the ears."

"The way you're talking about it, anyone would think you were trying to sell it to him," the other Frenchman intervened. "What you ought to do is share that bread with me. I have a right to it. If I hadn't told you that they were going to give us new clothing, you wouldn't have had it."

"Maybe. But the coat was mine."

Alain thought it best to leave. He borrowed a needle and some thread from a *stubendienst,* sewed his own number on the jacket, and then put it on. It was so thick that it reminded him of the garments he had seen worn by animal trainers, to protect themselves from bites. With this, he thought, I won't have to be so afraid of the cold.

An S.S. guard had come in. Everyone present leaped to attention, including the block chief, in his little corner. Groping his way backward, Alain managed to find the door. His legs were still very weak, but he thought it prudent not to remain there. He began wandering aimlessly among the barracks buildings, trying to find a place that was at least partially sheltered.

120

As he passed the Institute of Hygiene, Herbert Alstein was just coming out.

"But what are you doing here, my dear friend?" Alstein asked.

Alain explained that he was ill, that he had a day of exemption from work and did not know where to go.

"I met another of your friends," Alstein said, "Monsieur Philippe Drouhin. He was introduced to me by a former deputy I knew when I was stationed in Paris. I believe he was your classmate in school. What profession is he in now?"

Without even being conscious of what he was doing, Alain answered the innumerable questions he was asked about Philippe.

"Dr. Ding is away today," Alstein told him, "so I have the time to go over to the *Arbeitsstatistik*. Come into our mess hall. You can wait for me there, quietly and comfortably warm. I hope that, in a little while, I'll be able to tell you something of your chances of being assigned to the factory."

The room was empty. Alain sat in a corner. It was, as Alstein had said, very comfortable.

Presently, Alstein returned.

"I have good news for you," he said. "But you are as red as a poppy. What's wrong?"

"I have a fever," Alain replied.

"Wait a second. I'll go and get you some aspirin. Have you had anything at all to eat?"

"Nothing since the bread yesterday morning."

"But you can't go on like that. Stay right there; I'll be back in a minute."

When Alstein came back, Alain swallowed the aspirin tablets with a few mouthfuls of a steaming yellow liquid.

"That's great," he said. "It reminds me of the chicken bouillon my grandmother made me drink when I was a child and had a cold."

Alstein laughed.

"It's not chicken bouillon," he said, "but rabbit bouillon, typhous rabbit to be exact. Don't make such a face. It's sterilized."

121

He explained that the lungs of rabbits which had previously been inoculated with typhus were used in making the antityphus vaccine. The laboratory assistants put the remains of the animals through a sterilizer. They provided both bouillon and meat, which was shared among the personnel of the Institute of Hygiene.

Reassured, Alain went on sipping at the hot broth.

"I am pleased to be able to tell you," Alstein said, "that you and Monsieur Drouhin will very shortly be assigned to the factory as engineers. . . . No, don't thank me. It is a pleasure, one of the rare pleasures available to me here, to use whatever small means I have to help my French friends. So far as you are concerned, for that matter, your assignment had already been decided. Someone, and someone very highly placed, I was told, had intervened before I even inquired. In Monsieur Drouhin's case, I had no difficulty having his name placed on the list of engineers. That does not, however, console me for my failure to be of any help at all in the case of Monsieur Geoffrin. I could do nothing to avoid his transfer to Dora."

"But what is this Dora place, really?" Alain asked. "The mere name seems to spread terror everywhere."

"To tell you the truth, no one knows anything very precise. It's a camp, a dependency of Buchenwald, located west of Berlin, near Nordhausen. None of the men assigned there has ever been brought back here. The only certain thing, unfortunately, is that the mortality rate there is extremely high. This camp periodically receives a list of the numbers of the dead. An equal number of deportees is then sent to replace them. You must have been aware of the frequency and size of these transports. That will make it possible for you to judge the number of human lives consumed by Dora. Each month, it corresponds roughly to its total work force. I hope that Monsieur Geoffrin's splendid constitution will permit him to survive. I have not yet abandoned the project of having him returned here, even though, as I said before, no one has ever left Dora after having been assigned there. But in any case, the danger of being sent there no longer exists

122

for you or for Monsieur Drouhin. The S.S. command has ordered the *Arbeitsstatistik* to keep all engineers, electricians, and mechanics here."

Alain had the impression of surfacing in calm waters after a desperate struggle somewhere in the depths.

As he entered the door of the mess hall in his own building, Alain was greeted by a stream of oaths from a *stubendienst*. He understood nothing of the ugly German phrases except their tone. But why should he care what they meant? He had a good, warm coat. He was going to be assigned to the factory. He had only to tolerate this mad dog. When he was tired of barking, he would stop. With his hands thrust deep in his pockets, Alain walked into the room, thinking only that he would go and sit down on a bench. Before he had time to make a move to protect himself, the *stubendienst* leaped forward, and his clenched fist caught Alain full in the face. Alain staggered backward, trying to regain his balance, but his legs folded beneath him. He watched the tables, the light bulbs, and the beams of the room revolve slowly around him. He was neither surprised nor disturbed. There was a superior logic to the manner in which events unfolded, and there seemed no point in arguing it. He was going to sleep, and that was just as it should be.

When he regained consciousness, his first impression was not of pain but of surprise. The tip of his tongue encountered two incisors which were not in their accustomed place and were as loose as childhood teeth on the point of falling out. His mouth was full of blood. The *stubendienst,* perfectly calm now, was eating a slice of bread and paying no attention to him. Alain was forced to support himself on a bench in order to get up. He staggered toward the washrooms and sat down on one of the toilet seats. The draft of cold air in there revived him. He put his fingers to his swollen lips and then carefully tested the two teeth. They were held in place only by shreds of the flesh of his gums, and he pulled them out without difficulty. He spat blood and went to rinse his mouth. The cold water set off fireworks of pain.

He sat down again, feeling weak but somewhat better. Now that he knew that he was going to work in the factory, he was beyond the reach of things like this.

23.

||||||||||||||||||||||||||||||||||||||||||||||||||||||||||||||||||||||||||||||||||||||||||||||||||||||||||

Alain swallowed the aspirin tablets Alstein had given him, with his ration of soup that night. Encased as he was in the quilted jacket, he sweated profusely. He had an unquenchable thirst and a constant need to urinate. Every hour throughout the night, he was forced to leave his compartment, go to the toilets, and then drink deep of the icy water. It seemed to him that he could feel it flowing through his body, washing away all the impurities left there by the fever. When he awoke in the morning, he felt exhausted but cured. Only his swollen lips and the toothless portion of his jaw still caused him pain. He devoured his ration of bread and the little square of margarine, and this restored some of his strength.

At the entrance to the quarry tool shed, he found Philippe and Paul Genteau, already carrying the barrow. In the halflight of dawn, they walked directly in front of him without seeing him. He called out to them.

"Well, don't we say good morning to our friends anymore?"

They came to an abrupt halt, as if they had been caught in some guilty act.

124

"Here," Genteau said, obviously embarrassed, "this is your place."

"I didn't recognize you," Philippe stammered. "But I'm damned glad to see you again. Are you better?"

Alain could not help laughing at their confusion, and that sufficed to clear the atmosphere.

"I'm cured," he replied. "And, as you can see, I am now warmly dressed. Padded, in fact, to such an extent that I don't have to worry about the *kapos*. So, Genteau, you keep my place."

Genteau refused. Philippe protested he would give up his place. A moment later, each of the three was accusing the two others of not wanting to team up with him. The day was beginning to get brighter, and Philippe noticed Alain's swollen mouth.

"What happened to you?" he asked.

"It's nothing. I got punched by a *stubendienst*."

Philippe moved closer to Alain to get a better look. Genteau took advantage of their momentary inattention and vanished.

"Damn it, he's gone!"

"I should have expected that," Philippe said. "That guy does you a favor as if he were stealing from you—by hiding."

"We'll have to find him. We can take turns with the barrow."

But when they did find him, he stubbornly refused.

"You know," Alain said to Philippe, "this time, it's certain. We are going to be assigned to the factory."

"Have you seen Desbrosse again?" Phillippe asked ironically.

"It has nothing to do with Desbrosse. It's Alstein—"

"Alstein?" Philippe interrupted him. "The elegant secretary at the Institute of Hygiene?"

"The same."

"In that case, it may be true."

"It *is* true."

"Well, whether it is or not, I'm grateful to you for having spoken to him about me."

125

"But I didn't have to speak to him about you. He told me you had been introduced to him by a former deputy."

"Yes, a friend of my parents. Or, I should say, an acquaintance, because there's no particular reason to be proud of knowing him. Since you had spoken to me about Alstein, I told him about our past friendship. But I didn't ask him for anything. In view of his lack of enthusiasm about doing anything for you, I didn't think it was worth the trouble."

"Well—" Alain began, but Philippe interrupted him again.

"Now that I think about it," he said, "there was one thing that was odd. When he learned that we knew each other, he subjected me to an absolute barrage of questions about you and about myself."

"When was this?"

"Wait a second—day before yesterday, yes, the day when you were taken ill. If it had happened before that, I would have told you about it."

"Three cheers for the mutual assistance society."

"What do you mean?"

"That each of us served as a witness in the other's defense with Alstein. I'll bet that he asked you where I lived."

"Yes, he did."

"And what my apartment was like?"

"Yes. And a great many other things. But I still don't understand what you're getting at."

"Alstein helps those Frenchmen who deserve help. But how can he be expected to know if the people who ask for his help are really what they claim to be, unless there is someone else to vouch for them. I am very, very grateful to you, Philippe."

"Fine, but why did he take an interest in me?"

"Because I confirmed what you had told him about yourself, just as you confirmed what I had told him about myself."

Throughout that day, Alain and Philippe discussed the prospects opened to them by the news they had received from Alstein.

126

They could already see themselves, installed in a well-heated office, leaning over documents and plans, with no fear of the bludgeons of *kapos*.

"And busily at work aiding in the victory of the Third Reich," Alain said. "That will be the moment for deciding the proper use of your gauge for measuring blameworthy and praiseworthy actions."

"I was thinking the same thing," Philippe replied. "But it's a little too soon to start worrying about that. In the first place, we aren't in the factory yet. And in the second, we don't know what we will be supposed to do."

"Obviously, we could always bring to our new tasks the same zeal with which we transport these pebbles."

"Perhaps—who knows?—we could even do our part to hinder the work of others. Everything will depend on what sort of men we have supervising our work."

There was nothing to do but wait. And this period of waiting, even though it was lit by hope, was more anxious than that of the past weeks, because now they felt that it must soon end. Every day, before the morning roll call, when the block chief called out the numbers of those men who were being transferred from one *kommando* to another, Alain's heart pounded against his ribs.

When his own number was called, he was certain that he had at last arrived at his goal, but that morning every Frenchman in the block received the slip of paper denoting a change. It was not a change of *kommando* but a change of block. All the French were assigned to either block 26 or block 31.

Alain had not seen any of the senior *kapos* recently, and he had long since given up hope that they would keep their promise.

In the quarry that day, the Frenchmen talked of nothing but their regrouping. Indifferent to one another until this moment, they suddenly became aware of the ties that bound them together. The concept of nationality had been destroyed by their dispersion among blocks of other nationalities. Now, it was abruptly resurrected. They called back and forth to one another, questioning, answering, while pretending to work, and gathered in little groups whenever possible to discuss this new event. The reasons behind the regrouping were the subject of all conversations. The most extravagant hypotheses were formulated, and traded from one group to another. To make them more plausible, their bearers embellished them with newly invented details.

Every Frenchman selected his own *truth* from the mass of rumors that circulated. Some of these rumors died swiftly, to be replaced, in the minds of those who had believed in them for a moment, by a version more in conformity with their need for hope or their inclination toward tragedy. Since it is reassuring to believe what a great many others also believe, the number of admitted *truths* was finally reduced to two. The optimists *knew* that General de Gaulle—or Marshal Pétain—had obtained preferential treatment for the French deportees and that their regrouping was the prelude to a substantial improvement in their situation. The pessimists *knew* that this regrouping made the French into hostages who would be executed if the Allied bombings continued to wreak havoc in Germany.

Alain and Philippe were both pleased and disturbed by the regrouping. Pleased, because it would offer an opportunity for improving the living conditions of all of the French in the camp. Disturbed, because of the chance that this opportunity would be lost. Moving around from one group to another, they had attempted to distract their compatriots from speculating on the causes of the regrouping and lead them to considering the advantages that might accrue from it. But their efforts had been without result. The excitement of the moment could be satisfied only by sensational revelations, of a type to lift some of the men to heights of joy and drive others to despair.

128

"We should have prepared them," Alain said, "so that they would have been ready to take advantage of the regrouping."

Philippe shrugged. "That would have been difficult. You scarcely believed that it would happen yourself. It would have been unwise to raise their hopes."

"No one would have listened to us, in any case," Alain said wearily.

"At this moment," Philippe observed, nodding toward a nearby group of Frenchmen, "our comrades resemble Chinese coolies. They are seeking, in the most unlikely rumors, the same satisfaction to be found in an opium pipe."

"Yes, because reality is so unbearable they'll accept anything as the price of escape from it."

"But that isn't going to solve anything. What we are facing is a concrete problem."

"Oh, the problem itself is simple enough. Tonight we are going to find ourselves gathered together, as Frenchmen, under the orders of a new block chief. We'll then proceed to divide ourselves into two categories. One will be those who consider themselves privileged beings, protected by tutelary gods named De Gaulle or Pétain. That group will be undisciplined, demanding, and quarrelsome. The other will be the despairing types who consider their fate already decided. They will have only one desire, to be left alone, and they will abdicate their self-respect before anyone has asked them to."

"Yes, that's about it. On the one hand, the stubborn and restless; on the other, the unreachables, who will evade any attempt at organization."

"I was doubtless wrong," Alain said, "in talking to the senior *kapos* about democratic order and freely accepted discipline. I wanted to bring about our regrouping, but I hadn't thought about the material conditions it would take place in. They destroy the whole structure. The natural behavior of men requires a period of preparation for events."

129

"That, actually, is the foundation of your whole idea of regrouping."

"And that's why the whole thing is going to be useless, even before it has had a chance to develop. Our comrades are convinced of one of two things: either they are saved, or they are condemned. In either case, they don't realize for a moment that their fate might depend on themselves, individually or collectively. So, what is the point of having obtained the regrouping?"

"You're almost as pessimistic as the worst of them. You and I are not the only reasonable Frenchmen in the camp. You're ready to give up now, because you've been listening to those who have lost their grip. But there are still those who have heads on their shoulders, cool heads, rational heads. They aren't saying anything, because if you want to deflate a rumor, you must be able to replace it with the truth. And they don't know that truth."

"We've been going around telling the truth, from one group to another. And you saw what happened."

"The time wasn't right. Let the fever drop. Before anything could be done, the regrouping had to come. And we have that."

"Yes, we have that. But taking proper advantage of it is going to be a long process."

"Oh, well, we have plenty of time."

The French deportees took their places for roll call with the blocks they were about to leave, and then moved to the barracks to which they had just been assigned. Charlie had spent a few days in that barracks, after leaving quarantine, and the block chief had not seemed to him a bad sort.

"I've already worked for him, as interpreter," Charlie said. "Everything will be all right if he'll let me do it again."

Charlie greeted the block chief as though he were an old friend. His youthful, open smile and his knowledge of German allowed him to carry it off.

130

"I'm glad to be back here, with you," he said.

"Ha," the block chief grunted. "Well, I'm not happy, finding myself saddled with a bunch of Frenchmen. They had better watch their step, or else—"

"They'll watch their step, I can tell you that. But in any case, you can be sure I'll do anything I can to help you. If you should need an interpreter—"

"I will. You stay here. I've prepared a little speech for them, and you'll translate it."

At curfew time, the block chief had all the tables and benches in the mess hall pushed back along the walls.

"Roll call," he said.

"He's going to take a count," Charlie translated, and almost before anyone had noticed, he took charge of the operation. "Don't behave like a bunch of jackasses. The faster the count is made, the faster we'll get to bed."

"By fives," the block chief said.

"Form three columns of fives, side by side," Charlie said.

The columns were formed.

The block chief and the *stubendienst* counted the deportees. Then they compared their figures and held a whispered conference. Alain began to be worried.

"Silence!" the block chief shouted. "I am going to speak to you."

"Silence," Charlie cried. "I am going to translate what the block chief wants to say to you."

"I know all about you Frenchmen. You're a bunch of bastards. But I know how to enforce discipline."

"He wants to welcome you here. He is prepared to give up use of the bludgeon if we can maintain discipline ourselves."

There was a murmur. Charlie was not the only Frenchman who understood German, and the freedom of his translation had not gone unnoticed.

"Silence!" the block chief bellowed again. "I demand absolute obedience. When you come into this building, I want you to wash

131

your boots or your galoshes. I want everyone to wash himself thoroughly in the morning. You Frenchmen are naturally dirty, but I'll change that. In the dormitory, there is one sleeping mat and one cover for each two men. I want to see order strictly maintained in there. If it is not—the *stubendiensts* have strong arms and good bludgeons."

"The block chief, naturally, wants order maintained and is counting on us, as Frenchmen"—Charlie made this word ring like a note from a trumpet—"to see that it is, without having to call in the *stubendiests*. Let's show him that we are worthy of our reputation. We must always remember to wash our boots before we come into the building. We must always be sure to wash ourselves in the morning. In the dormitory, there is one sleeping mat and one cover for each two men. There's no point in fighting over them. But if there are some bastards who pinch extra covers, we should let them know ourselves that this is not the way Frenchmen behave, and not wait for them to be beaten up by the *stubendienst*."

"To bed!" the block chief shouted.

Charlie planted himself solidly in front of the pile of covers. "Don't shove," he said. "There are enough for all."

The human tide rushing into the dormitory almost swept him away. The long habit of a daily battle for the conquest of a cover and a place to sleep impelled a few of the men to their customary assault on the door. But they were swiftly recalled to order by those around them. Alain had remained behind, to see what would happen, and he heard someone say, "There's no point in being with other Frenchmen if there are still some of them who behave like Russians." The tide began to ebb of its own accord. A strapping young fellow volunteered to assist Charlie, and together they succeeded in distributing one cover to each two deportees.

Alain was the last to go in.

"There are a few left over," Charlie said. "I'm going to give

132

them to the oldest men. Try to find a free place for us, and I'll join you in a few minutes."

There was a hum of conversation throughout the dormitory. A few of the more anarchical types criticized Charlie for "acting as if he were the block chief." The others were beginning to sense the advantages that might result from their regrouping. Alain could only hope that their imagination would not lead them so far that they might be disappointed later.

Charlie joined him in the compartment and said, "What do you think? It didn't go off too badly."

"It was sensational," Alain said. "The block chief seems to be a solid-gold type."

"Hmmm. Well, you know, I did a little editing in the translation of his speech. The main thing now is to make it work well enough so that no one can blame me for it."

24.

|||||||||||||||||||||||||||||||||||||||||||||||||||||||||||||||||||||||||||||||||||||||||||||||||||||

The block chief thrust his head into the dormitory and barked, *"Aufstehen!"* His powerful bass voice reverberated in the icy air, echoed by the yawning and grumbling of men, the creaking of timbers, and the groaning of the sleeping planks as the deportees turned and twisted and sat up. Before the boots of even one of their number clattered against the flooring, there was a sound of whistling, and the startled men recognized it as the reveille of the French army. As the clear, familiar notes echoed through the building, they were picked up by a swelling hum of many voices. For an instant, the deportees were twenty years old again and waking up in their own bunks in their own barracks. Men began talking to one another spontaneously. Some of them were actually joking. That first awakening in block 26 was different from any that had preceded it. The spell was momentarily broken when the *stubendienst* came into the dormitory, bludgeons in hand, prepared to herd the men into the washrooms. But they found little use for the weapons they carried. The file of deportees flowed like water toward the door.

Such remarks as were exchanged—"Stop pushing, will you, you bastard!" "Get a move on, you stupid ass!"—seemed almost affectionate by comparison with the usual battles between deportees of different nationalities.

Around the washbasin, things did not go as well. The *stubendienst,* probably as a result of their annoyance at not having had the opportunity to use their bludgeons as much as they would have liked, conceived the idea of forcing the deportees to wash their feet. In the resulting disorder, they found the pretext that they had been seeking. Contrary to past habit, however, the rage for vengeance engendered by the sting of blows received was not rented in brutal quarrels among the deportees. The unity of language made it possible for everyone to express his feelings, knowing that he would be understood without resorting to force. A mutual hatred for the *stubendienst* fused into a stream of obscenities that did no harm to anyone. They calmed the inflamed tempers of the injured men and created an air of solidarity among the French. It was reflected in the distribution and sharing of the bread. There were quarrels and battles, inevitably; but they were less violent than usual and more quickly resolved.

When he took his place in the column to march out for roll call, Alain found himself standing next to one of his friends from Nantes, Marcel Dupuy. He had been in the camp for two months, but they had never seen each other before. A little group of men from Nantes had already formed, with Marcel at its center, and Alain discovered that, among them, there was a fishmonger from the neighborhood where he had lived. The

134

poor man repeated his story endlessly, to anyone who would listen. Some French prisoners, being sent from Nantes to the prison of Fresnes in Paris, were being taken through the streets of the city in a German army truck. One of them had leaped out and fled. The German police, who were responsible for the number of men in their transfer, had held a short sidewalk conference. The fishmonger happened to pass at just that moment, on his bicycle. They had seized him and tossed him into the truck. Two weeks later, in spite of all his protestations, he had been put on the train for Buchenwald, still under the name of the escaped man. The loss of his bicycle, which he had last seen standing against a wall, was the only thing his mind could still encompass. The fate that had overtaken him was too enormous to be within his grasp. And since he could not comprehend it, it had no place in his thoughts.

Had it been simply a matter of another French deportee he had chanced to meet in the quarry or on the square, Alain would probably have paid little attention to the human derelict who poured out such a story. But this was a comrade, a man whose prison he shared. No longer just part of a mass, he was a part of a French society. Alain did his best to console him.

"Come now, old man, you're making too much of it. What difference does it make if you lost your bicycle? That won't prevent you from putting away your share of muscadet when we get home."

"Yes, but what will my wife have to say when I get back? She doesn't even know what happened to me. She'll be very angry with me. Do you think for a minute that she'll believe me when I tell her how I lost my bicycle?"

"But we'll all be there to tell her that you didn't run off with some pretty girl."

"Of course, of course. But I had my name on the plaque of my bicycle. Someone may have taken it back to the store. A bicycle is a pretty important thing these days."

135

The old man wandered on and on, his voice fading into a gentle murmur. As death approached, the flickering candle of his mind illuminated only one small corner of the world, waiting for the moment when misery would snuff it out completely.

At the opposite pole, there were those who unconsciously attempted to personify, before dying, the character they would like to have been. Freed by events from a past they could not control, and having nothing further to fear from the future, they needed only an audience before which to play their chosen parts. The regrouping of the French offered them this audience, and there was a sudden emergence of directors of vast enterprises who were actually small-town shopkeepers, of Casanovas who were really henpecked husbands, and, most numerous of all, of heroes of the Resistance who had been arrested for some daring act against the Germans. The character each elected to play was invariably one of greater stature than his own, and each felt himself obliged to demonstrate the qualities he claimed to possess. Megalomania has its good points; it creates obligations.

The natural authority of certain of the deportees was recognized by their comrades, and these men became mentors for the entire block. A system of organization based on seating at the tables in the mess hall was born spontaneously, and everything else flowed from that.

The return to the block, after the day's work, was no longer a prolongation of an ordeal. It became a time for conversation. The relative calm that prevailed limited the brutal interventions of the *stubendienst*. At night, every man returned to his own sleeping compartment, which was always the same one. At Charlie's request, the block chief had agreed to allow a cover to be folded and left there, thereby eliminating the nightly battle over covers.

After the morning roll call, the French marched together to the columns for the various *kommandos*. And they took their places in the columns together, offering a united front against attack from other groups.

136

A few of the French deportees, who for some reason had not been included in the regrouping, still lived in blocks with prisoners of several different nationalities. Whenever they could, they mingled with their comrades in blocks 26 and 31, just as provincial visitors seize every occasion to mingle with the inhabitants of the capital. They found in this contact the element of solidarity, the comfort of belonging to a community and being able to choose their own friends, all of which had been beyond their reach so long as they were dispersed throughout the camp.

The regrouping of the French had not eliminated from their ranks the good-for-nothings, who are always present. But now they were surrounded by men who spoke their language and knew them for what they were. They were discreetly watched. When necessary, the threat of punishment was generally sufficient to put an end to their schemes.

A wind of equality and justice blew through this corner of the camp. Since some of the fatigue duties were rewarded with a supplementary ration of soup, they were assumed on a rotating basis by deportees designed by the chiefs of each table.

Christmas, 1943. The block chief requisitioned all the silver paper in which the chocolate in the deportees' packages was wrapped. He made stars and icicles from it and used them to decorate a little pine tree he had set up in a corner of the mess hall. The sight of this tree recalled family holidays together and gave rise to a general depression.

One morning, in an attempt to dissipate the gloom that shadowed everyone, Charlie conceived a harmless joke. He whispered to some of his comrades, in strictest confidence, that he had learned from a reliable source that the Holy See was sending packages to the deportees and that they would be distributed on Christmas Eve. He had planned, as a second phase to the operation, to reveal the contents of the packages, and it would then immediately have been apparent to everyone that the whole thing was a well-planned joke. But he was overtaken by events. Within an hour after he had whispered the first part of his story, no one was talking of anything but the packages. There were many who stated flatly that they had already arrived. Some were considering the idea of offering a ration of bread in exchange for some of the cigarettes that were certain to be included in the papal shipment. Lively arguments developed on the relative merits of Italian and French tobaccos.

That night, when his *kommando* returned to the block, Charlie asked all the table chiefs to put an end to the story by explaining that it had just been a joke. But it was too late. On Christmas Eve, 1943, there were still men who were convinced that Santa Claus was going to bring them a handsome gift. Their dreams had filled it with the most unlikely treasures. With their ration of soup that night they received one tiny sausage, a surprising, derisory supplement to the usual standard of the camp.

On Christmas Eve, curfew had been set back to midnight. Some German friends of the block chief came to pay him a visit, and they sang the Christmas songs together. Their voices were very good. That of the block chief, in particular, had a deep bass resonance. The French listened in silence. It was no longer possible to forget previous Christmases, spent with their families. The façade each of them had tried to maintain collapsed; the chin that had been carried high slumped against the chest.

"Last year, I was in London," Alain said. "I spent the night drinking with friends who were as anxious as I was to avoid thinking of their children and their wives in France. It wasn't very gay, but it was better than going to bed and spending the entire night feeling sorry for ourselves because we weren't at home. Look at those men sneaking off to the dormitory now. In a few minutes, they'll be bawling like children."

"And do you think the ones who are staying out here are

138

any happier, celebrating Christmas with an empty belly, their head in their hands, clenching their teeth as if that could keep the tears from coming?"

"There must be something we could do to occupy their minds."

"It would help if we at least knew how to sing."

"Wait a minute—there is one guy who claims to be a composer. Perhaps we could persuade him to sing some of his compositions."

The musician declined, however, saying that he was a pianist. One after another, the deportees slipped furtively off to the dormitory. Those who remained in the mess hall formed little groups and talked among themselves in muted voices.

From one table, at the opposite end of the room from that occupied by the Germans, there came an occasional burst of laughter. The other men turned to stare at it.

"Whose turn is it now?" Charlie was asking. He had just told one of the stories from his inexhaustible repertory. Other men came to join the group where there was laughter, and then returned to their own tables to tell their comrades what they had heard. The needed impetus had somehow been found. The smoldering embers of memory were drowned in a flood of barracks room stories, just as Alain had drowned them in alcohol the year before.

Roll call was not held until eight o'clock the next morning. It had snowed all night, but the sky was clear. The first light of dawn touched the deep, immaculate blanket of white that covered the barracks. In the streets of the camp, the footsteps left by the teams of men who had gone to bring the bread from the kitchens had not soiled the virginal apparel of the earth. Heavy boots and galoshes sank into the powdery snow without a sound. The blocks formed for roll call in silence. To the left of the gate, the trees of the pine forest stretched silvery branches almost to the fence. The sky became progressively paler, pink at first, and then yellow, before stretches of clear blue appeared between the high, thin clouds.

"What a great morning this would be," Charlie said, "for skiing."

25.

||||||||||||||||||||||||||||||||||||||||||||||||||||||||||||||||||||||||||||||||||||||||||||||||||||

One night, the block chief called Charlie to his corner to give him a package. The food and cigarettes it contained were packed in a sturdy wooden case. Inside the case were the parts of a ring bolt, a padlock, and two keys.

Charlie gave a generous share of what he had received to the block chief, who then asked what he planned to do with the box.

"If you'll give me your permission," Charlie answered, "I could keep it above the cupboards in the mess hall. That way, I could keep some of what comes in the packages and wouldn't have to eat it all at once."

"But it will be stolen."

"No, it won't. I'll close it with the padlock."

The block chief thought it over for a moment and gave his consent.

Charlie screwed the ring bolt in place, borrowed a pencil from the block chief and wrote his number, in large characters, on the side of the case. Then he padlocked it carefully and placed it on top of the cupboards in the mess hall.

The following Sunday, when Alstein brought his typewriter to the block to help the French deportees write their postcards home in German, he was asked by every one of them to ask that the next package be sent "in a wooden box that can be locked" and that it contain "things to cook." Little by little, at either end of the mess hall, wooden cases were lined up and then piled on top of each other above the cupboards.

In this way the deportees were able to save some items of food and cook them on the little round stove in the mess hall on Sundays, using an iron pot or an old tin can. Groups were formed, whose members shared whatever was sent to them. Some of those who did not receive packages were occasionally invited to be guests. On a Sunday afternoon it was often necessary to stand in line for hours before getting a place on the stove. Grayish noodles danced in boiling water beside a pot of flour cereal. The pat of margarine distributed with the morning bread was saved to be used with the noodles or the cereal. When the cooking was finished, the little group of friends installed themselves at a table, and each of them took his turn dipping his spoon into the common pot. These revels could not fail to stir the appetite of those who had not been invited and had not received a package. They swallowed their saliva, pretending to see nothing and rolling their eyes in envy, or openly begging.

Since no one set himself up as the standard-bearer of vice, the application of elementary moral principles was sufficient to maintain order. A few of the men had become moral guardians with no mandate other than that of a natural authority.

One day, the evening soup was replaced with boiled potatoes. It was a simple matter for those who had gone to pick them up at the camp kitchen to pilfer a few on the way back. The block chief noticed that one small container had less in it than the others when it arrived, but before he had the time to do anything about it the bearers had been searched by three of the table chiefs and the potatoes were immediately discovered. One of the thieves was a high-ranking official, the other a young boy. Charlie managed to persuade the block chief to turn the thieves over to the justice of their compatriots, instead of consigning them to being beaten to death by the *stubendienst,* as was the normal practice with thieves. Some of the deportees held a brief meeting and decided that the older thief should be forced to stand behind the *stubendienst* while they went ahead with the distribution of the potatoes, holding a sign that read: "I am a thief." In this way, every man in the block would pass in front of him, read the sign, and remember his face. Everyone was in agreement that the young boy should be granted a reprieve. In view of his age, it seemed obvious that responsibility for the theft must rest with the official.

The question of whether the thieves should receive their ration that night was hotly debated. It was finally decided they should: to deprive a deportee of nourishment, even if it was no more than a few boiled potatoes, came far too close, in their famished condition, to a condemnation to death. And in any case, it was a form of physical, if not of bodily punishment.

Charlie had a great deal of difficulty explaining these subtleties to the block chief. But he succeeded, largely because it was beginning to dawn on this thickheaded man that the minds of these Frenchmen operated in a way that was unfathomable to him. Although he was troubled by a vague fear of being thus mystified, he conceived both a certain contempt and a bit of admiration for such a way of thinking.

But everything that had been achieved was almost lost.

The block chief had somehow come into possession of a mangy yellow mongrel. He played with the dog throughout the day, lavishing on it all the unemployed tenderness of his sentimental Bavarian heart. Before leading the men of his block out for roll call, he would pat the dog's head and scratch its ears, urging it, in his deep bass voice, to be patient until he returned to the barracks.

One night, when he went back to his corner, after the roll

call, the dog had disappeared. Everyone in the building was enlisted in the search, but the dog could not be found. A childlike despair, on a scale proportionate to his enormous physique, overwhelmed the block chief. Although he had shut himself up in his corner, the sound of his grief could be heard throughout the mess hall. There was something grotesque in the spectacle of a man who was totally indifferent to the fate of his fellow man inordinately afflicted by the disappearance of a little dog.

A particularly spiteful *stubendienst,* who had never forgiven the French for depriving him of the pleasure of using his bludgeon to his heart's content, went in to see the block chief and began talking to him in carefully guarded tones.

Within a matter of minutes, fury took the place of grief in the block chief's childish brain. Suddenly, there was no doubt in his mind that these French pigs had killed his dog. They were thieves and murderers, degenerate bastards who were too cowardly to turn over the criminals themselves. Well then, they would all taste the punishment called for by such a crime; and all the more so because theirs was a crime against the discipline and authority of which he, the German block chief, was the representative. He was going to teach these Frenchmen the price of thinking they could attack the very foundations of society. He was going to do away with them all, rid the world of their contemptible species.

The more he shouted, the more enraged he became. There were few among the French deportees who understood the obscenities he hurled at them, but the general meaning was clear to everyone, and their faces reflected consternation and fear. Summing up the general opinion, Rageot murmured: "If he doesn't find that mutt, we're going to be up the creek." The block chief opened the cupboard at the foot of his bed, took out the bludgeons, and distributed them to the *stubendienst.*

The deportees began a rush toward the door, but when they arrived there they collided with the chief of another block, who was coming in. He shoved them brutally out of his way.

143

"Franz," he cried, "look!"

He was carrying the bloody carcass of the dog, and now he held it up for all to see, dangling from his fingers like a dirty handkerchief. He took his colleague by the arm and led him outside.

The *stubendienst* were no longer certain whether they should carry out their mass attack on the French. They sat down, dangling the bludgeons between their legs, waiting for the block chief to return.

He came back a short time later, sobbing like a baby. Without a word, he took the bludgeons from the hands of the *stubendienst* and replaced them in the cupboard.

The next day, the deportees of block 26 learned what had happened from some of their friends who still lived in one of the multinational blocks. Their block chief had surprised three Poles in the toilet room, in the very act of cutting up the body of the dog. He had left them under guard of his *stubendienst* and gone to find his colleague. Together, they had beaten the three Poles almost to death, and then they had hanged them.

A fortnight later, stuffed and mounted, the dog was returned to his customary place at the foot of the bed of the chief of block 26. Each night, the chief sat beside it, patting its head and talking to it as though it were still alive.

"It's a strange thing," Charlie said. "Our peace has been assured by the sacrifice of that yellow mongrel."

"Be careful of what you're saying," Alain replied. "You are around the Germans so much that you're becoming a little bit like them. You're getting sentimental about what happened to the dog, but you forget the three Poles who were murdered."

"No, I'm not forgetting them, but it's that stuffed dog that constantly reminds our block chief that we deserve his confidence. As for the Poles, they escaped from here days ago, in the smoke from the crematorium chimney, so they no longer serve any purpose."

144

26.

||||||||||||||||||||||||||||||||||||||||||||||||||||||||||||||||||||||||||||||||||||||||||||||||||||||||

Roll call was ended, and the *kommandos* had left the square.

A hundred or so of the deportees, among whom were many French, gathered near the gate of the camp. They had been summoned here, that morning, by a slip of paper from the *Arbeitsstatistik*. The rumor had spread that they were going to be taken to the factory. The fact that Alain, Philippe, Genteau, and several other engineers had all been included in the list made it seem possible that the rumor was true.

Even as they waited and shivered in the icy wind that swept the square, unable to see even one another in the predawn darkness, the deportees let themselves be carried away by optimistic dreams.

"Now, there's no more need to worry, we'll get through somehow. The winter is getting on. The middle of January, and we've already seen the worst of it. It won't be so bad from now on, and we'll be indoors, in the factory. In March we'll see the first signs of spring. And everything will be better when it isn't so cold."

"The Allied invasion is sure to take place as soon as the weather is good."

"And after that, it won't be long."

"We can count on being home by the beginning of summer."

"We'll be home before that. Hitler will collapse as soon as the success of the invasion is assured. The German army can't fight on three fronts at once—in Russia, in Italy, and in France.

145

It will revolt against the regime to prevent the invasion of German territory."

"It won't be a month between the time of the invasion and our liberation."

A *lagerschutz* walked across the square toward the group of deportees, who had been waiting for two hours now. He called them off by number, formed them into a column, and led them through the gate. He stated the number and destination of the crew to the S.S. guard and handed him a paper. In what he said, Alain picked out the words "Mibau Werke"—the Mibau factory.

THE FACTORY

Every man carries his own Patmos within himself. He is free to go or not to go to this dreadful promontory of thought, from which one gazes out into the darkness. If it should be that he never goes, he remains a part of ordinary life, of ordinary conscience, of ordinary virtue, of ordinary faith; and that is good. For mental tranquility, it is best.

Victor Hugo, Essay on William Shakespeare

27.

IIIIIIIIIIIIIIIIIIIIIIIIIIIIIIIIIIIIIIIIIIIIIIIIIIIIIIIIIIIIIIIIIIIIIIIIIIIIIIIIIIIIIIIIIIIIIIII

On their arrival at the Mibau factory, the deportees were split up among the different workshops.

Alain was placed under the orders of an extremely tall German who wore faded and patched blue mechanic's overalls with an enormous swastika sewn across the chest.

While waiting for his work assignment, Alain perched on a high stool in front of a brand new workbench which still exuded the good, clean odor of resin. A Frenchman next to him was busily at work filing down a little piece of metal clamped in a vise. A diagram was spread out on the bench in front of him, and when he referred to it, his lips moved silently, like those of an old woman counting the stitches of her knitting.

Alain watched him for a moment, vaguely astonished at the extent of his concentration.

"Have you been working in the factory for a long time?" he asked.

The Frenchman cast a frightened glance around him before answering. "A month," he said at last, as though he were betraying a secret.

"What are you making?"

"A mold."

"A mold for what?"

"I don't know."

Alain slid down from his stool and walked over to look at the diagram.

"Get back where you were," the Frenchman implored, his eyes riveted to the piece of metal in the vise.

Then, since Alain made no move to leave, he repeated rapidly, in an anguished tone, "Get back where you were, I'm telling you. You're going to make trouble for me. You're not supposed to pay attention to what the others are doing. It's forbidden."

He spoke in a strangled whisper, without looking at the man beside him, like a timid girl who dares not rebuff an overardent suitor too openly, for fear of attracting attention to herself.

"All right, all right," Alain murmured.

The diagram was too far away for Alain to be able to make it out. But his neighbor seemed to think he could, because he moved it even farther away.

"You seem to be in a godawful sweat," Alain commented.

"I don't want to be hanged," the Frenchman replied, as though he were talking to himself.

"And who's going to hang you?"

"The big blue foreman."

"The big blue foreman?"

"Yes, the *meister*."

"What in hell do you mean?"

"The German civilian in the blue overalls. He just walked by, and he looked as if he was watching us. That's why I couldn't answer you."

150

"Is he as bad as that?"

"He hates Frenchmen."

"From the looks of him, he hates everyone," Alain said drily.

"Maybe, but the French in particular."

"And what about the Russians?"

"He's satisfied just to think they're no good."

"Well, well!"

"You see, the thing is that he's in over his head."

"What do you mean?"

"He's the foreman, and the Frenchmen who work for him are more than a match for him, professionally. So, he asserts his authority by behaving like a bastard. With him, the more stupid you are the better off you are."

"Thanks for the tip."

"What do you do? In civilian life, I mean."

"Engineer."

"Don't boast about it."

"Right."

"I made the mistake of doing just that. And it didn't help me. Look out!"

The tall man in the blue overalls was on his way back toward them. He spoke to Alain in German. When he realized that Alain had not understood him, he muttered an oath, then shouted an order, addressed to no one in particular.

A deportee who served as his interpreter came running from somewhere in the shop.

"Are you an engineer?" he demanded, speaking to Alain.

"One could say that—"

"What's that supposed to mean? Everyone who came in this morning is an engineer."

"Then why are you asking me the question?" Alain asked.

"It's not me that's asking, it's the *meister*."

"Tell him that I am an engineer, but that I can do whatever he wants me to."

151

"You seem to want to make trouble. I can tell you right now that it's not a good idea in here."

"You misunderstood me—"

The *meister* interrupted them, speaking rapidly in German.

"Follow me," the interpreter said.

Alain was led to a dilapidated piece of machinery and given instructions. His work consisted simply of piercing holes in little plates of stamped iron.

The foreman watched him work for a moment before he walked away, shrugging his shoulders and spitting on the floor.

Alain's neighbor, who was operating a lathe and had apparently paid no attention to him until now, glanced at him out of the corner of his eye and murmured, "Be careful. Your predecessor was hanged."

"What did he do?"

"He had broken his drill, and when he went to get a new one, the warehouse keeper made a mistake. He gave him one for four and a half millimeters instead of four. For the next several hours, without realizing that he was doing it, he was making holes that were too large."

"And he was hanged for that?"

"Yes. The *meister* accused him of sabotage, and the S.S. took him away. From what I heard later, he was executed the next morning in the courtyard of the crematorium."

"But it wasn't his fault that the drill was too big."

"He was Russian, and the warehouse keeper is German."

Philippe was assigned to a shop in which the assembling of wireless sets was slowly beginning to take shape. His particular job was soldering.

"You know," Alain told him when they had been working in the Mibau for a week, "moving from the quarry to the factory hasn't made me any better off, on an intellectual level."

Philippe smiled. "Have you already forgotten the cold, and

the constant fear of the *kapos,* that made us behave like a flock of frightened chickens?"

"I wonder if the boredom caused by what I'm doing now is preferable."

"Absolutely. It's restful. Isn't it exactly that same kind of mental repose you were looking for when you lay on a beach in the sun before the war?"

"That was before the war."

"What do you mean by that?"

"Simply that there is a war now, and it isn't the moment for lying in the sun."

"Do you mean that it's the moment for shivering in the quarry all day and being beaten with a bludgeon? In the factory we are warm and sheltered and the *kapos* don't bother us."

"I don't know how to explain it to you," Alan said mournfully. "It's just that I feel useless."

"It isn't a question of being useful." Philippe was categorical. "It's a question of survival."

"That's not enough."

"Before we were transferred to the factory, it was a considerable accomplishment."

"True, but it was a kind of test we had to pass. It couldn't go on forever. Now I have the feeling that we are getting bogged down in a state of futility."

"We have to resign ourselves to it."

"Resignation is not one of the virtues with which nature gifted me."

"I know that," Philippe said. "But you may have acquired it, since your arrest."

Alain shook his head. "I'm afraid I never shall. In prison, I was constantly studying the problem of escape—"

"In the first place," Philippe interrupted him, "you didn't solve it; and in the second place, your ambition was limited

153

to saving your own skin. I share that ambition and I intend to retain it, and that's why I'm grateful for the factory."

"In Fresnes—"

"You're not going to tell me that you contributed something to the Allied cause from your cell."

"No, but I did help to uphold the morale of my comrades by sending their messages—"

"—to their families or their girl friends."

"And here, it was because of me that the French were grouped together."

"All of that has just one purpose—to survive, and, insofar as possible, to help others to survive. We can't do any more than that. So, wrap yourself in your cocoon and count the days—"

"Count the days while I work for the Germans. Because we are working for them, you know."

"Oh, we're really not doing anything very much."

"Anything we do is too much."

"And what would you like to do about it?"

"Sabotage."

"Sabotage what, and how?"

Alain shook his head again. "That's exactly what I've been asking myself."

"Considering the kind of work you've been given to do," Philippe observed. "I don't see how you could go about it."

"For the moment, I know that I can't do anything. But what bothers me is the thought that the way things are going now, when the opportunity does come I won't be able to seize it."

"On the contrary, you will be in good shape."

"Not morally, and that's what counts."

"Well," Philippe said with resignation, "in any case, if you are too impatient you will do something stupid. And what would you gain by getting yourself hanged for nothing? I would advise you to weigh the risks carefully before trying anything."

"That's just what I'm doing. But this routine is getting me

154

down. What a relief it would be if I knew I was accomplishing even the most insignificant act of sabotage. In a war like this, any form of production has a military potential and should be sabotaged."

"Provided the damage inflicted is greater than the cost of the operation."

Alain was in agreement with this, but he emphasized the impossibility of applying it. How could they evaluate either the extent of any damage they might cause or its cost?

"If we accept the premise that we are going to die here," he concluded, "any form of sabotage is worthwhile, even if its effects are infinitesimal and it is punished by hanging. On the other hand, if we are convinced that we still can save our own skins, it would be better to refrain from sabotage. When you resolved to take part in the Resistance, did you ask yourself a great many questions?"

Philippe replied that there had been one question in particular, and it had not been an easy one to answer: How to go about it? He had wanted to get to England. But in view of the difficulty of accomplishing that, he had given up the idea and had tried to find a means of making himself useful where he was. It had taken months before he had finally succeeded.

"One day," he said, "one of my colleagues at work swore to me that he belonged to a serious Resistance organization. Shortly after that, the BBC broadcast the message we had agreed on as a signal. That proved to me that my colleague had been telling the truth, and I placed myself at his orders."

"Right," Alain said, "but from that moment on, did you ask yourself, every time you did something, if what you were doing was proportionate to the risks you ran?"

"Obviously not. How could I have?"

"That's what I wanted to make you say. You decided to serve a cause, without worrying about whether you would live to see its victory."

"I was convinced that if I was captured, I would be shot. We all thought that, if that's what you mean."

"But now you are saying to yourself: 'I escaped death that time: there's no question of exposing myself to it again. So, no sabotage.'"

Philippe stared at Alain in astonishment.

"But I never said that. What kind of argument are you trying to force me into?"

"I'm not trying to force you into any argument. But you just told me that in your opinion it would be best to refrain from any act of sabotage. I just want you to know that I do not agree."

"You misunderstood me. I simply pointed out the futility of being hanged for no purpose. When I was in the artillery, I was taught that my first concern should be to make good use of every shell. Here, we have to be sure we are making good use of whatever weapons we possess. That's all I meant."

"Obviously, I agree with you on that. But, to carry your comparison a little further, each of us, in this camp, is both the artilleryman and the shell. Under those circumstances, it's entirely possible that concern for our own survival might prevent us from finding a target worth the expenditure of the shell."

"The peace and quiet of the block and the factory have done nothing to calm you down," Philippe said, smiling. "If anything, they seem to stimulate you."

Philippe was afraid Alain's impatience for action might compel him to seize the first opportunity for sabotage that came along, and he was determined to try to prevent this.

"Take your time," he said. "Time is certainly the thing we lack least. Choose your target, and don't fire until you have done everything possible to make sure of hitting it. Don't confuse cowardice with a concern for effectiveness. This isn't a matter of getting yourself hanged just to demonstrate to yourself that you are still serving a cause."

"Of course," Alain said, "but the useful things that we can

156

do don't just grow on trees. Maybe when we know what we are producing in the factory we'll be in a better position to gauge the value of sabotage. And then, perhaps, the day will come when we will find the means of carrying it out."

28.

|||||||||||||||||||||||||||||||||||||||||||||||||||||||||||||||||||||||||||||||||||||||||||||||||||||

Work crews of several men each were set up in the shop Alain was assigned to. The members of these crews were put to work assembling the pieces made in the factory during the previous month. Each of them carried out a single operation, always the same, and then passed the piece on to his neighbor for the next step in the assembly-line process.

Alain took advantage of the half-hour noon recess to go from one bench to another, examining the products that came off the assembly lines. He tried, without succeeding, to imagine the whole of which these products might be the component parts. When he realized that he was not going to be able to satisfy his curiosity, he lost interest in the new assembly lines that were being established.

In time, the German foremen remembered that there were a number of highly qualified engineers in the shop and decided to entrust them with the final adjustment of completed pieces. With a group of other men, Alain was moved into one of the little rooms off the main one.

The appliances on which they worked were programing mechanisms. It was clear that their function consisted of controlling an operation that took place in ninety seconds and included a dozen distinct phases.

In a nearby room another team ran the final check on a type of vertical gryoscope. In a third room horizontal gryoscopes were verified and adjusted. Both of these gyroscopes were equipped with Swedish electric motors turning at thirty thousand revolutions per minute. They were fed by twenty-four-volt direct current. So were the programing mechanisms.

Alain was intrigued by this discovery.

That night Alain stood next to Charlie in the formation for roll call.

"You know," he said, "the job in the factory is getting more interesting. You should try to get yourself transferred there."

The idea was not particularly tempting to Charlie, since he believed that it would not be disagreeable to work outdoors once the winter was over. Moreover, his *kommando* was being taken to Weimar more and more often now.

"It's a change," Charlie explained, "seeing something besides the camp, deportees, and S.S. guards. Yesterday, our truck broke down and we walked through part of the city."

Charlie described the empty windows of the stores, the queues in front of the food stores, and the German population itself, poorly clothed and poorly shod.

"Do they still ignore you?" Alain asked.

"I had a long discussion about that with one of my German friends. This wasn't the first time he had been marched through Weimar. He told me that, at first, his compatriots stopped in the streets to watch the internees pass. At that time, they were all Germans. The civilians laughed and spat at them. And three months ago, as I told you, they pretended not to see us. Now, a few rare passersby discreetly show some signs of compassion."

"Perhaps they have relatives among us."

"There have always been Germans who had relatives among us. But until now that hasn't made them any more friendly."

158

"Well then, what do you think has caused the change in their behavior?"

"Lassitude. Don't forget that it has been a long time since the Wehrmacht raced from one victory to another. Their confidence in their beloved Führer is probably beginning to wane, so we seem a trifle less contemptible to them."

"I think you are taking dreams for realities," Alain said drily. "I haven't seen the slightest sign of any decline in the fanaticism of the S.S."

"I'm talking about civilians, not about the S.S."

Charlie told him that, the day before, a civilian had intentionally dropped a cigarette in the path of the *kommando* column. An S.S. guard had noticed it and had cursed the man roundly, threatening him with dire punishment.

The German internees had commented on the incident at great length. A few months earlier, not only would it never have entered anyone's head to offer a cigarette to internees, but if someone had done so, the people around him would have turned him over to the police.

"To complete the story," Charlie said, "I should add that the S.S. guard pounced on the cigarette before any of us could make a move toward it, and he certainly didn't put it in his pocket for use as evidence for the prosecution."

"That's just an isolated occurrence," Alain said. "You're jumping to conclusions when you conclude from it that the morale of the population is deteriorating."

"I'm not reasoning anything of the sort. For that matter, it's difficult to talk about the morale of the population. They are all terrorized by the Gestapo. Some of the Free French workers* have told me some interesting stories on that subject."

* There were two categories of French workers in Germany, those who volunteered their services because of the good pay promised by the Germans, and others who were drafted by the Vichy government and sent to Germany. Neither were treated as prisoners.

"Then you have managed to talk to them?"

"Yes, or at least to some of them. I even found one who agreed to write to my family for me."

Charlie then outlined for Alain the practical problems he and his Free French friend had had to solve. Letters mailed to France by the free workers were required to carry the name and address of the sender. They were strictly censored, as were any letters the free workers received. Passing on news of a deportee would certainly have cost the worker his freedom if he had been discovered.

Charlie had patiently worked out a formula which, without alerting the censors, would be sufficiently clear to put his parents on their guard against any imprudent reaction. The letter had been written as though the addressee was a cousin of the sender. It stressed that the writer had met Charlie completely by chance and did not expect ever to see him again. Then it went on to mention that Charlie had been hoping to receive a wooden box of such-and-such dimensions, secured with a padlock. Charlie had never asked for anything of the sort on the card he was permitted to send, but the free worker had commented, as though jokingly, on the impatience with which he was awaiting it.

"It worked very well," Charlie said. "The proof is that I received the case, but my parents have never mentioned it."

He sighed, shook his head, and added, "My friend has just gone off on a leave of absence to France. He promised that he would go to see them. He will be able to talk to them." His voice was unsteady, but he regained control of himself in a moment. "He'll explain to them that if they receive further letters from a free worker and the name of the street, on the address, is printed in capital letters, they can safely answer it. They can say anything they might want to write to me, so long as they give a fictitious name for the sender. The censor won't see anything wrong."

160

"If they want to gild the lily," Alain said, "they can always toss in a few lines glorifying the collaborators and damning the Gaullists."

"Don't worry, my father is shrewd enough to think of that all by himself. When he learns something of the way things are handled here, I'm sure he will find some means of overcoming the obstacles."

"When is your messenger scheduled to come back?"

"Unfortunately, I have a feeling that his leave of absence will last a long time. I think he intends to disappear while he is in France, perhaps even to cross the frontier into Spain."

"Did he tell you that?"

"No, but his concern with arranging things so that this correspondence could go on through someone else led me to suspect it."

"Be careful, Charlie. One of these days, you're going to run into some character who will tell you he'll do anything he can to help you. Then, as soon as you have given him a message to pass on, he'll race to the Gestapo with the whole story. I wouldn't trust any Frenchman who voluntarily works for the Germans."

"Oh, I know there are many collaborators among them. That's why I'm extremely cautious. I haven't yet asked for a thing from any of the others. And I won't, unless my friend really does not come back; and then only when I am as certain as I can possibly be that I'm not dealing with an memory.

"Or with someone who doesn't know how to hold his tongue—"

"Don't worry about that. I was arrested because one of my comrades in the Resistance talked too much. It was a lesson I haven't forgotten."

"It hasn't prevented you from telling me about your projects."

"Of course not, but I know you."

161

"You're not taking any risks with me, but as a general rule, it's better to say nothing."

"Yes, papa."

"Don't get angry, it's for your own good that I'm telling you that."

"Yes, papa," Charlie repeated.

During the factory recess period the next day, Alain went into the room where the vertical gyroscopes were being checked. He hoped to be able to examine them and possibly to learn their purpose. The foreman walked in just as a comrade from block 26 was explaining to Alain the workings of the apparatus. The German immediately began to shout, his voice rising with every phrase. Alain could grasp only the words that had now become familiar to him—"forbidden," "spy," "sabotage"—and the curses that punctuated this diatribe. Pushed bodily outside the gyroscope control room, Alain expected to be handed over to the S.S. But the *meister* led him off toward a bench laden with casings for the programing mechanisms. These were a kind of cylindrical box of white cast iron, painted black on the outside. The factory that produced them must have been damaged in a bombing raid, because the interior of the boxes was spotted with areas of rust, apparently caused by drops of rain. The foreman seized Alain by the shoulder, seated him on a high stool, and handed him a piece of emery paper. It was not the moment to make a pretense of not understanding. Alain set to work cleaning the interior of the box. The *meister* remained standing beside him for a long time, savoring the joy of humiliating a representative of his enemies. He went away at last, leaving Alain to his new task. From that time on, Alain was never entrusted with any other job. Day after day, for five months, he polished the rust-bitten interiors of iron boxes.

162

No other form of work could have allowed him so much intellectual freedom. He took advantage of it to make a mental inventory of the information he had thus far gathered.

Vertical gyroscopes, horizontal gyroscopes, and programing mechanisms were being manufactured in his own shop. In Philippe's shop, there was an assembly line for remote-control wireless receiving sets. When these were completed, another team of deportees, to which Genteau belonged, tested and checked them. Alain made inquiries concerning the electric current that fed them. It was the same that was used for the gyroscopes and the programing mechanisms. Taking infinite precautions, lest his curiosity attract attention, he also managed to learn that the connecting pieces for the four different kinds of appliances were of the same type. He concluded that they were complementary and intended to form part of a single machine.

The association of two gyroscopes, a programing mechanism, and a remote-control receiving set led him to think that this machine was an airplane. But this hypothesis was contradicted by the fact that these instruments were nothing but crude assemblages of iron. Not only were they too clumsily made for them to be of any prolonged use, but the metals employed in their construction were of low quality, and obviously selected for reasons of economy, without thought to their weight or thickness. They had nothing whatever in common with the lightweight, sturdy, and meticulously crafted mechanisms characteristic of aviation material.

This was not, however, the only consideration that made it seem unlikely they were intended for an airplane.

A year earlier, shortly before his arrest, Alain had sent to London a report of great interest to the planning staffs. The author of the report was one of the directors of the organizational committee of the French aviation industry. Profiting from the relationships he had established with the directors of principal German aviation firms, he had set about making up an estimate of the production capacity of each firm. It was, of course, impossible for him to ask any direct questions. Not only would he not have obtained a reply, but he would automatically have become suspect. He had therefore drawn up a very subtle plan of investigation and had followed it through with unflagging patience and precision. Alain had openly admired the method he devised for learning what he wanted to know. It had led him, by three separate paths, to a series of estimates which were considered completely authentic. Alain remembered, in particular, that the author of the report had succeeded in obtaining information on the number of man-hours of work required for the manufacture of each type of plane. By asking innocuous questions on such subjects as the rate of assessments paid into corporate funds, on the over-all amount of these funds, and on the average wage of factory workers, he had arrived at a reasonable estimate of the total number of man-hours of work. He had, in fact, verified this result by compiling a chart of the rate of absenteeism among the factory workers and of the number of hours thus lost each month.

Alain strained to recall every detail of the report, working at it with the same patience he might have applied to unraveling a tangled ball of yarn; but physical exhaustion clouded his memory.

He decided to attack the problem from another angle. For several consecutive days, during the recess period, he counted the number of cases of gyroscope motors that were stored in the shop where he worked. The number of pieces in each case was stenciled in black. At the end of his count, Alain reckoned that the supply of motors in the factory would permit construction of more than ten thousand complete mechanisms.

Even though he no longer remembered the estimates of German aviation production, he was quite certain that no single type of aircraft could be produced in units of ten thousand, and certainly not at this rate of construction. The foreman had

164

ordered him to polish a minimum of forty casings per day, and by observing the work of the assembly lines Alain had assured himself that this was roughly the number of mechanisms the assembly lines turned out each day. Forty mechanisms per day, twenty-five work days per month, added up to one thousand mechanisms a month and twelve thousand a year.

The numerical disproportion between the production of the Mibau factory and the possible construction of a type of aircraft to which this production might correspond was obvious.

Alain remembered one other detail that also tended to prove his theory that the mechanisms were not intended for airplanes. When he had been working on the final checking of the programing mechanisms, he had been struck by the absence of any device for resetting the instrument. This indicated that the mechanism could be used only once. He considered it certain that since the programing mechanism could be utilized only once, the machine for which it was intended could also be utilized only once. And this would explain why the gyroscopes were constructed with no concern for durability.

Little by little, he thought he was beginning to see the light.

The only kind of military instrument that could be employed only once is an instrument that carries an explosive charge and destroys itself on impact. In this case, since the instrument was radio-controlled, it was obvious that it was provided with an autonomous propulsion system.

Alain could think of only two instruments that fit this definition —a naval torpedo, or some kind of land vehicle.* But neither one of these would have required a vertical gyroscope as part of its directional mechanism. Moreover, remote control by radio of a naval torpedo seemed an unlikely possibility: Hertzian waves are not conducted under water. His own reasoning had entrapped him in a vicious circle. He had established, to his

* It should be borne in mind that at the beginning of 1944 jet propulsion had not yet been adapted to military weapons and that the first rocket, the V-2, was not put into service until September, 1944.

165

own satisfaction, that the electrical and electronic appliances produced by the Mibau factory were intended for use in a single instrument, but if this was true, that instrument must function in space, in the manner of an aircraft. And it was not an aircraft. Somewhere he must have made a mistake.

The solitary research he then undertook to locate his mistake became an obsession with him. After several days of hesitation, he decided that, despite the risks involved, he must discuss the matter with Genteau. His classmate from the École Supérieure d'Électricité might help him find a way out of the impasse.

The following Sunday he went looking for Genteau, and when he found him he insisted that they go for a walk. The fine rain that fell was mingled with particles of snow that stung their faces, but there was no other way of talking at length without being overheard. Alain enumerated his findings, outlined the path of reasoning he had followed, and gave the conclusions he had arrived at. Genteau informed him that, after a final check had been completed, the wireless receiving sets were tested on a vibrating plate. This, in itself, indicated that the machine on which the sets were to be mounted was subject to vibration. It was logical to assume that this vibration was caused by the motor of the machine.

"But in that case," Alain said, "I have obviously made a mistake somewhere in my deductions, since they lead to the conclusion that we are manufacturing equipment for pilotless aircraft, and that certainly can't be correct."

"Your line of reasoning seems perfectly correct to me," Genteau assured him.

"But my solution is impossible!"

"Yes, I'm well aware of that. But what can you do about it?"

"It's exasperating."

"Exasperation is one of the few things of which there is no lack here."

"But you don't see any omission or mistake in my deductions?" Alain persisted.

166

"None at all."

Alain was profoundly disturbed. Far from opening up, the vicious circle seemed to have closed more tightly than ever before.

29.

‖‖‖

That night, on returning to the barracks after roll call, Alain slumped on a bench in the mess hall and waited for the order to go into the dormitory. His eyes were focused on nothing; he wanted to sleep, to forget. It was the only way to rid himself of the questions that tortured him, of the answers he could not find.

Charlie came into the room and sat down beside him.

"What's wrong?" he asked.

Alain turned wearily from his thoughts.

"Nothing special. It's just that it's been a long time since the noon ration. I didn't get very much, and I'm hungry."

"I was looking for you this afternoon. We had a feast." Charlie leaned forward and whispered, "There was a pot of lard in the package I received."

"Great!" Alain exclaimed, but there was no conviction in his tone.

"And that's not all. In the lard, there was a scrap of paper that said: 'from Oscar.' "

"And what does that mean?" Alain asked, not understanding Charlie's excitement.

"It means that my buddy—you know, the free worker I met

in Weimar, the one who wrote to my parents—he has been to see them. Now they know what's going on here."

"It might be better if they didn't know."

"Oh, don't worry about that, Oscar wouldn't have told them anything that would disturb them too much. But I'm sure he did explain how they can answer if they receive news of me from another of the free workers."

"Then Oscar won't be coming back?"

"What do you think? He had ten days' leave, and he has been gone for more than a month."

"But then why is it you've just learned that he saw your parents? Didn't he go to see them as soon as he arrived in Paris?"

"He promised me that he would, but the last card I received from them was sent from the Vendée. They must have gone to spend a few days there, with some friends who are fortunate enough to be lacking in nothing and generous enough to share what they have with their guests. The last package I got before this one was also sent from the Vendée. Do you remember the ham that was in it? So, I imagine that Oscar wasn't able to see my parents until after they returned to Paris."

Charlie got the box in which he stored his provisions and opened it. Alain turned his head away so that he wouldn't see the treasure it contained. They were a torture to his empty stomach, stirring up yearnings impossible to appease.

"Here," Charlie said, "eat this. It will do you good."

He handed him a slice of rusk on which he had spread a layer of lard. He closed the box and then, after studying it thoughtfully for a moment, opened it again and took out two lumps of sugar. He pushed one of them toward Alain and put the other in his mouth, sucking on it as though it were a candy.

Alain would have liked to express his gratitude to Charlie and to share with him the joy of contact with his family. But somehow, he could not manage it. He realized, with a sense of panic, that he was becoming resigned. Resigned to accepting

168

food without being able to give anything in exchange, resigned to having no news of his family and being unable to send any, resigned also to the knowledge that the Mibau factory was turning out equipment whose purpose he could not determine and whose production he could do nothing to sabotage.

"I must ask you to forgive me, Charlie," he said, "for accepting what you give me without even protesting. I know very well you don't expect anything in return and you're doing this from simple friendship, but I'm ashamed I have nothing to offer you, other than the pleasure it gives me to know that you've managed to get in touch with your parents."

"What's the matter with you?" Charlie demanded. "Are you losing your mind? That's the first time I've ever heard you make such a stupid remark. You're not cut out to play the self-pitying role, you know."

Charlie cast about for some means of countering Alain's distress. Aside from a few items of food, he could give him nothing, and he knew that acceptance of these only embarrassed his friend. They had been here for months now, side by side, sharing the same sleeping compartment and the same cover. Earlier, in the tormented atmosphere in which they lived before escaping from the quarry *kommando* and before the establishment of the French blocks, there had been things they could do to help each other. Now, that ordeal was past. The block was still a prison, but it was a tranquil one, and they were in *kommandos* where they were no longer shadowed by the constant menace of being sent to Dora. Under these circumstances, there was nothing a man could do for his friend.

"Do you know what's happening?" Charlie said. "We have become bourgeois—dull, middle-class citizens, and we're bored, like all middle-class citizens. Obviously, for members of the bourgeoisie, we don't lead a very gay life. We're not as well housed as we would be in a charity shelter, we never have enough to eat, the work we do could be done by any unskilled laborer, and every morning and every night we stand around in the square in the snow and the wind, waiting to be counted. But we are bourgeois just the same, because we aspire to nothing more than maintenance of the status quo. Our most extravagant ambitions don't go beyond spending Sunday afternoon with our fellow bourgeoisie, sharing our packages. I wish you could have seen this block this afternoon. There were little groups of men at every one of these tables, sampling the things they had received, very discreetly, not dipping too deeply into their reserves, wanting to be sure they would last until the next package arrived. And all of this very calmly, watched by those who receive nothing and had not been invited. But there were few of those. They prefer to go out for a walk or to visit others like themselves, in blocks where no one is playing at having a dinner party. But they were bourgeois too, poorer bourgeois. They are simply another variety of the same species."

"There's a good deal of truth in that," Alain admitted. "But I don't quite see how it could be otherwise. What can we do except wait? We have no means of acting—they've seen to that. Now that Oscar has gone, you're trying to set up a new contact with your family. Others are trying to change to a better *kommando*. Some of us, in the factory, still hope to find an opportunity for sabotage but without running too great a risk. None of this is a very healthy sign. Do you have something to suggest, something that might provide a way out?"

Charlie shook his head. "No, damn it, I don't. We just have to admit that these Kraut pigs have got us tied hand and foot. They've not only made us incapable of thought by exhausting us physically, they've also made sure we have nothing to think about. No news, no books, no problems beyond economizing what strength we have, in order to go on living."

"Yes, living like animals."

The block chief was opening the door to the dormitory.

"Let's go to bed," Charlie said. "There's nothing we can do about it."

30.

||||||||||||||||||||||||||||||||||||||||||||||||||||||||||||||||||||||||||||||||||||||||||||||||

The first quarter of 1944 was drawing to a close, but there was still no sign of the warmth of spring. Dawn was beginning to break when the *kommandos* left for work, and it was not yet dark when they returned at night. But the cold was still almost as sharp as it had been in December, and it snowed frequently. In the streets of the camp a brief thaw occasionally buried in mud the ashes that had been spread on the ice. But a new coating of frost formed almost at once, causing the wooden soles of the deportees to slip and slide, making walking almost impossible. The men on the ration detail set one foot carefully in front of the other, their backs bent almost double, so that the bottom of the tin they carried between them would be only a few inches from the ground and its contents would not be lost if one of them should lose his balance. Even so, the tin sometimes overturned and the hot liquid spilled. The Russians would race to the spot, hurl themselves on the ground, and lap up the soup with their tongues, like famished animals, ignoring the frozen mud that had melted into it.

For a long time now, nothing had happened that was of any interest to the French community as a whole. Those who worked in the factory were content to wait for liberation. Until then, they foresaw only a bleak, monotonous future, and they did their best, aided by what had now become habit, to endure a situation which it seemed nothing could alter. Those who worked in the quarry lived in constant terror of being sent to Dora. The most active among them were always involved in some kind of scheme that might result in their transfer to the factory. If they received packages from home, they automatically became targets for the swindlers who claimed to be in a position to help them and promised to do so, in exchange for cigarettes and food. The lure of the factory was so powerful that a great many poor wretches allowed themselves to be duped and cheated.

The turnover in the population of the two French blocks was high. Deportees who died or were sent away in one of the transports were replaced by others, either recent arrivals in the camp or men who, until now, had still been scattered among the blocks of other nationalities.

In the *kommandos* the French were mingled with German internees and with other prisoners, but there were few who maintained any relationship outside their own group. Their need for companionship, restricted as it was by misery, was amply satisfied by the presence of their compatriots, and they were seldom tempted to break away from the isolation imposed by language.

As time went on, the French community assumed more and more the characteristics of an island within the camp. Physical exhaustion sapped the intellectual energies of its members, and the number of their personal relationships dwindled proportionately, to such a point that they came to be governed as much by chance assignment as by any deliberate choice. "If this goes on," Philippe said, "the majority of us will no longer know anyone except the man who works beside him and the man who shares his bed." The real world, the world of free men, was forgotten. Even the outline of the camp itself was gradually fading. The weary brains of the deportees were aware of nothing beyond a constantly shrinking circle, in which each one was the minute dot at the center.

172

31.

One night Charlie came running up to Alain.

"I've got good news," he said. "Geoffrin has just come back from Dora. He's in the block of the Institute of Hygiene."

Alain was shocked. "I thought that anyone who was sent to Dora never came back," he said.

"Geoffrin is the first who ever has, and he will doubtless be the only one."

"But how did it happen? Why did they make an exception in his case?"

"It wasn't an exception, it was the result of an extraordinary *tour de force*."

"Alstein?"

"Yes. He never accepted the fact that Geoffrin was sent to Dora despite everything he could do. So he took every opportunity to persuade Dr. Ding that it would be in his own interest to have Geoffrin on his staff."

"Did Ding know that he had been sent to Dora?"

"No, of course not. If he had, he would just have written him off. It wasn't until after he had convinced him that Geoffrin really was indispensable that Alstein told Ding where Geoffrin was. He claimed that he had just learned it himself, and then, without giving Ding time to draw a breath, he got him to sign a letter he had drawn up. It was addressed to the S.S. officer commanding Dora and demanded Geoffrin's return."

"Oh, come on," Alain said, "you're not going to tell me that doctors, even if they are members of the S.S. and directors of an institute of hygiene, have the power to give orders to a camp commander."

"Alstein knows that better than we do."

"Well then?"

"Well, the difference between Alstein and us is that he also knows how S.S. officers are likely to react. You see, there are circumstances—sometimes merely as a result of the whims or ambitions of their generals—when they are given missions that are completely outside the normal chain of command, missions that can only be carried out by violating rules. So the position of those who have the job of strictly enforcing rules is not simple. If they interfere with a mission ordered by someone of high rank, they are handed a one-way ticket to the Russian front. But if one of their superiors discovers they have helped a mission that displeases him, the same fate may be in store for them. No matter what they do, they are taking risks."

"And the commander of Dora decided to take the risk of sending Geoffrin back here?"

"Not at first. But when Geoffrin failed to show up here, Ding's vanity was wounded and he blamed Alstein for having pushed him into something that could only result in failure. Alstein claimed that this wasn't so and suggested that Ding follow up his letter with a telegram. Ding agreed. With that for ammunition, Alstein took it on himself to write the telegram in terms Ding would certainly not have approved, and sent it off without showing it to him."

"What did it say?"

"Something like: 'If you do not put deportee number such-and-such at my disposal without delay, the production of anti-typhus vaccine for the Wehrmacht will be interrupted and you will be held personally responsible. Signed: Dr. Ding, Director of the S.S. Institute of Hygiene.' "

"And that worked?"

174

"Apparently the commander of Dora, after reading the telegram, decided to send Geoffrin back rather than run the risk of being accused of having caused a stoppage in the production of vaccine. He must have thought Geoffrin's return here would very probably go unnoticed and therefore not cause him any trouble, while the telegram signed by Dr. Ding fairly reeked with the threat of Russia."

The following Sunday, Alain paid a visit to the block of the Institute of Hygiene. He found Geoffrin there, sitting in a corner of the basement room, well away from the other deportees and talking in muted tones with Charlie. He looked like an emaciated old man. The bones of his cheeks and jaw seemed about to burst through the waxy surface of his skin. His neck was as thin and as knotted as a twist of rope. His eyes, sunk deep in their orbits, glittered with fever.

"It's good to see you again," Alain said, "very good. But you don't seem to have enjoyed your trip very much."

Geoffrin looked up at him, without answering, and then glanced at Charlie, who nodded slightly, indicating that it was safe for him to speak.

"You're right in that," he said. "Dora is not an ideal vacation spot. It was a good thing I left when I did. I don't think that I could have stood it very much longer."

"That's fairly obvious," Alain replied.

"Oh, it's all right now. But I have a feeling that the commander of Dora allowed me to return to Buchenwald only because he thought my chances of arriving here alive were small, and the chances of my survival once I got here were none at all. For that matter, I wouldn't have had a chance if I hadn't been lucky enough to be assigned to these luxury quarters."

"Were you ill?"

"No. Exhausted. At Dora, there are no ill people; or rather,

175

illness is so brief a passage between life and death that it is scarcely worth talking about."

Geoffrin went on to describe life at Dora. The underground factory had been built in tunnels dug into cliffs of white quartzite by deportees. As Geoffrin spoke, Alain began to realize that the *kapo* of the canteen had been right in saying that Buchenwald was a sanitarium. It was indeed, compared with Dora. The deportees at Dora were covered with lice, and each month they were compelled to spend a part of the night outdoors, completely naked, at the height of winter, on the pretext that their clothing was being disinfected. Geoffrin gave numerous examples of the sadism of the "green" *kapos*. One day one of them had hanged nine deportees he suspected of sabotage. He had simply strung them in a line from the arm of an electric hoist. They had remained there until nightfall, hanging in the main tunnel through which all their comrades passed. Another *kapo* had found a Russian sleeping in a corner and had beaten him to death.

"But what are they building in the tunnel?" Alain asked.

Geoffrin glanced to left and to right, making certain he could not be overheard by his neighbors. He leaned toward Alain, then abruptly seemed to change his mind. He sat up straight again and turned away from Alain and Charlie.

"I never found out," he said.

An awkward silence fell on the little group. Alain reproached himself for having put Geoffrin in an embarrassing position. He would have liked to offer some form of apology. But, more than that, he would have liked to know the answer to his question. The words that came to mind, however, served only to emphasize his unsatisfied curiosity and Geoffrin's surprising behavior. He could not speak.

Alstein came in and sat down beside Charlie, without saying a word to anyone. Each Sunday, like a priest making his weekly rounds through the most miserable neighborhoods of his parish, Alstein paid a visit to the Small Camp, bringing to some of the

176

Frenchmen the moral comfort of his presence and some portions of typhous rabbit which had been cooked in sterilizers.

His friends' eyes automatically focused on Alstein. It was totally unlike him to have greeted no one when he arrived. Alain thought he had the appearance of someone who had just had a meeting with the devil.

"Have you been to visit your poor?" Alain asked gently.

A few seconds passed before Alstein gave any evidence of having heard him. He had placed his right hand on the edge of the table, and now, to conceal its trembling, he clasped it between his knees. When he spoke, it was as though he were emerging from a dream. His German accent was more pronounced than usual, and his words came more slowly.

"I have just come from the Small Camp, in fact," he said, "and I hope you will forgive my emotion."

There was another period of silence, and then Alain, hoping to break it, said, "Is some friend of yours dead?"

"We are accustomed to death," Alstein replied. "But madness—"

He had spoken as if to himself. When he continued, his voice was more controlled, growing firmer as he told his story.

"You all know Professor Verville, at least by name. In France, when my situation was difficult, he was a sort of spiritual guide to me, and I could not have had a better one. I would have liked to get him out of the Small Camp, and when he arrived I was imprudent enough to tell him this, without taking full account of the fact that his age constituted an almost insurmountable obstacle. Even so, I might perhaps have obtained his assignment to the tailoring *kommando,* but the intransigent Catholicism of his writings, and the fact that they are so widely known, resulted in the failure of all my efforts. I told him this, and he recognized my inability to help. It seemed natural to him that the religious character of his work should stand in the way of any alleviation of his martyrdom. He even derived a certain satisfaction from the fact. But week after week, his strength has waned, and for some time now the gradual decay of his body has troubled his mind. He lives surrounded by a court of feeble-minded old men, and I suspect him of preaching some form of heresy to them. He seems to have made them into fanatics. This man, who used to be so modest, now demands that I address him as Master; and when he speaks of the French deportees in the Small Camp he calls them 'my disciples' or 'my apostles.' To him, the Germans are the Pharisees. He has gotten it into his head that I have made a pact with the S.S. and that, if he is still in the Small Camp, it is not only because I have done nothing to get him out but also because I have worked to keep him there. Today, he did not confine himself to showering me with reproaches. He unleashed his pack of faithful, and I found myself surrounded by old men, threatening me with their bony fists and screaming oaths and curses. I was forced to knock some of them down, simply to get away. It was worse than being forced to defend oneself against a woman or a child. The agony of the mind is infinitely more frightful than any agony of the body. The spectacle presented by Professor Verville is a devastating thing."

32.

All through the next day, Alain was sketching out plans that might induce Geoffrin to reveal to him what was being produced in the underground factory at Dora. On his return to camp that night, he was tempted to go to see Geoffrin again, but he was afraid of being indiscreet and confined himself to leading Charlie off to the toilets to talk.

"What Geoffrin told us yesterday about Dora was really frightful," he said.

Charlie nodded agreement. "Yes," he said, "we were damned lucky not to have been sent there. Conditions there must be really rough, to have affected a man of his constitution that way. And from what he was telling me before you came in, it was even worse while the tunnel was being dug. The deportees lived underground, without any running water, without latrines, and without any sleeping quarters. Day and night, there were teams at work blowing up the rock of the mine. No one could sleep. The gases and dust released by the explosions were slowly asphyxiating everyone. The constant explosions caused blocks of stone to fall from the roof of levels that were already in use, crushing anyone who happened to be beneath them. The situation didn't get any better until the camp itself was built. Since then, the deportees spend twelve hours of each twenty-four there. The rest of the time, they are working in the tunnel, one week by day and the next week by night."

"But what are they doing?"

"Geoffrin hasn't told me that. And you certainly must have noticed that he doesn't seem inclined to talk about it."

"Yes, I noticed that, but I can't understand why."

"He was threatened before being sent back here. The commandant of the camp himself warned him that if he revealed anything at all, he would be hanged."

"That didn't prevent him from telling us about the situation at Dora."

Charlie nodded again. "Yes, about the situation, but not about what is being manufactured. It's of no importance whether we know what conditions are like at Dora—that the food there is even worse than it is here, or that the *kapos* are 'greens' who kill men simply to amuse themselves. If you or I were to repeat any of that, it would be swallowed up immediately in the flock

179

of lies and rumors that are already circulating, and the S.S. wouldn't give it a second thought. But suppose that one fine day they were to discover that exact information was circulating at Buchenwald regarding whatever it is that is being constructed in the tunnel. The Gestapo would be notified at once. And they would conduct an investigation and establish a connection between Geoffrin's return and the leak in this information. If it was correct, Geoffrin would automatically be held guilty, and you know what would happen next."

Alain shook his head thoughtfully but said nothing.

"For that matter," Charlie went on, "even if the information was incorrect, Geoffrin would be lucky to escape a noose."

"Why? His return can't have gone unnoticed at the *Arbeitsstatistik*—where the Gestapo certainly has spies—or at the S.S. headquarters of the camp. It must have caused some surprise in both places."

"Yes, but no one dares do anything now, for fear of getting his knuckles rapped. Rumors, even false rumors about what is being manufactured at Dora, would furnish a pretext. And the result would be a nice little massacre. Geoffrin and Alstein would not be the only ones to be liquidated."

"Oh, I realize Geoffrin has good reason for being careful, but just the same, he might have confided in us."

"You're not being very logical," Charlie said. "You never miss an opportunity to reproach me for talking too much, and now that you've come across someone who keeps his mouth shut you're complaining about it. What difference can it make to you what's being manufactured at Dora?"

Alain did not reply at once. He seemed lost in his own thoughts.

"You know," he said at last, "it wouldn't be a bad idea at all to have some secret equipment manufactured by deportees rather than by ordinary workmen. It would limit the number of people with any knowledge of it who could circulate freely, and as a result it would reduce the chances of a leak."

180

"Yes," Charlie said, "but I can't picture deportees manufacturing anything of any real importance."

"Why? Buchenwald furnishes a lot of personnel for the aviation factory at Schönebeck."

"The men who are sent there are just manual laborers."

"We can't be sure of that. Right here, in the Mibau factory, the majority of us are employed as workmen, even though those who were conscripted last were selected without regard for their professional qualifications. I'm not saying that you could call them a crew of skilled workmen, but the work is broken down into such simple operations that the majority of it could be accomplished by anyone. Think of it for a minute. Even if it requires three deportees to replace one ordinary workman, the saving is considerable. The work force of the Mibau alone would make it possible to mobilize a regiment of able-bodied Germans who, without us, would have to be classified as skilled workmen. At this particular moment, there can't be any doubt that that's important to the Wehrmacht."

A Frenchman from one of the other blocks had suddenly appeared in the doorway.

"Come look," he shouted. "The sky is full of planes."

In the toilets the noise of conversation had drowned out that of the motors. But outside, it was perfectly distinct. The clear sky was filled with a throbbing sound, as deep and regular as the breathing of a sleeping man. The deportees lifted their heads and held their breath, listening with every pore in their bodies. When their eyes grew accustomed to the darkness, the first thing they could pick out was the fleeting reflection of moonlight on gleaming wings. Then the planes themselves became visible. Hundreds of bombers, very high, formed a slowly turning carrousel. New formations arrived and joined the circle, swelling it to ever larger proportions. It unrolled at last into a graceful scroll, and the planes moved off in successive columns, all in the same direction, as if they were going to a parade.

181

The silence was broken by a sneeze, followed by fits of coughing held back until now by emotion.

"My friend," a voice said, "there are people who will sleep badly tonight."

"Let's go in," Alain murmured. "It's cold out here now."

He and Charlie went into the empty mess hall.

"What we have just seen is a good omen," he said.

"How many planes do you think there were?"

"Several hundred, at least."

"They seemed to be just carrying out an exercise, as calmly as if they were at home."

"Yes, they did. But they are a long way from their bases, you know."

"I can't help wondering why they kept circling the way they did."

"I think that several formations coming in by different routes had a rendezvous point here, before going on together to carry out a massive bombing raid. I remember that the English did it that way when they made their first big raid on Cologne, in 1942. I was in London at the time, and an account of it was in all the newspapers."

There was a sudden screaming of sirens, and groups of *lagerschutz* began racing through the streets of the camp. The words they shouted were incomprehensible, but the deportees understood enough to return hastily to the blocks. It was the first time an air raid alarm had been sounded at Buchenwald, and it was not sounded until after the planes were far away. As the sirens continued their long, drawn-out scream, the stumbling flight of the deportees before the onslaught of the *lagerschutz* degenerated into a disordered rout. An S.S. guard came into the mess hall, looking for the block chief, who had already returned to his own cubicle. Those of the prisoners who had managed to retain some semblance of calm seized their comrades by the shoulder or the arm, shaking them, forcing them into a posture of attention. The S.S. guard was shouting and waving his arms and nodding toward

182

the windows. The *stubendienst* hastened to close the black curtains, which were gaping open on every side, allowing the light to escape.

After he had obsequiously conducted the S.S. guard to the door, the block chief called Charlie and ordered him to translate the instructions he had just been given. "In the event of an air raid alarm, all deportees must be in their own blocks. On the *lagerschutz* and the firemen are permitted to be outside. Deportees must make sure that all windows are completely sealed by curtains. Any deportees found outside their own block during an alarm will be clubbed by the *lagerschutz,* their numbers will be taken, and they will be assigned for two weeks to the shit *kommando.* Any block that shows a light after sundown will be deprived of rations."

Like a stone dropped into the stagnant waters of a pond, the passage of the bombers had created a profound and sudden disturbance in the empty, monotonous existence of the deportees. It furnished nourishment to imaginations deadened by physical weariness and unvarying routine. For a long time now, the thought of an Allied invasion had no longer stirred any emotion. It had been announced too often, and the hope it brought had been too often false. The air raid alarm, the agitation of the *lagerschutz,* and the visit of an S.S. guard at such an unaccustomed hour were facts, a whole set of new facts, witnessed by everyone, sweeping like a fresh wind through the submissive world of the deportees. Motionless and silent beneath the cold arch of the sky, they had listened to the throaty whisper of the airplane engines. And then, without transition, the sirens had shattered nerves drawn taut by listening. The collective emotion overflowed into a kind of drunkenness, in which minds already weakened and receptive surrendered willingly to the seductive lure of the imagination.

183

Far into the night, there was a steady hum of conversation in the sleeping compartments. The block chief, clearly disturbed himself, made little attempt to enforce silence. Prisoners who made the journey to the toilets observed him talking gravely with the *stubendienst*. One of the *lagerschutz* was sitting with them, smoking a cigarette.

Normally, after being awakened in the morning, the deportees functioned like automatons until the time when they left the camp to go to work. They dressed, bathed, formed in columns, stood in the square for roll call, and went to the formation area of their *kommandos* in a state of lethargy from which only the daily rationing of bread managed to stir them for a moment. But even this rationing no longer aroused any passionate response. The table chiefs had conceived a set of rules that assured a fair portion for everyone. If an argument did arise, a makeshift scale consisting of a strip of wood, suspended from a cord and equipped with wire hooks at either end, made it possible to check the weight of the slices and insure their equality. The problem occasioned by the ends of the loaves, whose thick crusts contributed to the weight of the slice and were considered less nourishing by some and more nourishing by others, had been resolved. Each man, in turn, received an end slice and could then exchange it, if he so desired, with someone who preferred the crust. These acquired habits, the absence of any disrupting element, the elimination of the brutalities of the *stubendienst,* and the exhaustion of the men themselves, assured the smooth accomplishment of daily rites. The deportees played their part in them in a half-sleeping state that reminded Charlie of the way that he had participated at morning mass when he was a child.

But the morning following the air raid alarm was different. As soon as the block chief had shouted his ritual *"Auf—stehen,"* animated conversation broke out everywhere. The events of the night before had fermented for hours in overexcited minds. The yeast of hope had leavened the facts beyond recognition. Many of the deportees saw in them proof that the Allied invasion had taken place.

When he was a small boy, Alain had forced himself to forget the sum of the coins in the change purse he carried to school. As a student, he had deliberately underestimated his chances of successfully passing his examinations. He denied being a pessimist, however, and in fact he was not one. It was in order to convince himself more firmly of the necessity for effort that he voluntarily cheated a little. "You see," he had said to one of his friends, "basically, I'm a weak person. If I permitted myself to believe that whatever I desire is in my reach, I would not be able to make the effort required to attain it, and the consequent failure would destroy what strength I have. I prefer a fertile anxiety, rewarded by a happy surprise, to an illusory and sterile tranquillity that will bring me nothing but disillusionment."

The remarks he now heard on every hand, claiming that the invasion was an accomplished fact, irritated him all the more because he was forced to be constantly on guard against his own inclination to believe them. At first he had told himself: It's a rumor, a hoax like all the others. The sight of those bombers has set everyone to imagining things, because they never saw anything like it before. That's all there is to it. But little by little, Alain had yielded ground. The invasion certainly will take place someday, he thought, and it will not be announced to us by some irrefutable piece of evidence. So perhaps that day has come. Nothing proves that it has, but there is nothing to prove that it hasn't.

Marcel Dupuy had slipped into the place next to Alain in the column that was forming to go out for roll call.

"You know," he said, "this time it looks like it's the real thing."

"What looks like it's the real thing?" Alain demanded.

185

"The invasion."

"The invasion? Since when have you been listening to the BBC?"

"What do you mean? Haven't you heard what everyone is saying?"

"I've heard," Alain said, "what someone who doesn't understand German claims to have overheard last night, on his way to take a leak, from the whispered conversation between the block chief and a *lagerschutz*. I also heard one of our Communist comrades stating positively, last night, that the planes were Russian. He had recognized the particular sound of their motors; there was no doubt about it. Moreover, according to him, only the Russians could possibly send planes this far. I'm surprised he didn't claim he had seen the stars on their wings. This morning he is stating that those same planes were American, and in order for them to be able to fly over Thuringia the Allies must already have secured air bases on the continent. I've heard a bunch of jackasses telling each other a bunch of fables to amuse themselves, but every one of them, just like you and me, went back into the block as soon as the alarm sounded and hasn't been outside since. So where do you think they have dug up their information, if not in their own disordered imaginations?"

"But in that case," Dupuy said desperately, "how do you explain all those hundreds of planes?"

"I'll answer you with another question: In what way would the invasion explain them? Do you really believe that if the invasion had just begun, the Allies could spare hundreds of bombers to pound God knows what target a thousand kilometers away from their bases? Isn't it more normal to think they would be using them to destroy German formations, highways and railroads, the nearby air bases from which German fighter planes could attack them?"

"Yes, of course," Dupuy conceded. "You are certainly right. But why are you so annoyed?"

186

"Because it annoys me to listen to such stupidity. And it annoys me even more to see friends like you taking it seriously."

"But that's no reason for getting so angry."

Alain was in a rage—in fact, a rage against himself. Because he too had been uncertain for a time and had allowed himself to be carried away by the flood of rumors. Now he was experiencing the bitterness of being forced to turn his back on the hopes the rumors had raised.

"You know," he confessed, in a calmer tone, "I would have preferred to tell you that the invasion had really taken place. But don't worry about it, the time will come. The whole thing is to hang on. And in order to hang on, we have to be just as sparing of our reserves of morale as of our physical reserves."

For two more days the forest fire of rumors spread, consuming all reason in the deportees. The spark that had set off this fire was forgotten. But it was constantly rekindled by new sparks, struck on nothing more substantial than a fevered hope. The thought of approaching liberation summoned the delights of normal life from the limbo of memory. The life of the camp by comparison, assumed again all the frightfulness that time and custom had gradually erased. The deportees rediscovered its hunger, its cold, the interminable roll calls, the stench of the sleeping quarters, the even worse stench of the toilets, the eternal coating of greasy filth in the mess tins, their own misery and the hideous countenances of their friends. Habit had lulled their suffering into a kind of sleep. The hope of soon escaping had only served to reawaken the suffering, making it as intolerable as it had been on the first day.

When at last the deportees were forced to admit that the invasion had not taken place, discouragement overwhelmed the weak. The effort required to readapt to their condition was too great for them to make, and they allowed themselves to be sucked down in the whirlpool of despair. Every morning the number of the dead was greater, their bodies lying beside the buildings around the square.

33.

IIIIIIIIIIIIIIIIIIIIIIIIIIIIIIIIIIIIIIIIIIIIIIIIIIIIIIIIIIIIIIIIIIIIIIIIIIIIIIIIIIIIIIIIIIIIIIIIIIIIIIII

The cold, which had seemed to persist indefinitely, yielded at last one Sunday morning. The sky abandoned its icy hue, the sun shed a little warmth. The sharp bite of the wind was gone, the movement of the breeze was soft and tepid. The last icy stalactites that hung from the roofs of the barracks glittered in the sunlight, dripping little streams of water before they broke away. Lying on the ground, their shattered fragments gleamed like bits of crystal. Little groups of the healthiest deportees wandered through the streets of the camp. Their muscles were no longer knotted with cold. Their shoulders, for so long hunched against the wind, moved freely again, and the harsh lines of their faces relaxed.

Alain had walked over to Genteau's block but had not been able to find him. He went on walking, not knowing quite where he was going, avoiding the puddles of inky water, splashing through the mud. He had unbuttoned his coat and was whistling softly to himself, his hands in his pockets, his mind wandering. He came to the end of the last row of barracks. In front of him was a little square with a magnificent oak tree at its center—the only tree in the camp. Beyond the square was the *Effektenkam-*

mer, a two-story building whose concrete mass loomed above the low structure of the kitchen and the bakery. It was the first time Alain had ventured this far by daylight. He had been brought to the kitchen several times, as a member of the carrying crew, but always well before dawn.

As if they were still obeying orders, all the Sunday strollers turned back at the boundary of the square. Alain was on the point of following their example when he suddenly paused, seized by a temptation to investigate this unknown corner of the camp. It was undoubtedly forbidden. He glanced around him, looking for a sign, but there was none to be seen. After a moment's hesitation, he left the crowd and walked on alone toward the oak tree, half-expecting to see a *lagerschutz* come racing toward him, bludgeon already raised. But nothing happened. The trunk of the tree, very straight and very tall, opened out above his head in a spread of enormous branches. An inscription indicated that Goethe used to come and sit beneath this oak, in search of inspiration. But for the deportees its celebrity stemmed from a prediction: The tree's death would announce the collapse of the German Reich. Alain leaned back against the wooden railing that encircled the base of the tree, lifting his face toward the sun, welcoming the warmth of its rays. He had an odd sensation of dizziness. It had been a long time since he had been alone. Everywhere in the camp, the crowd hemmed in, absorbed and crushed the individual, annihilating his thoughts, suppressing his initiative, making him just another member of a herd—deaf, blind, wandering aimlessly through the streets. No one was sufficiently certain of his own personality to dare to break away. Alain himself felt ill at ease in this unaccustomed solitude. He straightened up and forced himself to walk around the tree. For an instant, he considered walking the length of the *Effekten-kammer* building, to see what lay behind it, but he decided not to. He walked back to the end of the street, rejoined the mainstream of deportees, and in their midst, rediscovered the peace of mind a mass provides its members.

Then he saw Geoffrin, bareheaded and wearing no coat. He had already seen Alain and was coming to meet him.

"What a transformation!" Alain exclaimed as they shook hands. "Conditions at Buchenwald seem to agree with you."

"It's primarily conditions at the Institute of Hygiene that agree with me," Geoffrin replied. "I wouldn't have recovered so rapidly anywhere else."

He did, in fact, seem a great deal better. The post he occupied gave him the right to wear his hair long. It had not been cut since he left Dora, and now formed a thick, even brush on his skull and temples. He was freshly shaven, and even though was still very thin, he had again that air of strength, of physical and moral equilibrium that had impressed Alain on their first meeting.

"After having lived in the bedlam of Dora," he was saying, "you can imagine what it's like to be back among civilized, intelligent men, doing something that is properly organized and effective."

Alain could not help interrupting. "Is effectiveness really so desirable," he asked, "when we are working for the Nazis?"

"The antityphus vaccine that we produce is not reserved for the German army," Geoffrin said. "It was given to you when you arrived in the camp."

"In that case," Alain said, "if vaccination is possible, why do the Germans live in terror of an epidemic of typhus and take so many precautions to avoid an invasion of lice? Anyone in this camp who has even one is sent off to be disinfected. It's one means of obtaining a day of rest. In my block, there are corpses of lice that are passed from hand to hand, in exchange for a cigarette or a bread ration."

"That's because the vaccine does not prevent contagion. It simply attenuates the effects of the illness—in principle, at least."

Obviously, Alain thought, under those circumstances its production does have a certain value for us.

Geoffrin surmised the direction of his thoughts.

"Don't think for a minute," he said, laughing, "that while I was at Dora I spent my time regretting that I was not more usefully employed. And I don't imagine that you are very deeply concerned about the efficiency of the factory where you work."

Alain shook his head. "If I were concerned, it would be with finding some way of reducing its efficiency. But I'm afraid I'll never be able to do anything about that. For several weeks, though, I've had the feeling that it would be worth trying."

"What are you manufacturing?" Geoffrin asked.

"To tell the truth, I never stop asking myself that question, but I have nothing to go on but conjectures. The conclusions I've come to are absurd. It seems to me we are constructing electrical appliances designed to equip a self-propelled projectile, navigating in space, subject to vibration and remote-controlled by radio."

Geoffrin stopped walking. He seemed to be listening to some far-off sound, or searching for something in his memory.

"What makes you suppose that?" he asked at last.

Alain explained it to him at length. Once again, as he outlined it step by step, his reasoning seemed to him to have no flaw.

Geoffrin questioned him on physical details such as the dimensions of the appliances built at the Mibau and the method employed to connect them. Alain thought that his curiosity might permit a reciprocal curiosity about what was being manufactured at Dora. He was wondering how he might approach this subject without seeming indiscreet when Geoffrin slipped an arm through his, began walking again, and murmured in his ear: "If I were in your place, I would keep what you have just told me strictly to myself. Your conclusions are correct. In the Mibau, you are undoubtedly building the equipment for the machines that are being constructed at Dora—enormous rockets designated by the name A-4.* They carry a very large explosive charge and are

---

* It was under the name A-4 that the V-2 rocket was planned and built. It did not receive the later designation, which means "reprisal weapon No. 2" (Vergeltung Waffe 2), until it was placed in service, following the V-1, which was a small pilotless jet plane.

propelled by motors of an entirely new type. It's unquestionably in order to maintain the secrecy of this construction that no one leaves Dora. Be careful; it isn't a good idea to know too much about it, either for you or for me."

He released Alain's arm. There was a long silence between them, and then Alain said only: "Thank you. And don't worry, I'll be sure to hold my tongue."

The code A-4 left no room for doubt. It appeared on drawings and documents Alain had managed to glimpse. He suddenly felt an overwhelming need to be alone, to digest what he had just learned. He made a pretext of an appointment and began walking back toward Goethe's oak. The square was still deserted, but it seemed less disturbing to him than it had an hour before. This time, he had the courage to go on walking. He passed the *Effektenkammer* and came out on an unused field that extended to the boundaries of the camp. An S.S. guard shouted something from a watchtower and pointed his submachine gun toward him. Alain turned back in the direction he had come and sat down at the foot of the oak.

The certainty of the military importance of the Mibau left him stunned. Its production must be paralyzed—at any cost.

Since his entrance into the factory, three months earlier, he had tried his best to do just this. Philippe, Genteau, and doubtless some others had also tried. But they had accomplished nothing.

Was it impossible?

Alain began to wonder why the Germans had taken the pains to hide the construction of the rockets in a tunnel at Dora that could not be reached by bombing, while the production of the electrical equipment, without which the rockets could not be used, took place in a factory whose flimsy buildings lay in plain view, unprotected even by antiaircraft batteries.

In spite of what Geoffrin had told him, he was tempted to find in this apparent anomaly a reason for doubting the importance of the Mibau production. But the evidence was incontrovertible.

The heavy-equipment transports required at Dora for construction of the rockets could not escape observation from the air. They would clearly indicate the existence of an industry that warranted a bombing, while the Mibau, seen from the sky, must seem no more than an extension of Buchenwald. Moreover, even if the Allies established a distinction between the factory and the camp, it was probable that they would not take the risk of massacring deportees without being certain that destruction of the factory was worth it. And even if they had known that electrical and electronic equipment was being manufactured there, they would not necessarily have suspected the importance of the Mibau. In order to measure that, they would first have to know of the existence of the rockets, and then establish a link between them and the production of Buchenwald. It was not certain that the English possessed information about the rockets. That the Germans used deportees to assemble them was evidence of their concern for the preservation of the secret. The foremen of the Mibau themselves were doubtless ignorant of the nature of the machines for which their product was intended. In any case, the absolute rule forbidding the return to Buchenwald of any deportee from Dora showed determination to avoid any correlation.

Without the stubbornness and audacity of Alstein, this rule would not have been violated. Alain marveled at the sequence of chances that had led to his realization that the destruction of the Mibau would make the production of Dora useless. It was because he had known him before the war that Alstein had fought with such determination for Geoffrin's return to Buchenwald. But this would have been impossible if the position Alstein occupied at the Institute of Hygiene, and the qualifications of Geoffrin, had not furnished Alstein both the means and the pretext. Charlie, too, had known Alstein for many years and had introduced Alain to him because Charlie and Alain had established a bond of friendship. Why? Alain no longer remembered. The origin of their relationship had not been

193

marked by any significant fact. He had found Charlie a likable person, and then they had had occasion to do each other mutual favors. Alain would doubtless not have attracted Alstein's interest if he had not been instrumental in the regrouping of the French deportees and had not had Philippe's backing. And he had been instrumental in the regrouping only because an informer had reported to the senior *kapos* that Alain had worked directly under General de Gaulle. It was Alain's friendship with Alstein and Charlie that had gained him Geoffrin's confidence. But this confidence would have borne no fruit if Alain had not been employed in the factory and if he had not met Genteau again in the camp.

Beneath the opaque shell of events, he discovered a network of linking elements as complex and as ordered as the bloodstream of the human body, with its thousands of greater and smaller arteries, of veins and capillaries.

A miracle of this same nature had been necessary before he could know what the Mibau represented in the German war plans. A superior force must have presided over the accomplishment of this miracle. And since such a force existed, it was self-evident that it would continue to work, and furnish him with the means of paralyzing the Mibau's production.

Alain was seized with a feeling akin to drunkenness. He, a miserable deportee, emaciated and starving, was going to shatter the results of years of work on the part of German scientists and industrialists, to save thousands of human lives and—who could tell?—perhaps affect the outcome of the war.

After roll call that night, Alain led Philippe to the noisiest corner of the toilets, near the ventilator, where he could be sure that his words would go no further than his friend's ears.

Making no attempt at any preliminary explanation, he simply

194

announced, "I'm going to try to paralyze the Mibau's production."

Philippe was stunned by the determination of his tone and his appearance. "What the hell's gotten into you?" he demanded. "Do you have a fever again?"

"No, no, nothing like that. But I've had enough of stalling around, not doing anything useful."

"Oh, fine," Philippe said mockingly. "And since you're in a mood for exchanging confidences, I can tell you that I've decided to assassinate Hitler. Obviously, my project is going to be a good deal more difficult to carry out than yours, but you'll have to admit that it has one considerable advantage over yours: it will be much more effective in the matter of bringing the war to an end.

"You've got to listen to me," Alain said, "I'm not joking."

"And just how do you plan to go about paralyzing the Mibau's production?"

"I haven't any idea—yet. I wanted to discuss that with you."

"Don't you think," Philippe said, "that it would be better to wait until we can talk this over quietly? We might be overheard here."

Alain shook his head. "No, this is urgent. I've already waited too long."

"Very well," Philippe conceded. And then he added, in the tone usually reserved for speaking to someone who is not quite sane, "Who are you thinking of including in your little secret?"

"No one. I'm still at the stage of generalities. I'm talking to you about it because I want your advice."

"Well then, I'll give it to you: Drop the whole thing."

"You don't understand," Alain protested. "You think I've gone crazy."

"Well, you do give that impression."

"Well, I haven't. At this point, I can see three possible solutions: first, sabotage; next, the destruction of the factory; and last, a call for a bombing raid. What do you think?"

195

"I think that sabotage, at the level of polishing iron boxes, isn't going to be very effective; that you lack explosives to blow up several acres of factory; and that, insofar as a bombing raid is concerned, you're going to have difficulty bringing it about."

"You're a terrible pessimist," Alain laughed. "But I would like you to think about what I've just said. I'm suddenly eaten up by a need for action. I'm sure the attempt to do something is worthwhile. And I know now what I left undone before. I approached the problem without being convinced that it could be solved, without being convinced that it *must* be solved. Now I'm absolutely sure that what we are manufacturing is extremely important."

"What makes you so sure of that?" Philippe demanded.

"It's obvious," Alain said, "that the equipment we're making is designed for weapons of a kind we know nothing about but which are certainly enormously powerful. The Krauts would not be amusing themselves installing gyroscopes, programing mechanisms, and remote-control receiving sets on machines that did not need them."

Philippe nodded.

"Until now," Alain went on, "when I discussed with you and Genteau what was being manufactured in the Mibau, I was concerned only with the nature of the machines this equipment was being made for, and I lost sight of the fact that no matter what they were, they were unquestionably formidable weapons."

He slept badly and woke up exhausted and nervous.

All day, as he polished his iron boxes, Alain attempted to classify the ideas that were floating through his mind. If I don't force some kind of discipline on myself, he thought, I am certain to fail. He tried to draw up a mental work plan, but he was so weary that he was forced to give up.

196

After evening roll call, he went back to his block to think the matter out. An image from his childhood memories flashed through his mind. When he was a little boy, the freight cars in the marshaling yards were still drawn by horses. One day, he observed a Percheron reared up on its hind legs, pushing with all its strength against its collar. The chains that extended the traces of the horse's harness were hooked to the side of a freight car. The horse was panting laboriously. From time to time, its hooves slipped on the paving stones and sent out little showers of sparks. A fog of sweat rose from the animal's straining body. The freight car remained, it seemed, motionless, an inert mass dominating the powerful, stubborn struggle of the horse. It had seemed to the wide-eyed Alain that this struggle would never end. But a moment or so later the animal's muscles relaxed. He had regained his normal stance and shook himself to loosen the pressure of the collar against his shoulders. It was only then that Alain had realized that the car was moving very slowly forward. The chains, with the pressure on them relaxed, unhooked automatically and fell to the paving stones. The heavy car slowly passed the sweating, trembling horse. Then it reached a sloping portion of the track and, from one switching point to the next, rolled faster and faster, until it struck against the rear of the forming train, sending a great clatter of crashing metal through the silent station.

That's it, Alain thought. I am that horse. For a long time to come, I am going to have to apply all my strength to this task, without allowing myself to become discouraged, even if my efforts seem to produce no results. One day, things will begin to move. And then the switches will open automatically and my project will go on to completion, under its own power.

Sleep was overtaking him. Without realizing what he was doing, he said aloud, "I simply have to be as stubborn as that horse."

Charlie was lying beside him in the sleeping compartment. "What horse?" he demanded. "It's mules that are stubborn."

But Alain did not hear him. He was already asleep.

197

34.

|||||||||||||||||||||||||||||||||||||||||||||||||||||||||||||||||||||||||||||||||||||||||||||||||||||||||||||||||||||

On Monday, Alain spent the entire day considering various ways of paralyzing the Mibau's production.

As long as his work consisted of nothing more than the polishing of iron boxes, he would have to give up any thought of sabotage. For that matter, he would be in no better position if he should again be assigned to regulating programing mechanisms. Before their casings were sealed, a German civilian checked every one of the mechanisms assembled and adjusted by deportees. Any malfunction would be discovered immediately. To break a few tools, or to put a few of the machines temporarily out of order, would, at best, obtain only a brief satisfaction for which a disproportionately high price might have to be paid.

Between sabotage and the destruction of the factory itself lay the possibility of rendering its means of production unserviceable. The attainment of this goal with limited means constituted a new form of the art of war. It permitted the achievement, temporarily at least, of the same military purposes as a bombing raid, while at the same time safeguarding the patrimony of the occupied countries. A well-placed charge of plastic explosive— in an electrical station, for example—could force a stoppage in an entire industry for months. In England, Alain had received special training in this field; but even had he been able to gain access to the transformers that supplied the Mibau, he would have been able to do nothing, because he had no explosives.

Fire appeared to be the only possibility for one working from the inside. The wooden framework, the flimsy roofings, covered with tar paper, were easily combustible. At the same time, this flimsy construction would limit the amount of damage. Tools and equipment, even though they were not materially affected by the fire, would be damaged by exposure to the elements. The difficulty of starting a fire was not insurmountable, but the means of extinguishing fires had been well planned. Heavy canvas hoses were installed at intervals along the water mains, and extinguishers had been placed almost everywhere. There was no point in even thinking of cutting off the water. The best plan was to attack the hoses. Alain tried this and came very close to being caught by an S.S. guard as he was attempting to cut into the canvas with a piece of file.

He came to the conclusion that in order for the fire to have some chance of spreading, it would have to break out when the factory was deserted.

Alain settled finally on the idea of a delayed-action firing device. He planned to ask either Alstein or Geoffrin for some saltpeter. There surely should be some of it available in the laboratory of the Institute of Hygiene. He would make a wick from a strip of shirt material, soak it in a solution of saltpeter, and then let it dry. The wick would burn slowly, and it would suffice to set fire to matches. He knew that it was possible to obtain a box of these in exchange for a bread ration.

In one corner of the tool warehouse there was always an accumulation of crumbled and shredded wrapping paper. On the rows of shelves above, there were lines of bottles of gasoline, kerosene, and oil. The pine board partitionings oozed with resin. There was no doubt in his mind that it was possible, in this area, to cause flames high enough to reach the roofing in a matter of seconds.

Getting into the area after the departure of the warehouse supervisor presented a risk, but Alain was determined to take it.

And it should work, he thought.

But it was obvious that a bombing raid by Allied aircraft would be infinitely more effective. He imagined the effect of a few bombs dropped some moonlit night—the twisted roofs, the blown-out walls, the blasted water mains and electric cables. That was something that would be worth the risk.

If the Allies knew what the Mibau was producing, they would undoubtedly carry out such a raid. The problem was in informing them about it. There were only two ways to do this—to carry the information, or to send it. Carrying it meant escaping. There was no possibility of that. Therefore, it was necessary to send it, which meant finding someone on the outside who could and would deliver it.

The end of the workday in the factory took Alain by surprise. The return to camp and the distribution of the evening ration prevented him from following the course of his reflections. During the roll call, he realized with satisfaction that he had never before carried an analysis of the problem so far. The difficulties to be overcome were now defined.

He returned to his barracks filled with optimism. Genteau was waiting for him and caught him by the sleeve just as he was about to enter the door.

"We still have an hour before curfew," he said. "Come over to my block. Almost no one there speaks French. We'll be able to talk there more easily than in yours."

On the way, he explained to Alain that Philippe had told him of their conversation of the day before.

"I've known for a long time," he said, "that we were constructing matériel that was militarily very important."

"Why didn't you tell me that?"

"I thought you realized it yourself."

Alain stared at him.

"And besides, what good would it have done you?" Genteau continued.

"I might have tried to do something."

"To do what?"

200

"I don't have any idea yet; but I can tell you that, now, I am constantly searching for something. I would have set about it sooner."

"That would have only resulted in making your helplessness harder to bear."

"Because you think there is nothing I can do?"

Genteau sought another avenue of approach.

"Listen," he said, "until now I thought of you as an old friend, a buddy—"

"But now—" Alain exploded.

"But now I am placing all my trust in you."

"I'm touched. And to what do I owe this honor?"

"A man can be an absolutely marvelous guy, deserving of total confidence in normal conditions, and be nothing more than a dangerous character here, simply because he might be indiscreet."

"What do you mean by that? Are you insinuating that I am indiscreet?"

Genteau ignored the question.

"Since the conversation I had with Philippe at noon," he said, "I've decided to let you in on something: We are listening to the English broadcasts every day."

"What?"

"Yes. You heard me right."

"You've gotten hold of a radio?"

"No, we built one."

"We? Who is 'we?'"

"The crew assigned to checking the receiving sets."

Alain was swept up by an impatience to know everything there was of the news. Genteau summed up the situation for him. In Italy a landing intended to outflank the Gustav Line did not seem to have lived up to expectations. A pocket had been formed, but to all appearances, it had been effectively contained by the Germans. Frontal attacks in the direction of Cassino were dragging on. Things were going better on the eastern front. Russian troops were developing a powerful offensive in the south and had liberated practically all Soviet territory, with the exception of Byelorussia. Odessa had been evacuated by the Germans, and battles were raging throughout the Crimea. Allied aviation was extremely active over Western Europe. All the communiqués mentioned raids day and night and pointed out the exhaustion of the German pursuit aircraft, underlining the fact that, if the figures for enemy aircraft shot down were declining, it was because this form of game was becoming increasingly rare. There were repeated accounts of the enormous destruction caused in Germany by aerial bombardment, and of the spreading paralysis of the enemy's production capabilities. The communications networks of the occupied countries in the West were the targets of pinpoint raids, and the constant pursuit of locomotives testified to the Allies' particular concern with diminishing the capacity of the transport system.

"All of that isn't bad," Alain said, "but it doesn't really let us hope for an invasion in the near future. Obviously, so long as the Italian business is not concluded, there's not much chance of seeing another front opened up. The most gratifying part of it all is the aerial supremacy of the Allies, which certainly seems more pronounced every day. But what is the BBC saying to the French people at home?"

"They're doing everything they can to restrain their impatience."

"That's not very comforting."

"Yes, in a sense it is. I have the impression that the Resistance has developed considerably, on the military level, in the period since we were arrested. Now, they talk of the F.F.I., the French Forces of the Interior, as of something that is really important. And it is surely not easy to hold the Maquis in a state of inactivity. The high command is doing its best to avoid a situation in which they would attract too much attention too soon and so be wiped out before they could cooperate in a combined action. You can imagine the sort of thing they are saying: You represent a powerful trump; train hard, gather reinforcements; you are

202

going to be heroes. But wait a little while. You will be informed when the time has come to launch the attack."

"Well," Alain said, "one thing is clear. The Liberation isn't scheduled for tomorrow."

"Did you think it was?"

"Of course not. But I had hoped the invasion would take place at this time of year, so that everything might be decided by autumn."

"You're not the only one. And it's for that reason that it's best to try to keep morale up here. The regrouping of the French has made that even more difficult than before. That's one of its inconveniences. If we were still scattered, the appearance of those bombers the other night would not have created the wave of hope it did, nor left behind the wrecks of all the poor chaps who will never recover their lost illusions."

Genteau outlined his plan. It consisted primarily of taking advantage of the BBC communiqués to stem the abrupt shifting of opinions among the prisoners. To do this, it was necessary to call on those Frenchmen who had some influence with their comrades.

"Yes, I see," Alain said. "It would be their mission to counter the false rumors and give exact information, saying that it was more likely to be the truth—without, however, ever quoting it as such. It's a good idea. How many men are there in your crew at the factory?"

"Seven."

"Good. Seven, to begin with. If each one of them passes the news to three or four others, there will be enough to cover all the blocks."

"Of the seven, there are only four Frenchmen. That's what makes the operation difficult. If we want to avoid any excessive risks, we must strictly limit the number of people who know the source of the news. Outside those few people, it must be passed along as just a common sense evaluation—even though those who do that now may eventually be suspected of having the gift of prophecy."

203

Alain saw new vistas opening before him. It was not just that he would now be in possession of firsthand information; he would also be in a position to make good use of it, and this was what intrigued him. He thanked Genteau profusely for having included him in the setup of the plan. It was agreed that Philippe would act as liaison between Alain and Genteau. Since they belonged to the same *kommando,* Genteau would bring Philippe up to date on the daily communiqués during their return from the Mibau each night.

For an instant, Alain was tempted to repay the confidence Genteau had shown to him by telling what he had learned from Geoffrin. Their friendship might be made that much stronger. But he abandoned the idea. It was not necessary, and it might result in all sorts of complications. Perhaps in Genteau's judgment the fact that Alain would commit such an indiscretion might be of greater importance than the information he revealed.

All through the next day, Alain thought about the conversation he had had with Genteau. He decided at last to discuss with him the practical possibilities of sabotaging the factory's production. The new link that had been established between them made it possible. That night, he walked over to his friend's block.

Genteau did not believe that a fire could be effective. Even if it was possible to start it, it would have no chance of spreading. The roofing and framework of the buildings would not provide sufficient fuel for the flames. The point of origin, even if it was not discovered immediately, could be easily isolated, and the damage would be insignificant.

After they had discussed the matter for a few minutes, Alain was forced to agree with him.

"Well then," he said, "we'll have to arrange for the factory to be bombed."

Genteau burst out laughing.

"Obviously," he said. "The same way you catch little birds. Just put salt on their tails."

204

"Perhaps, but it should be possible to get word to the Allies."

"That's not the problem. But even if we should succeed, we wouldn't be much farther ahead."

Alain was bewildered. "What do you mean?"

"We've already considered setting up radio contact with London," Genteau said.

"You mean you have the equipment?"

"We have everything we need to build a transmitter."

Alain's heart pounded against his ribs.

"If you don't know what wave length to transmit on, and you don't have a call sign or a code, I can supply you with those."

"That isn't the difficulty."

"Are you afraid the broadcasts will be picked up and traced?"

"No. We're not in France, and there is very little chance that the Germans keep a close watch over their own territory."

"Well then, what's the problem?"

"The problem? Granting that we succeed in getting our message across, no one in London would believe it."

"You think not? That would depend on what it said."

"No matter what it said."

Alain thought about this for a moment.

"You're probably right," he sighed. "I know the people in the Intelligence Service, and they would be sure to think that the Krauts were setting up a trap for them."

"And that, for one reason or another, they wanted to provoke a bombing raid on a concentration camp."

"It might be possible to identify the sender for them."

Genteau shook his head. "That wouldn't solve anything. They would simply think he was acting on German orders, voluntarily or involuntarily."

Alain's soaring hopes plummeted back to earth. No matter what message they put together, it would be regarded as the work of the Gestapo, with the willing or unwilling complicity of some of the deportees.

"The only thing we can do," Genteau concluded, "is sabotage."

"Sabotage—sabotage!" Alain burst out. "Just yesterday you told me that I couldn't do it. Today you demonstrate to me that the factory can't be set on fire and you claim I am wasting my time in trying to have it bombed. What then, in your opinion, can I do? Just go on polishing my boxes and wait to see what happens?"

"I'm afraid so."

"Then you're giving up entirely?"

"Not entirely. There are some things you don't know. Half the total production of the radio receivers is rejected by the inspectors. Does that mean anything to you?"

"But the other half of the production is accepted." Alain was thinking of the rockets in the underground tunnel at Dora that Geoffrin had described to him, and for a second time he weighed the possibility of telling Genteau about them.

"It's too much, of course," Genteau agreed. "But we haven't yet said our last word."

"Neither have I," Alain replied. "You have decided to sabotage by making poor equipment. Go on with it. As for me, I'm going to have to find some other way, since that one isn't open to me. I'm not claiming that I'll succeed, but let me try. If I fail, at least I can't reproach myself for having done nothing. And in any case, it will keep my mind busy."

"I wouldn't try to prevent you from doing anything you can," Genteau said. "But be careful."

"Our efforts are sure to complement each other. You are slowing down production. And I will be trying to stop it altogether. And I assure you, doing that is worth any risk."

That night Alain went to sleep to the sound of sirens announcing an air raid. The distant sound of bombers' engines penetrated the open windows of the sleeping quarters, mingling with the snores of the deportees, and he dreamed that the Mibau was being crushed beneath a rain of bombs.

206

‖‖‖

35

The alert that night, the second in a period of weeks, strength-ened Alain's determination to bring about an air raid on the factory. Basically, it was a matter of transmitting to the Allies information they would accept at face value. This brought up two distinct problems—that of the messenger, and that of the message. The message would have to be detailed enough to be convincing, and obviously, it would have to be in writing. These requirements engendered a third problem, one of a strictly practical nature. It was not enough for him to have paper and pencil available; he must find some means of making use of them without giving himself away. No one at Buchenwald ever wrote anything more than monthly postcards, on forms that were distributed and col-lected on a specified date; it was impossible to sit down any-where, to do anything, even for a few moments, and be sheltered from the eyes and ears of the other prisoners. To make matters worse, it would be necessary to prepare the message at the last moment, to write it out in one brief session so it wouldn't be discovered during a search.

Alain considered asking the *kapo* of the canteen to provide him with a quiet corner when the proper time came, but he abandoned this thought almost at once. The German Communist prisoners had not, because they were Communists, ceased to be Germans. Certainly, they fervently hoped to see the Nazis crushed; but at the same time they feared the defeat of Germany, and they would do nothing to hasten it. Had it been otherwise, in fact, they could have informed the Allies of the Mibau's activity long before this. They knew all the details of its production. They were very probably even aware of the existence of the rockets being built at Dora.

In spite of the relative sparsity of its population, the block of the Institute of Hygiene did not offer any better possibility of privacy. Anyone who did not belong in this block and yet went there for purposes, presumably, of writing, would be certain to attract attention. Moreover, it would be necessary to share the secret with Geoffrin and Alstein. And that, in case of accident, would be for them a superfluous risk.

Alain was exasperated by the problem—ridiculous, on the face of it—posed by the simple matter of finding a corner where he could write out his message once he had discovered a means of transmitting it.

During the month of April, even though it was still snowing, all outer coats and jackets were collected by the block chiefs and returned to the *Effektenkammer*. At the same time, the deportees were forbidden to go into the sleeping quarters in their clothing. Each night, they had to leave their rags and whatever form of boots they had in the mess hall and go to bed wearing only their shirts. The number of nocturnal thefts multiplied immediately. In the morning, curses and moans filled the air. Battles for repossession of pilfered shreds broke out everywhere. A few of the stronger and more unscrupulous stripped their comrades of their tatters, claiming that they had been stolen from them. Throughout the camp, a flourishing market sprang up for boots and garments from which the numbers had been removed. Bread, cigarettes, and matches were the materials of barter.

In an attempt to remedy this situation, the Frenchmen in block 26 convinced their block chief it was necessary to set up a nightly guard in the mess hall. Several of the strongest and most trustworthy deportees were selected to stand watch. In one day, the thievery stopped.

Alain's name was on the list of those appointed. Once each week he gave up two hours of sleep to protect the possessions of his comrades. That opened the way to a solution of the problem of writing the message, even though he was not always alone during these two hours. Acquaintances who couldn't sleep came to sit and talk with him, and there was constant traffic between the sleeping quarters and the toilets. It was only necessary, however, to find a way of discouraging the indiscreet; and he would then be able to write without being noticed.

Genteau provided it for him. Along with the other members of his control group in the factory, he had been authorized to collect some of the personal belongings he had been carrying when he arrived in the camp. Among these was a treatise on vectorial calculus that he had asked to have sent to him when he was interned in France.

"I'll make you a gift of it," he said to Alain. "And as you know, it doesn't make the most stimulating reading. No one will be tempted to borrow it from you. And it isn't likely to cause you any trouble with the S.S.; even they would find it hard to qualify it as seditious. Moreover, it gives you good reason to have paper and a pencil, so that you can work on the exercises in it. I'll get those for you."

Every time he was on guard duty, Alain immersed himself in the study of vectorial calculus, conscientiously blackening his little scraps of paper. To those who asked him: "What are you doing?" he replied, "Come and look," and if the curious person was inclined to overstay his welcome, he added: "All right, now that you've seen what it is, get out of here and let me work." He acquired a reputation as a pedant among those comrades— always the same ones—who slept badly or had weak bladders, but they grew accustomed to seeing him writing during his period on guard and ceased paying any attention to him. In the morning Alain gave Charlie the book, the remaining paper, and the pencil, and they were locked up in his chest until the following week.

Gathering information on the products manufactured in the various sections of the Mibau did not present any difficulty. Simply by talking with friends in his own block during the roll call, Alain managed to get the information he was looking for without creating suspicion. He discovered that the last two of the main buildings were manufacturing artillery caissons and Mauser rifles, of a model dating from the first World War. With these exceptions, the whole of the Mibau was given over to the production of equipment for the A-4 rocket.

Both the trip to the factory in the morning and the return to the camp at night now took place in daylight, and Alain was thus able to make all the topographical observations he needed to draw up a plan of the camp and its annexes, concentrating on the specific location of landmarks that could most easily be picked out from the air.

As for a messenger who might be able to carry the information to France, Alain had come to the conclusion that his only hope lay in the free workers who returned to France on leave. His next line of research, therefore, would have to be directed toward his comrades who came in contact with free workers—and this was true of Charlie.

Alain questioned him on the subject.

"What's the status of your underground liaison with your family?" he asked him.

"It's at a dead end," Charlie sighed. "I did meet one rather nice guy. A lieutenant in the reserves, a prisoner of war who was released and who works in a maintenance office in the Weimar station."

"You have some strange friends."

210

"Oh, of course, working for the Nazis can hardly be considered a reference. He could have tried to escape, or at least have gone on twiddling his thumbs in a POW camp. But in spite of all that, he's still a nice guy."

"Have you asked him if he would deliver messages to your parents?"

"Yes."

"And?"

"And he told me to go to hell."

"And that's what you call a nice guy?"

Charlie shook his head. "I don't know how to explain it to you," he said. "The fact that he turned me down didn't change my opinion of him. He could have been evasive about it, found some excuse, talked about the danger involved, brought in his family—he's married and has two children. But he didn't do anything like that. He just said no."

"What did he actually say?"

"Something like this: 'Look, my friend, it isn't worth taking such a risk for such stupidity.' His tone was friendly, but it was clear that that was the end of it, so I dropped the subject. I had the feeling that if I had asked him something else—to help me attempt to escape, for instance—he might have thought about it before answering, but since it was just a matter of writing a letter, he said no immediately."

"Do you see him often?"

"From time to time, when he comes to the area where my *kommando* is working. Sometimes, that happens several days in a row, and then we may go a week or two without seeing each other."

"Listen. I'm going to ask you to do something for me."

"You're not by any chance thinking of trying to cut out of here, are you?" Charlie asked.

"No," Alain replied. "Don't worry about that; I haven't lost my mind. But I would like you to try to find out just what this

211

guy is made of. No matter how disappointing it might have been, his reaction to the business of the letter was probably wise. But try to find out if he would be receptive to playing a part in something really serious, if the opportunity should arise."

"If you could tell me something of what it's all about—"

"Out of the question," Alain interrupted, laughing. "And for that matter, it's no more than a remote possibility."

"All right—all right—but what kind of job are you thinking of asking him to do?"

"None, for the time being. I'm simply thinking that it would be a good thing to know that we have someone we can rely on outside the camp. Concentrate on getting some kind of idea of how reliable he is. Is he discreet, or does he talk too much? Does he have any guts? Why is he working for the Krauts? Why doesn't he try to get out? That's the kind of question I'd like to have the answers to."

Not content with having a single path that might lead to his goal, Alain set to work finding others.

A man named Delage, who had been one of his cellmates in the prison at Fresnes, seemed a possibility. Alain had seen him again at Buchenwald before Delage was transferred to Weimar, to a camp whose occupants worked in a factory, the Guslov Werke. Alain had heard it said that the deportees in this camp were in contact with some of the free workers. Through the intermediary of friends who had been sent back to Buchenwald for a few days, he had occasionally received news of Delage and had sent him messages.

He knew that transient deportees were billeted in block 17. The following Sunday he walked over there right after the morning roll call. A double enclosure of barbed-wire fence isolated the barracks from the rest of the camp, but there was no guard at the gate. He went into the area and wandered around for a time, looking for Frenchmen. He had the good luck to find one who had just returned from Weimar. He did not seem overly bright, but in view of the questions Alain wanted to ask, he thought this was just as well.

From the conversation he had with this man, he learned exactly what he had hoped. The deportees who worked in the Guslov Werke were actually in contact with the free workers. Relations between the two groups were forbidden, but in spite of this they managed to talk with each other. On several occasions, free workers going home on leave had offered to bring news of the deportees to their families and had brought messages back, which proved that they had carried out their mission. Any deportees in Weimar who might be ill were sent back to Buchenwald for treatment. The face of the man Alain was talking to was swollen from an infection, and he had been sent back to Buchenwald for a few days of rest.

This information made Alain highly optimistic.

"Do you know a man named Delage?" he asked.

"Yes. As a matter of fact, he's one of my best buddies. We're in the same block."

"When you go back, tell him I would like to see him as soon as possible. Tell him to find some way to come back here, the same way you did, for a few days. My name is Alain, and I was his cellmate at Fresnes."

"No kidding," the man said, "you're Alain? I'm glad you found me. Delage has often told me about you. You're from Nantes. I'm from Saint-Nazaire, myself. I got picked up for hiding some Englishmen after the commando raid. You can count on me. I'll let Delage use my own trick."

"What trick?"

"To get this inflammation in the jaw. I rub the gum and the inside of the cheek with glass wool I take from the insulation of the heating pipes. It swells up right away, and it doesn't cause much pain. I learned about it while I was in the navy. It's a good way of getting out of the dirty jobs."

Alain could do nothing now but wait.

36.

||||||||||||||||||||||||||||||||||||||||||||||||||||||||||||||||||||||||||||||||||||||||||||||||||

Developments in the working conditions at the Mibau moved at a swifter pace than either Alain's projects or military events.

The rumor that a night shift would be installed had already circulated on several occasions, but nothing had ever happened to confirm it. Now it was revived, and this time a new group of *meisters* arrived, to be briefed in their duties by the original foremen. From fragments of conversations the deportees were able to overhear, they learned that the new schedule would be put into effect the following week.

Alain had not seen Genteau for several days. The nightly roll calls had been too long. When he at last succeeded in contacting him, he at once brought up the matter that had been tormenting him for days: the new control group for the radio receivers would know nothing of the sabotage and would be doing nothing about it, at least not at first. Therefore, they would reject far fewer of the receivers than the present crew. The Germans would be sure to notice it, and the consequences were easy to foresee.

"Don't worry," Genteau said. "Formation of a new crew couldn't have taken place at a time less likely to be harmful to our security, and I hope it will include at least a few members reliable enough to be trusted with our system of sabotage."

"Just what is your system?"

"It's based on a systematic deterioration of the tubes."

"How do you go about it?"

214

"Oh, it's very simple. We let them drop from a little height, just enough to loosen the electrodes slightly."

"And your engineer doesn't notice anything?"

"No, because it doesn't affect the tuning of the sets as long as they're immobile. It isn't until the German civilian takes them over for a final check, on the vibrating table, that nothing works. Then, sets that we have adjusted perfectly turn out to be unstable and have to be rejected."

"That's very clever."

"We stumbled around for a long time before getting there, but now we have the technique mastered completely."

"And you've never been suspected?"

"Yes, I think we have."

Genteau, who was apparently in a confidential mood, told Alain that an inspector had arrived from Berlin three weeks before, carrying with him some carefully wrapped and sealed boxes. They contained tubes. The German engineer who supervised the crew of deportees and the civilian who was responsible for the final tests on the vibrating table had greeted him with great deference and placed themselves under his orders.

The inspector had declined their services. He had ordered the deportees to stand aside from the test benches and to keep out of his way, and then he had set to work.

As the radios came down from the assembly line, he had equipped them with the tubes he had brought with him and then adjusted and regulated them. His obvious competence had been extremely disturbing.

Genteau and his comrades, waiting in the corner of the hall, had already come to the conclusion that their sabotage had been discovered, and they were under no illusions regarding the fate that awaited them. They attempted to talk among themselves in a natural manner, but their eyes were irresistibly drawn to the man whose hands, slowly turning the delicately tuned knobs of the control mechanisms, seemed to be determining the precise moment of their hanging.

215

"We didn't know the answer until the next day. The proportion of defective sets was higher than ever."

"But how do you explain that?" Alain asked.

"I don't explain it."

"But you must have some theory about it?"

"Not the slightest, except perhaps that the tubes brought by our visitor had been sabotaged before being given to him. But that is highly unlikely. Only the final result mattered, and it surpassed our fondest hopes. Our engineer breathed a sigh of relief when it was proven that he could not be blamed for what was happening."

After it had been established, through some miracle, that the tubes were not responsible for the losses, and once the control crew had been cleared of all suspicion, Genteau had moved at once to take advantage of these developments. He suggested a technical explanation for the faulty functioning of the receivers: the wire sections of the coil were inadequate, he said, and the vibrations of its spirals caused their instability.

"Does that actually influence them?" Alain asked.

"Theoretically, yes, but the practical effect is certainly negligible. But one engineer was so fascinated with the idea that he sent off a report to Berlin, and last week we were visited by a delegation of generals of the Wehrmacht and the Luftwaffe, along with a few civilians. He had a long discussion with them, and when the time came for them to leave they made a point of congratulating us. The Luftwaffe general made us a little speech and shook our hands."

"You must have had a hard time keeping a straight face."

"Not too hard, because that imbecile said some interesting things."

"What?"

"Briefly, that our work and our zeal could have an effect of which we couldn't possibly be aware, and that they might, of themselves, change the face of the world."

Genteau went on to explain that, since the generals' visit,

216

manufacture of the radio receivers had been suspended pending arrival of orders, which had just come in. Not only were the new sets to be built in accordance with Genteau's recommendation, but all of those that had already been accepted were going to be modified.

"If the men who are assigned to alter them are in the least bit awkward," he added, "or, of course, if they should bother to sabotage them, which would be easy and involve no risk, not one single set will be functional."

"In that case," Alain said, "if I understand you correctly, the entire production of the past four months will be zero."

"Just about."

Alain could find no words to express his admiration.

Genteau called to his attention the fact that the results obtained thus far were not entirely to their advantage, however. Assembly of the radios had now begun again, and as a result of the addition of the night shift, the rate of production would be doubled. No matter what else happened, it would not be possible to reject the same percentage of sets as before, since they would be provided with the modified coil. Moreover, between the time when the new control crew was formed and when the first sets would come off the assembly line, Genteau would have only one Sunday in which to meet the control crew members, evaluate the degree of confidence that might be placed in them, and convert at least one of them to the sabotage program. If none of them seemed reliable enough, morally and technically, it would be necessary to abandon the whole plan. In that event, with the additional output resulting from the night work, the number of acceptable sets completed each week would be four times greater than it had ever been before.

"So," Genteau concluded, "it's more necessary than ever that the bombing of the factory take place soon. When do you think it might be?"

Alain shook his head gloomily. "I still don't have a messenger."

"Do you have any hope of finding one soon?"

217

"I have two leads. But the annoying thing about it is that, from now on, there are going to be deportees in the factory all the time, except on Sunday. Unless the Allies are willing to slaughter us, they're going to have to choose their time very carefully."

The system of two work-shifts began the following week. The night shift left for the Mibau after the evening roll call and returned at the beginning of the morning roll call. The day shift left after the morning roll call and returned at the beginning of the evening roll call. That left the factory empty for only two or three hours each day, and from Sunday morning to Monday morning.

Alain preferred working at night. During the day, the block was almost empty. Distribution of rations to the members of the night *kommandos* was carried out in an atmosphere of relative calm. In the sleeping quarters, each man had a mat to himself and shrouded himself in covers borrowed from the neighboring compartments. The air coming through the open windows was fresh. Alain slept soundly until the end of the afternoon and then was free, until time for the ration distribution, to walk by himself or to visit friends in other blocks who worked, like himself, at night.

The war news broadcast by the BBC circulated through the camp without causing any curiosity about its origin. The mere fact that it was coherent inspired confidence. In the Far East, after the long series of British and American reverses, the Allies were nibbling away slowly but effectively at the far-flung Japanese defenses. Soviet troops were methodically reducing the enemy pockets left behind by their overwhelming offensive. In Germany itself, and in the occupied countries of Europe, bombers based in Britain continued their devastation of major targets and their destruction of the German pursuit forces. The exact date of the

218

invasion now seemed of little importance; it was certain to be soon. Next winter's snow would shroud a camp in which there were no prisoners, where smoke no longer rose from the chimneys of the crematorium. No one doubted this. The deportees awaited their liberation as an exhausted boxer awaits rescue by the bell. The weakest among them sank into a bottomless, boundless lake of torpor. The strongest, those who worked in the factory, went feebly through the motions of their daily ordeal, marked by the pangs of constant hunger and the long periods of standing in the square, with the bitter wind in their face and the melting snow at their feet.

A burning impatience left room in Alain's thoughts for nothing except finding a messenger.

Each time that Charlie managed to talk with his friend in Weimar, he reported the results to Alain. Since they did not know the man's real name, they had agreed to call him Oscar, in memory of his predecessor.

"That will bring us luck," Charlie had said.

At the beginning of his captivity, in 1940, Oscar had been a disciple of Marshal Pétain. His admiration for the old hero bordered on an idolatrous masochism. In his eyes, France, and he himself as a Frenchman, were atoning for the sins of the politicians. His POW camp might have been a monastery, in the sense that he dedicated himself to a patriotic mortification. He offered up his own suffering, relative though this might have been, for the redemption of his country in a renewed world. It was for that reason that he had turned his back on the idea of escape. Then, a time had come when he was first aware of doubt; and at last he became certain of his error.

This, at least, was the story Oscar had told Charlie. It did not satisfy Alain.

"That may be true," he said, "but it doesn't explain why he is working for the Krauts now. You say he speaks German perfectly. Then why doesn't he get the hell out of there?"

"That's something I've wondered myself," Charlie said.

"The best thing to do would be to ask him."

"He's supposed to go home on leave sometime soon. Perhaps it is a kind of two-stage escape that he is attempting, first being made a free worker, and then deserting while on leave."

"Deserting while on leave." Alain said, "That's putting it very neatly." He was profoundly discouraged. Oscar was not the sort of man he needed. "When is he supposed to leave?" he asked.

"About a month from now."

A month from now would be the end of May. Alain would have liked to find another messenger, one who was more reliable and could leave at an earlier date. But he had still heard nothing from Delage. For lack of anyone better, he might have to be satisfied with Oscar.

"Ask him," he said to Charlie. "Put the question to him directly."

"What question?"

"Whether he intends to come back after his leave. And if he says no, ask him why he hasn't tried to get back home long before this. A link with France isn't easy to find; you know that as well as I do. But if it's a link we can't depend on, we'd be better off to abandon it right now and look for something else."

"What do you want to use him for?"

"To convey some information to someone in Paris. It's information so important that I consider it worth the risk of my skin, yours, his, and that of the person who receives it. I can't tell you any more than that. If we use Oscar and he turns out to be an informer, or even just a dupe, it'll be the end for all of us."

"It's a good thing you warned me."

"What? You mean you won't go along?"

"Yes, of course I will. More than ever. I trust you. Why shouldn't I agree to match your own stakes in the game? The whole thing now, obviously, is to find out whether Oscar is the teammate we need. Don't you think that if he were an informer, he would have agreed to send a letter to my family? He could have done that, and then I would have had complete confidence in him."

"That's true enough," Alain agreed. "Now, we have to find out if this repentant Pétainist is really someone we can rely on, or just a scatterbrained child. So long as he doesn't know what the information is, the risks are limited. The thing to find out is whether we can trust him with some papers to be carried to Paris, papers that would give him absolutely no chance of survival if they were discovered."

"Ah," Charlie said, "so it's a matter of papers. And who is going to give them to him?"

"You, of course. Who did you think it would be?"

Charlie considered this for a moment.

"Don't think that I'm backing out," he said, "but are there many of these papers?"

"No. A few sheets about half as large as your hand."

"Is that what you've been giving me to lock up in my chest?"

"Of course not. I'll write them out at the last moment. But what's bothering you?"

"I'd thought that it would be a verbal message you wanted to give to Oscar. I know you, and I'll go along with you. But what about him?"

"He knows you, and that will have to be enough for him. But whether he knows who I am or not is of no importance. If he were to be caught, he would talk. Perhaps sooner, perhaps later; but he would talk, and you would do the same thing before being hanged. Since neither you nor I could hope to get away, there wouldn't be any point in trying to gain time by playing it tough. That's why, if there should be a hitch, the best thing for you and for him would be to get to the end of it without waiting to be tortured. There would always be that much saved."

"Well, at least you're cheerful about it," Charlie murmured.

"It isn't a matter of being cheerful; it's a matter of seeing things as they are. And we have to make Oscar see them as they are. If he's going to back out, the sooner he does it the better. I don't want him to tell you that he'll do it and then, at the last minute, change his mind; or, even worse, get rid of my message as soon as you give it to him. I'm not looking for some halfway measure. I have to have someone who knows what game he's playing. That's why your deserter-on-leave still bothers me. But I can't afford the luxury of turning him down because he doesn't fit my idea of Robin Hood. I don't have an unlimited choice of messengers, and I can't place a classified ad for candidates."

The days dragged on. Little by little, Charlie added bits and pieces to his knowledge of Oscar. The man was totally unaware of the existence of the Maquis in France. He imagined the intelligence networks of the underground were open only to specialists of one kind or another. Since the "free zone" was now also occupied by the Germans, he believed that his escape would force him to go into hiding and thus to give up all possibility of future action. By remaining in Germany, he hoped someday to be able to do something for France. He did not know what or how. He was simply waiting for the great opportunity, powerless to bring it about, incapable even of focusing his search for it, but fiercely determined not to compromise himself without purpose. It was for this reason that he had refused to transmit Charlie's personal messages. In the course of his forthcoming leave, he intended to make contact with an underground network and to attempt to gain admission to it, in spite of his lack of experience. He hoped that he would be entrusted with the carrying out of missions that might have miraculous results.

In the final analysis, his explanations were plausible. The character they depicted formed a reasonable whole. And—there was no other choice.

In response to Alain's message, Delage had had himself sent to Buchenwald with an inflammation of the jaw so perfectly

222

imitated that the S.S. dentist had pulled a healthy molar, without any anesthetic whatever. Alain had told him what he expected of him, and Delage had immediately promised to undertake the task of finding a free worker who could be trusted. He was optimistic. According to him, it should not be difficult to find someone.

"The vital point," Alain had stipulated, "is that he be in a position to go to Paris on leave very shortly, or at least that his leave makes it possible for him to pass through Paris."

Delage had assured him that this would not present any great obstacle. But he had asked no questions regarding the object of this messenger's mission, and since he avoided the subject, Alain had been forced to ask him how he planned to maintain liaison between themselves.

"As soon as I've found the man you need," Delage had said, "I'll come back here to take care of all the details."

It was clear that he wanted to seem cooperative but that he had not the slightest intention of doing anything at all. Alain had told him that the final assault against the Gustav Line, in Italy, had already been launched. Its success seemed certain. The invasion would not be long in coming. There was no call for a prudent man, assigned to a good *kommando,* to take any unnecessary risks.

A few days later, Alain learned from a deportee who had come in from Weimar that "the friend he had asked Delage to find for him could not be located."

Alain had expected it, so he was not disappointed.

That same day, May 18, 1944, he learned that Polish troops had raised their flag on the summit of Monte Cassino. All of northern Italy was open to the victorious Allies.

That night, Charlie announced triumphantly that Oscar had agreed to the entire plan. He was going to be granted a leave,

223

and he expected to be able to start for home at the end of the month. He would arrange to meet Charlie regularly every day in the period preceding his departure.

By Alain's reckoning, he would be working on the night shift from May 29 to June 4. He would not, therefore, be able to do as he had planned and write out his message undisturbed while guarding his comrades' clothing in the mess hall.

Beginning the next day, instead of sleeping through until the afternoon, he propped himself against the wall of the sleeping compartment and devoted several hours to the study of vectorial calculus. His comrades thought he had gone a little mad and showed no interest in what he was reading or writing. He counted the days and mentally wrote and rewrote the message he would send to Paris. In time, he knew it by heart.

Charlie informed him that Oscar's departure had been postponed until June 5; then, until the twelfth.

37.

"You're going to have to give up your plans," Genteau said.

Alain looked at him. The mischievous sparkle in his friend's eyes gave the lie to his serious tone.

"Is there something new?"

"It would be too bad to destroy the Mibau now, because our living conditions are on the point of improving."

"Are you joking?"

"Not in the least. My information comes directly from the German engineer who supervises our crew."

"Then you're still on good terms with him?"

"Better than good terms. In his eyes, I represent the prototype of the technician whose professional fanaticism makes him forget everything that is not properly a part of his profession. The type of man to whom you could confide the construction of the machine that is going to cut off his head."

"In other words, a new Dr. Guillotin."

"For weeks," Genteau said, "this dear man has been moaning to me about the poor production rate of the Mibau. And in spite of the pains he takes to conceal his intentions, it's been perfectly clear that he was trying to get me to suggest means of accelerating production."

Alain laughed. "Are you making fun of me, or is he making fun of you?"

"Neither one. Our engineer honors me with his confidence and respects my zeal. If you doubt it, here is the proof."

Genteau took from his pocket a package of German cigarettes.

"Take one," he said. "They represent the wages of collaboration."

"I'll be curious to see how that affects their taste," Alain said. "And what good advice did you offer to merit such a reward?" he asked.

"I drew his attention to the inadequate professional background of the workmen and to their poor physical condition."

"I find it hard to believe that those observations could have impressed him with their originality."

"No, but they did permit me to assure him that the deportees were not demonstrating any lack of good will and that everything would go much better if they could be fed more substantially and given some interest in their work. It cost me nothing to say that. And it happens, as a matter of fact, that my ideas coincided with those of the engineer. Little by little, I allowed him to pick my brain. We got to the point of talking about production bonuses, supplementary rations, and even—hold on now—about special insignia for the best workers."

"Do you mean to tell me you suggested that?"

"No, of course not. Although it wouldn't have been such a bad idea: anyone wearing such a decoration wouldn't have lasted long. The Russian POWs would have seen to that."

"And you would have been the first on their list."

"I would have been the first, because I would certainly have been named commander of the Order of Collaboration. It was because of that, in fact, that I resisted the idea. I concentrated on the ineffectiveness of purely honorary distinctions, as compared with material advantages. So we gradually got around to examining the form such advantages might take."

"Do you think we are going to get any?"

"They have already been granted. Now it remains to be seen whether we will actually benefit from them."

"What do you mean?"

"That they may vanish into thin air before reaching us. The conversation with my engineer was very instructive."

Genteau then went on to explain to Alain that the S.S. functioned as a kind of separate community. It had its own properties, in both lands and goods, separate from the properties of the Reich, and it exploited them for its own profit. The factory, which had been constructed at the expense of S.S., formed a part of its properties in land, and the internees and deportees, considered as human livestock, formed a part of its property in goods.

Both factory and livestock had been rented to a consortium of private companies, through a legal contract. One article of this contract stipulated the daily rental of an engineer, a skilled workman, a common laborer, etc.

The companies had claimed that the personnel furnished did not possess a technical competence commensurate with the rental they had been asked to pay, that the workers' poor physical con-

226

dition compromised their efficiency. The S.S. had replied that production rates could be improved by more frequent punishments. But the companies, a bit more perceptive than the S.S., were well aware that a simple increase in the number of hangings would not solve the problem. Moreover, in view of the turn of military events, the majority of their own engineers were not very enthusiastic about delivering deportees to the executioner. The companies, therefore, were inclined to bring out the proverbial carrot and put away the S.S. bludgeon. The S.S. had accepted this manner of viewing the problem only on the condition that the companies provide the carrot.

"So," Alain exclaimed, "we are going to have a new system of priority rations? It's too good to be true."

"You're jumping to conclusions a little too fast," Genteau said. "Between a principle and its application, there is ample room for interpretation, and it's precisely there that things become complicated. The companies have the money. But in order to transform this money into rations, they have to call in the S.S.; and to distribute these rations they have to rely on the camp administration. And as it happens, the companies have no confidence in either the S.S. as a supplier or in the camp administration as a distributor."

"The engineer admitted that to you?"

"Of course not. But the implication couldn't have been clearer. That's what makes me doubt the effectiveness of the hybrid system that's going to be put into effect. Supposedly, we are to be given several supplementary soup rations each week. This will take place in the factory itself, so that the companies can check on the fact that they actually have been distributed. In addition, bonuses, in the form of a special scrip, are going to be given to the most conscientious workers, and this scrip can be exchanged at the camp canteen for provisions supplied by the S.S."

"I'd be very much surprised if we ever saw the color of the scrip," Alain remarked. "But it's a comforting thought, just the same."

227

"Yes, and it certainly demonstrates the importance of what we're producing."

Alain's expression was suddenly grim.

"When I think of all the time I've lost," he said, "I could kick myself in the ass."

In the Small Camp, Alstein had succeeded in drawing Professor Verville away from his entourage.

"It's useless to go over all that again," the old man was saying. "The matter is settled. I have given my number to the block chief. Soon, whether you wish it or not, I will have departed from this hell. The light-work *kommando* for which my disciples and I have volunteered is an excellent *kommando*. We will be treated with dignity and respect, and we will be properly fed. They have promised us this."

Alstein was momentarily speechless with horror.

"But, Professor," he managed to say at last, "you don't even know what this *kommando* is."

"What difference does it make what it is? We will be out of this camp, and we will be given work that is within the limits of our strength."

"That's what they tell you. But it isn't true."

Alstein closed his eyes and gathered his thoughts for an instant before continuing, speaking as emphatically as he could.

"There is no light-work *kommando*. You are going to be sent to another camp where you will be liquidated. That is the truth. Don't you understand that this story of light work is nothing but a decoy, brought out periodically, by order of the S.S., to rid the Small Camp of all those who are naïve enough to volunteer?"

The Professor began to weep.

Alstein mistook the cause of his tears.

"Don't upset yourself about it," he said. "I won't have any

228

difficulty getting you out of this trap. You can count on me. You will stay here."

The Professor's tired old body slipped gently down to the ground, coming to rest at the foot of the wall against which he had been leaning. He was sobbing like a child.

Alstein leaned over him and put a hand on his arm, in what he meant to be a comforting gesture.

"Don't touch me," the Professor hiccupped. "That a man such as you, for whom I have done so much, should take advantage of the authority conferred on him by his cursed race to persecute me! It is an offense against God, and it plunges me into an abyss of sorrow. But the just will triumph. Beware of your punishment. It will be on the scale of your sins. Go away. Go away, I tell you. Don't stand there and offend my eyes."

"I'll go," Alstein said. "But take this, it's some rabbit I brought for you."

The Professor seized the package and with unexpected vigor hurled it far out into the field.

Two old men ran to pick it up. They stopped when they were still a few paces apart, glaring at each other. With their elbows held tightly against their bodies, their heads thrust forward on long, fleshless necks, they had the appearance of two fighting cocks preparing to do battle. One of them, whose right arm ended in an iron hook, moved forward again, ready to strike. The other one dared not move. But at the moment when the one-armed man bent down to pick up the package, the other hurled himself at him, snatched the package, and fled.

Alstein returned to the Big Camp with his head bowed, his shoulders slumped. Alain saw him approaching.

"Look," Alain said to Genteau. "Judging from his appearance, he has certainly just paid his weekly visit to old Verville."

"Verville? The Professor? Is he still alive?"

"Yes. He must have arrived in the camp about the same time you did."

229

"How is he?"

"He has gone mad."

Alstein had stopped in front of them and extended his hand, forcing himself to smile.

"We were talking about Professor Verville," Alain said. "Is his condition any better?"

"Alas, no," Alstein replied. "His latest idea has been to volunteer for a light-work *kommando*."

"Perhaps it might be good for him to have something to do," Genteau ventured.

"Yes," Alstein agreed, "that would be good for him. But in reality, the light-work *kommandos* are extermination *kommandos*. I told him that, and I hope I can succeed in having his number removed from the list of volunteers."

38.

On May 24 it snowed for the last time. On the roll call square, the wind scattered little clusters of wet flakes, depositing them beneath the collars of the huddled deportees. The ground refused to accept a new mantle of white. The icy layer of mud that covered it clung fast to boots and shoes and managed even to work itself inside.

The belated return of the bad weather sounded a death knell to the hopes the prisoners had placed in spring. It seemed to them that their ordeal would never end.

When the weather changed for the better, their bodies warmed, but their minds and hearts remained frozen. No one any longer spoke of the invasion.

Tuesday, the sixth of June, began like any other day. In the workshops of the Mibau, the sun filtered through the angled glass panes of the roof, throwing rectangles of light across the floors and the benches. The deportees kept track of time by measuring the slow movement of these areas of light.

As the afternoon began, lulled by the constant whispering of the machines, Alain was struggling against sleep. All around him, his comrades were either working lazily or taking advantage of the unaccustomed absence of the foreman to work on little projects of their own. They were making cigarette holders of raw wood, and pocket knives with blades of inferior steel which, since they lacked a spring, folded back on themselves like a razor. A subdued murmur, stemming from dozens of whispered warnings, announced the return of the *meister*. He came into the shop as if he were on parade, walking at a martial gait, with his head held high. Alain thought he resembled a drum major. He came to a halt behind a row of workbenches whose occupants were observing him carefully from the corner of their eyes, even as they pretended to be totally absorbed in their work. Abruptly then, the strident sound of his voice drowned out the noise of the machines. His phrases were punctuated with laughter and embellished with menacing gestures, but as he glanced around the hall, without ever pausing to look at any individual, the deportees lifted their heads and began to watch him, more curious than they were disturbed. He finished with a bellowed "Heil Hitler!" and marched off, with the same conqueror's stride that had marked his entrance, toward one of the rooms in which the control crews worked. As soon as the door had closed behind him, the man who always interpreted for him was called on to translate what he had said. He seemed to have been stricken dumb and could do no more than repeat, "This is it, guys, this is it. The invasion. It's begun. This morning."

231

"Where?"

"I don't know; he didn't say."

"Well then, what did he say?"

"That the Allies had at last committed the mistake that would mean the end of them. That they were going to be crushed, thrown back into the sea. That Germany was invincible, that she possesses overwhelming secret weapons. In other words, a crock of shit. But one thing is certain: the Allies have landed."

The deportees had abandoned their work entirely and formed little groups. They were all talking at once, and everything they said was interrupted by great bursts of laughter in which there were hysterical tears. Alain had remained sitting on his stool, facing his piles of iron boxes. He heard snatches of the conversations around him: ". . . will surrender within a month, . . ." ". . . be home before the holidays. . . ." The reappearance of the foreman sent everyone scurrying back to his post.

"What do you think about it?"

The question had been addressed to Alain.

"I think . . ."

He left the phrase dangling. Too many things were crowding through his mind, demanding attention.

In the first place, was this really the invasion or simply an experimental operation, like the commando landing at Dieppe? If it actually was the invasion, the great adventure was about to begin. If it should fail, how many of the prisoners in the camp would survive another winter? Then, suddenly, a new question arose. Why had the Germans not yet employed the rockets being built at Dora? According to Geoffrin, hundreds of these weapons had been available in March. By now, there must be thousands of them ready for launching. Was it because they had been held in reserve so that the Allies would not be able to find a way to fight them? And would they now completely destroy the invasion forces? It's been two months since I knew of their existence, Alain reproached himself, and I still have not succeeded in getting the information out. Now, all leaves for the free workers would

232

surely be canceled. Oscar would no longer be able to get away. And in any case, it was too late to warn the Allies. If this attempt at invasion should fail, God only knew how many months or years would pass before a new attempt could be made.

Alain signaled to an Alsatian friend who spoke German perfectly. They went off toward the toilets, which were a kind of living room for the workers in the factory, just as they were in the blocks of the camp. That day the news of the invasion had transformed them into a forum, and Alain had to force his way through the mass of bodies.

"Exactly what did the foreman say?" he demanded.

"Nothing very coherent. You saw how nervous he was."

"Yes, but did he say anything to justify his certainty that the invasion would be repulsed?"

"No. He confined himself to claiming that Hitler had only been waiting for this moment to inflict an irreversible defeat on the Allies, and that he was holding in reserve some secret weapons that would guarantee ultimate victory. It was obvious that he was only repeating what he had heard on the radio a few minutes earlier. Believe me, if he had really been so certain of what he was saying, he wouldn't have shouted so loudly. I had the distinct impression he was primarily concerned with convincing himself. No matter what he may have claimed, he's tortured with anxiety."

There was a sudden outburst of shouting. An S.S. guard at the door had turned on one of the fire hoses and directed it against the occupants of the toilets. It was an everyday occurrence. The S.S. habitually employed this means of discouraging malingerers. In order to escape, the victims were forced to run directly through the icy jet from the hose. Hobbled by their pants, clutching them around their middles with both hands because they had not had time to button them, they presented their comrades with a laughable spectacle. But this time, the toilets were occupied by many more than the usual number of men. The crowd was too compact to flow easily through a door already partially obstructed by the S.S. guard who held the hose. The avalanche of water forced the deportees into the less exposed area where the showers were located. A second S.S. guard turned on the faucets, and they were deluged from above. A third guard, outside the door, stood ready with his bludgeon to catch the men across the back and shoulders as they fled. Alain succeeded in escaping him, but he was soaked to the skin when he returned to his bench.

It was not until roll call that night that Alain learned from Philippe what the BBC was saying. This time, it really was the invasion. The directives given to the French population proved this. The first operations seemed to have been successful. They had taken place at several points along the Channel coast east of Cotentin and north of Caen. Some of the landings were doubtedly only diversionary maneuvers, intended to force the Germans to scatter their forces. Nothing in the communiqués gave any indication that Allied troops had encountered any unforeseen defense measures. On the contrary, the overwhelming supremacy of the Allies in the air was repeatedly emphasized. It was so great that they had landed troops from gliders, after having silenced the German antiaircraft batteries. Philippe was always extremely precise in relaying the news as it had been given to him by Genteau. It was only afterward that he indulged in any comment on it. What he had to say that day was optimistic.

"We will have to wait a few days," he said, "before we know how things will turn out. For the moment, the important thing is to try to prevent an outburst of enthusiasm that might cause people to do crazy things. Genteau and I felt that it would be a good idea to remind everyone that it took the German armies a month to reach Paris in 1940. So I suggest you prepare our comrades for the inevitable delays in the campaign. The calendar of forecasts that we felt must be circulated is this: one month to secure a bridgehead large enough to contain the Allied forces, their air strips, and their reserves of gasoline and ammunition; one month to establish this bridgehead and bring up the reserves we have mentioned; at least another month to reach the German frontier. That makes three months. That doesn't predetermine the date of our liberation, so it leaves room for the hope of a military surrender or of some internal upheaval in the Third Reich—although that can't be seriously considered until German territory itself is threatened."

As soon as they had returned to their respective blocks, both Alain and Philippe set to work on the construction of psychological breakwaters. In the midst of a tidal wave of delirious, unthinking hopes, they attempted to insert a single long, calm wave, which, if all went well, might carry their comrades safely to the sunlit beach of their still-distant freedom.

The tables were littered with packages of food from home. Their owners were celebrating the invasion by using up all of their reserves, as if they had suddenly become superfluous.

Charlie handed Alain a biscuit spread thick with soft butter.

"You don't seem very happy tonight," he said. "What's wrong?"

"Nothing's wrong. But I hadn't thought it would happen like this."

"What do you mean? Is it the choice of the invasion area that disturbs you?"

"Well, it's quite a distance from the Normandy region of the Channel, and it would have been shorter if they had started from Calais or Ostend. But it isn't only that. You see, I've dreamed about this day too much not to feel let down. It's always the same thing; the great events you look forward to are like the gilded paper on those hoops used by acrobats in a circus. They're dazzling as you run up to them. But once you have jumped through, the paper hangs in shabby little shreds, and on the other side you find all the problems they concealed. The instant of leaping through doesn't even provide the caress you might have hoped for and savored. It's too short."

"That doesn't change the fact that today marks the beginning of a campaign whose ending means freedom for us. If it had taken place a week later, we would have been freed a week later."

Alain's only reply was to thank Charlie for the buttered biscuit. He undressed, made a package of his clothing, and set it down on a bench against the wall. Then he walked off toward the sleeping quarters, the tail of his tattered shirt slapping against his skinny thighs.

Shortly, Charlie stretched out beside him.

"You realize," Alain whispered, "that I left France on June 17, 1940. I went back three times after that—by parachute, by plane, and in a fishing boat. I led the life of a hunted wolf before being reduced to the condition of a starving dog in this camp. For four years, I gambled everything I had on final victory, including my stupid life. I volunteered for every kind of mission. And now—"

"And now," Charlie interrupted, "you're pouting like a little boy who has worked hard at school, who has done all his mama's errands, who has behaved properly at the table all week, and now finds himself sent to bed, on Saturday night, before the family has dinner."

"Yes," Alain conceded, "I feel frustrated. I would have liked to have a part in the festivities that have just begun. When we get back, it will all be over. The Japanese lanterns in the gardens will have been put out. There will be nothing left on the table but sour wine in the bottom of the glasses and soiled napkins on dirty cloths. It will smell of cigars that have been left behind. There will be nothing for us to do but straighten up and wash the dishes—"

"And count the dead and the wounded. You and your regrets make me laugh. Anyone would think that, for you, the battle that's taking place right now is a motion picture, and that when the lights go on at the end you'll find yourself perfectly safe in your armchair. If you were involved in what is happening to-day—"

236

"If I were involved, I would be afraid. I would even be thinking of myself as a jackass for not having found a soft job in London. But I would conquer my fear. You see, the real battle is the battle you wage against yourself, alone and hand to hand. And for the victory of that battle to be complete, you must have experienced the danger of it."

"Tell me something," Charlie said. "In peacetime, do you play Russian roulette?"

"That's a stupid question," Alain said. "Victory over oneself has no meaning unless one makes of it an offering, a sacrifice. It must take place within a framework of life. It must have value as an example, and it must serve a cause. The men who are landing in France, at this moment, are serving a cause, and those of them who succeed best in overcoming their fear are helping the others to overcome theirs. I envy them. Charlie, you must know as well as I do that there is a difference between the exaltation of combat, when you are surrounded by friends, and the terrifying solitude we lived through before we were brought here."

"Oh yes, I see very well. What you need is an audience."

"Don't make jokes. It's not the audience that is important, it's human contact. It gives flavor to everything that happens. You can't deny that a good dinner is even better when it is shared with friends."

"In our situation, I wouldn't scorn it, even if I had to eat it alone. But you're never satisfied. If I understand you correctly, what you are searching for is victory in a hand-to-hand combat against yourself. But in order for this lonely victory to be completely satisfying to you, you must have a company of friends around you. That seems to be self-contradictory. Don't you think you're being just a bit difficult to please?"

"Not in the least. Look, Charlie, you know very well that when a cyclist races alone, against a watch, he doesn't go as fast as he will when he is part of a team, racing against other teams. Then, because he has the support of his teammates and is fighting against others who want to win just as much as he does, he sur-

237

passes himself. Well, for my part, I have had enough of racing against a watch. I've been doing that for years. And as a reward, I would have liked to reach the finish line as a member of a team, to race faster—faster than I have ever raced before."

"And when you cross the finish line, you'll be handed a bouquet of flowers and be kissed by the local beauty queen, while the newspapers take pictures. You've chosen a bad day to look gift horses in the mouth. We are here, in Buchenwald. We can do absolutely nothing but wait for the Allies to get us out. They landed this morning. That's good news. Is it or isn't it?"

"Obviously, it's good news."

"In that case, why in the hell are you behaving this way today, of all days? You didn't by any chance think you might be granted some special favor and released on Invasion Day so that you could put on your uniform and go and play at being a soldier, did you? Listening to you, anyone would think you consider what's happening a personal insult, because you can't play a part in it."

"I'm afraid the invasion might fail," Alain confessed.

"Because you have no part in it?"

"Don't be ridiculous."

"You're the one who is being ridiculous."

"Come into the toilets. I want to talk to you about Oscar."

There were too many people in the toilets to be certain that a conversation would not be overheard, and too few for the sound of their own talking to be unintelligible. Standing barefoot on the wet tiles, clothed in nothing but their shirts, Alain and Charlie leaned against the entrance door.

"Well," Charlie said, "get on with it. We could freeze to death in here."

"All right," Alain began, speaking softly. "I know that right here in the Mibau, we are building electrical equipment for completely revolutionary weapons."

"What weapons?" Charlie asked.

"That's not important."

"How long have you known?"

"For the past two months."

"And that's why you've been looking for a messenger?"

"Yes."

"And you think the Germans have kept these weapons in reserve, for the Invasion?"

"That's what I'm afraid of."

"But how will we know if they're using them?"

"I'll know."

Alain's tone of voice was peremptory. He was shutting out any digression, any doubt.

"It seems," he went on, "that they didn't use them today. Even though thousands of ships and planes were involved in the landing."

"What do you make of that?"

"I don't understand it. But one thing is clear. It's more important than ever that the Allies be informed of what the Mibau is manufacturing."

"You want them to bomb the factory?"

"Yes. They must."

"But what about all our friends who work there?"

"What difference does that make to you? You don't work there."

"But what about you?"

"I'm hoping that the planes will come during the morning, or the evening roll call, or on Sunday, when there's no one there."

"Would you authorize me to tell all this to Oscar?"

Alain hesitated. "Only if it's absolutely necessary to get him to make up his mind."

"To make up his mind about what?"

"About carrying the information, no matter how great the risk may be."

"Well, there are two possibilities. Oscar may still be granted his leave, in spite of the invasion. In that case, you can be sure that he will take your papers. But leaves for the free workers may be canceled—"

"In that case, he will have to escape."

"Yes," Charlie agreed meekly, "that's what he'll have to do."

"Do you think he would attempt it?"

"I don't know. When would you want him to leave?"

"As soon as possible. Whenever he's ready. If it's to be an escape, he'll have to make preparations. And at the last minute, you will have to deliver my message to him and tell him to whom it should be given."

"How much time will you need to write it out?"

"A few hours."

"Which means that if you're working on the day shift in the factory, you'll have to know the night before Oscar leaves. But if you're working at night, you'll have to know two days in advance."

"Yes. Let's go to bed," Alain said. "You can understand why I was in such a bad humor. But I feel better now."

39.

The English radio was not lavish with its news. "Operations are developing in accordance with the general forecast." But no matter how bitter the local struggles were—and the communiqués made no attempt to disguise this—it was apparent that the Allies were gaining ground everywhere. Not so rapidly, perhaps, as their headquarters had planned; but nowhere had they been thrown back into the sea.

Charlie had seen Oscar again.

"He didn't reject the idea of an escape," he told Alain, "but he is hesitating. He thinks you may have some illusions about the Mibau's importance. If the Germans did possess some secret weapons, as you think they do, he feels they would have already used them. He asked me what kind of weapons they were. But you hadn't told me that. If there were some way in which we could convince him—"

The German radio did it for them.

On the night of the thirteenth, when Alain's *kommando* arrived at the factory, the foreman at once launched into a series of new and shattering disclosures. The first of the Führer's reprisal weapons, the V-1, had gone into action. It was a pilotless plane, crammed with high explosives. And it was already sowing panic and death in London. The population had retreated to underground shelters. All activity was paralyzed. Other and even more formidable weapons were about to be put into action. England would be completely destroyed. It was on her soil that the outcome of the war would be decided, and not in France, where the invasion troops were dragging their feet on the beaches.

The men who listened to the foreman's words were overcome with consternation. Alain made frequent visits to the toilets, in an effort to assure them that it was perfectly normal for the Nazis to do everything in their power to distract attention from the inability of the Wehrmacht to throw the invasion forces back into the sea. The V-1s were a propaganda weapon, and nothing more. On the military level, they had no effect. He put his entire reserve of arguments to work in support of this affirmation. But his own anxiety was so great that he defied all the factory regulations and walked over to Philippe's shop during the half-hour break at midnight. He had to know what the BBC was saying.

241

It was announcing, with no apparent emotion, that flying bombs, launched from the continent, had been falling on London at irregular intervals since early morning. The high command had expected this. Many of the launching bases had been destroyed, in advance of the invasion. The fact that the bombs were now actually being used would make the remaining bases easy to locate. And they, too, would be destroyed. No figures were given on the material destruction caused by the flying bombs, and it was not possible to make any estimate of the importance of their effect on civilian and military activity in the British capital.

Alain thought back to the bombings of 1940 and 1941. Instead of crushing the morale of the English people, they had raised it to new levels. But would the same thing be true now? On each of his visits to London, between missions, he had noted the slow progress of nervous fatigue in the civilian population, especially among the women.

How would this population react to both an incessant bombardment and the publication of heavy Invasion casualties? There was no reason to fear a capitulation, if only because of the presence of the Americans. But the war effort itself might be affected, and this in turn would affect military operations in France. It was undoubtedly going to be necessary to abandon any hope of a lightning war, such as the one the Germans had conducted in 1940. This alone justified assuming the risks involved in transmitting to the Allies the information about the Mibau. And it was now going to be a simpler matter to convince them the message was true. Both Oscar and the Allied intelligence services would be less inclined to doubt its authenticity.

During roll call on the night of the sixteenth, Charlie announced that Oscar had decided to attempt to return to France without leave and that the papers he was to carry must be given to him on Monday, the nineteenth. Charlie would not see him again before that date.

A cold shiver ran the length of Alain's spine.

242

"Good," he said. "The papers will be ready when you need them, and I'll explain to whom they are to be delivered. Do you think Oscar will succeed?"

"He told me he has been studying an escape plan for a long time. I didn't ask for any details, but he seems sure of himself. Aside from the importance of his mission, which he is aware of now, he has another motive for wanting to get back to France. His family lives in Caen, and things are pretty hot in that corner of the country right now. He wants to try to find them. I think, in fact, that it was basically this that made him decide to escape."

"His motives don't matter. The main thing is that he leaves and doesn't eat the message on the way."

40.

On Sunday the camp seemed more crowded than ever. The sounds of conversation and of shouting could be heard through the open windows of all the sleeping quarters.

When he had swallowed his soup, Alain decided against going back to sleep and walked over to Genteau's block. He woke him up and led him out to the street, where they might have some privacy.

"If all goes well," he told him, "my information will leave tomorrow."

Genteau stopped dead in his tracks. "You've found a way to get it out?"

"Yes."

"A reliable way?"

"I'll know that when the message arrives, if it does arrive. How do things stand with you?"

"All right. The cooperation between the day crew and the night crew couldn't be better."

"You're taking one hell of a risk. If my count is still correct, there are fourteen of you involved now."

"Eighteen," Genteau said. "Each crew has been enlarged by two new members." He clapped Alain on the shoulder. "I hope you succeed. It would be a wonderful thing."

They walked again, saying nothing. Alain was once more mentally reviewing the words of his message. In the end, he recited it to Genteau.

"Do you think it's clear," he asked, "and that I have said everything that must be said?"

"Yes." Genteau nodded. "But it's going to take you hours to write down all of that and to make the sketches and the maps."

"I'm planning on spending the whole night at it."

"Then come eat something with me now."

Before roll call that night, Alain rubbed the inside of his cheek with some glass wool he had been keeping in Charlie's wooden box. It burned but produced no inflammation, so he finally resolved to hammer at his jaw with his own fist. It reddened angrily and developed a noticeable swelling. He pretended that it was giving him great pain.

Accompanied by Charlie, he went to ask the block chief if he knew of any deportees who had recently received aspirin in their packages. As he had expected, his only reply was a sharp rebuke.

"He isn't going to be able to sleep a wink tonight," Charlie explained to the block chief. "Would it be all right with you if he replaces the men who are scheduled to be on guard in the mess hall tonight?"

"I don't give a damn what he does," the block chief replied. This was exactly what Alain wanted. He obtained a list of the regularly scheduled guards and went around to each one of them, displaying the inflammation of his jaw and telling them that there would be no need for them to stand guard that night. They were delighted.

"Tomorrow morning," he said to Charlie, "I'll give you the papers."

"Who is Oscar supposed to turn them over to?"

In the fifteen months since Alain had been arrested, many more of his comrades in the Resistance must also have either been captured or forced to go into hiding. He wanted to send Oscar to someone whose activity was so limited that he would not have been caught and who still had reliable contacts at a high level. As a security measure, he decided to plan on two receivers. Thus, if it should prove impossible, for any reason, to reach the first, Oscar could fall back on the second.

"What bothers me," Alain said, "is that if he should be captured, he'll be forced to reveal at least one of the names to the Gestapo."

"He could always pretend that it had been left to him to find some way of getting your messages to the Allies after he arrived," Charlie suggested.

"Don't take the Germans for greater fools than they are. There will be three of us who know that the message is intended for one or another of two specific individuals. Whether I want to or not, I am involving them in the whole thing."

"Whether *they* want to or not would be a more accurate way of putting it," Charlie said.

"That's what makes the problem so complicated."

"Yes. But you're not in much danger of having to listen to their reproaches, you know. If they are captured, we'll all be in hot water, each in his own pot."

"It still bothers me to think I'm handing them something like this, without any knowledge of whether they are in a position to accept it."

245

"You and your scruples make me laugh," Charlie said. "You seem to forget that if your message does go through, everyone who works in the factory is going to have bombs dropping on his head some fine day. And you haven't asked them if they are willing to go along with that."

"It isn't the same thing."

"You can't avoid some damage being done," Charlie persisted. "If our plan fails, we'll be the ones to get hurt. If it succeeds, it will be our friends in the factory. You're the only one who is risking his neck no matter what happens."

Alain told him then that he had finally decided on his sister and on one of his cousins as intermediaries for transmitting his information to the Allies.

Both his sister and his parents had been arrested in 1942 while he was in London; but they had been freed a year later, when he himself was captured. There was a good chance that his sister had retained her contacts in the Resistance but had also been cautious enough to remain free of suspicion.

As for his cousin, he had always been the prudent type. His business and personal relationships were extensive, and he had placed them completely at the disposal of the Resistance. His friends, in turn, had given him their confidence, because they knew that he would not allow himself to be carried away or compromised by any uncontrollable passion for action. He had furnished Alain with several extremely valuable agents but had made it clear that he considered his own role ended as soon as he had made the introductions. If Oscar went to him, he would probably not agree to take charge of the documents himself, but he would undoubtedly be in a position to put him in contact with someone who could transmit them quickly to London.

Alain considered that he was taking no additional risk in signing his own name to the message. If the Germans were to seize the papers, all of them written in his hand, it would be relatively easy to trace them back to him. Whether or not he made the matter a bit simpler for them was of no importance. On the other hand, his signature, together with his rank and mention of his earlier connection with the intelligence services of the Free French Forces, would hasten the progress of his information to men in authority who were also his friends, who had confidence in him, and would make the best possible use of the information he had sent, without wasting time questioning its authenticity or the importance that should be accorded it.

He gave Charlie the instructions he was to pass on to Oscar.

"My sister is unmarried, so her name is the same as mine. My cousin's name is Roussel. That's easy enough to remember. All he has to do is think of that schoolboy song 'Cadet Roussel.' They both live in Neuilly. Oscar can find the addresses in the telephone book. If he can't reach either my sister or Roussel, he'll have to find some way of getting the message through himself."

Charlie shook his head doubtfully. He didn't feel that they could rely too much on Oscar in such a situation.

"If that should happen," Charlie said, "he'll have to go to my parents. They'll help him."

"Very well," Alain said. "But I didn't hear a word of what you said. You'll have to decide about that for yourself. But thanks, friend."

For a moment, neither of them said anything more. Then Alain asked, "How much time do you think Oscar will need to get to Paris?"

"He hopes to be there in a week."

Alain reckoned that if all went well, his message would reach London sometime in the first days of July. The bridgeheads now held by the invasion forces should permit far more rapid liaison between France and England than had been possible in the past. And it should not require any lengthy period of time for the Royal Air Force to carry out the necessary aerial reconnaissance and set up the bombing. It was reasonable to hope that the bombing could take place before the fourteenth of July.

247

41.

|||||||||||||||||||||||||||||||||||||||||||||||||||||||||||||||||||||||||||||||||||||||||||||||||

Charlie went to bed. Alain set to work: his taste for precision was at last being gratified. For weeks, he had weighed every word of his message. Now he was setting it down, lovingly, on little squares of paper, with a fine, concise script, separating sections and paragraphs, imbued with the feeling that human lives depended on his diligence. The uncertainty of whether the message would be delivered no longer played any part in his thinking. The meticulous work with which he was occupied absorbed him so completely that he was freed of all anxiety and doubt. The hours raced by, but he took no notice. He reread and corrected every page, and when necessary, recopied it, so that it would bear no sign of erasure. The sound of reveille took him by surprise, just as he was finishing. He was abruptly aware of his fatigue and of the cold. He remembered that he had eaten nothing of the food Genteau had given him. He closed the treatise on calculus, checked his own sheets of paper for the last time, then folded them carefully into a little package, which he wrapped in a blank sheet and placed in his pocket. In the toilets, safe in the midst of the morning swarm of deportees, he flushed away the pages he had recopied. His legs were like rubber and he felt nauseous. His head was swimming. But he managed to find Charlie.

"Will you put my book away for me?" he said.

Then, when the box of provisions had been opened, he added, "Give me that open package of semolina." Charlie brought out the package, and Alain emptied it into his cap. Then he thrust the papers into the bottom of the little carton and poured the semolina on top of them.

No one, in the crush of hastily dressing deportees, was sufficiently awake to pay any attention to what they were doing.

"There," he said, handing the package to Charlie. "Now, as to the receivers—"

"Don't worry, I haven't forgotten. Your sister and Roussel, in Neuilly. Addresses in the telephone book. Right?"

"Yes, but I also mentioned, on one of the pages of the message, the name and address of a man I know is safely in England. I remembered having heard while I was in prison at Fresnes that he got away before they caught him. This way, if Oscar is caught, it will be easy for him to point the Nazis in the wrong direction, and neither my sister nor my cousin will be involved. Be sure to tell him that."

"Right. But while you were at it, why didn't you put down the name of some dyed-in-the-wool collaborator?"

42.

When Charlie's *kommando* had passed through the gate to the camp, it lined up along the shoulder of the Avenue of Triumph instead of continuing in its accustomed direction.

Charlie shivered. This was what happened when a search was to be made.

An S.S. officer pointed out some of the deportees with his walking stick. Charlie was one of them. They were ordered to leave the column and were taken back to the square, surrounded by S.S. guards.

Of the tens of thousands of deportees who left the camp in the *kommando* groups each morning, only a few were searched. Charlie never had been. The thought flashed through his mind that Alain was either a bastard or he had talked too much. In either case, he was finished.

He tried to put this out of his mind. It was not impossible that this search was simply a stroke of bad luck. If the S.S. had known anything, they would not have subjected him to a routine search. They would have taken him out of the line. Thinking of it in this way, he regained his self-control.

He and the other prisoners were lined up with their backs to the wall of the guardhouse. The S.S. watched their every move, rifles and submachine guns held loosely in the crook of their arms. There was no way of getting rid of the package of semolina. And neither could Charlie tear it up in his pocket, extract the papers it contained, and swallow them. He had noticed, when Alain put them in the package, that they were too bulky for that.

Some other deportees were brought back to the square and lined up beside the first group. They too were going to be searched. Charlie now felt certain that the message, which seemed to be burning a hole in his thigh, would not be systematically sought for.

One of the Russians dropped a long sharpened blade, concealed in a wooden sheath. An S.S. guard picked it up and tested its edge against his thumb. The knife's owner held out his hands in a gesture of mute supplication. The S.S. guard made a move suggesting that he was about to cut his throat, and the man automatically doubled up, shielding his neck and ribs. A sharp blow of the knee to his face straightened him up again. His body rested against the wall for an instant before sliding to the ground, a mass of twitching, bloody rags.

Charlie fingered the package of semolina in his pocket and

250

then turned to his neighbor, a German from his *kommando,* with whom he had always gotten along very well. Over his shoulder, suspended from a length of string, he carried a covered aluminum mess tin. It usually contained flour, with which he made a kind of soup during the noon recess. He had sometimes invited Charlie to share it with him, in exchange for a bit of chocolate or a cigarette.

"Do you think they'll take away your mess tin?" Charlie asked.

"No."

"I'm glad of that, because I brought some semolina, and I was going to suggest that we could mix it with your flour."

"That's a fine idea," the man said.

The S.S. officer ordered the deportees to take off all their clothing and spread it on the ground in front of them, with the pockets turned out and their contents placed on top of the garments. When they had done this, the little package of semolina, which had a bright red label, seemed to Charlie to be the center of all the first rays of the morning sun.

A noncommissioned officer, supervised by the S.S. officer, carefully felt through every piece of clothing and examined the objects lined up on the ground.

In time, he came to Charlie's neighbor. He lifted the cover of the mess tin and plunged the spoon it contained into the flour.

"There's nothing else in there," the man said, "you can see for yourself."

The S.S. guard circled the tin thoroughly with the spoon.

"All right."

He picked up the red package.

"That's semolina," Charlie said. "If we can light a fire during the recess, we were going to make soup with it and the flour."

He gestured with his head toward his neighbor's mess tin. His voice did not tremble, but it sounded as though he were choking. He listened to his own words with the curious feeling that they had been spoken by someone else.

The guard opened the package and pressed into it a finger he had moistened on his tongue. He brought the finger to his mouth, tasted, spat, and hurled the package at Charlie, who caught it before it could fall. A little spray of semolina whitened his face.

The S.S. guard moved to the next man.

Alain fought against sleep. Aside from a few hours on Sunday morning, he had not slept since Friday afternoon. Twice, during the morning, the iron box he was polishing slipped from his hands. He was awakened by the noise it made as it fell. When the half-hour recess was called, he rested his head on his arms and immediately went to sleep.

In the afternoon the man who occupied the bench next to his woke him up three times. On a fourth occasion the foreman kicked his stool out from under him. For an instant, Alain was certain that the factory had been bombed and he had been hurled into space by the force of the explosion. The laughter of his comrades, and his own bewildered air as he picked himself up, served to calm the *meister*. Alain resolved that, from then on, he would do his work standing up. By the time the workday ended, he was drunk with fatigue.

The cold air of the walk back to the camp revived him. But he felt a ball of agony at the pit of his stomach when he realized Charlie had not yet returned.

Charlie came back at last, glanced at Alain, and winked.

252

THE BOMBING

And the seven angels which had the seven trumpets prepared themselves to sound. The first angel sounded, and
there followed hail and fire mingled with blood, and they
were cast upon the earth: and the third part of trees was
burnt up and all green grass was burnt up.

The Revelation of St. John the Divine

43.

At dawn the next morning, having rested well, Alain woke up to a consciousness of his victory. The information had been given to Oscar. Alain could now look backward on all the problems that had been overcome.

For weeks his concentration on the task ahead had obliterated the world around him. Now he discovered that the factory was a furnace. During the noon recess several young Russians splashed about in the showers. He remembered having seen them do this week before last, when he was on the day shift, but it had never occurred to him to follow their example. Now, with his face lifted, his hands held out before him, he offered himself to the embrace of the cold water.

He returned to his workbench a few minutes late. The stream of curses from the foreman slipped off his back like drops of water. The knowledge of his power filled him with a smiling indifference. His eyes glittered wickedly when the two S.S. guards walked by. The man on the next stool noticed it and glanced first at the guards, then back at Alain, seeking an explanation.

"You look like the cat who swallowed the canary," he said. "What's going on?"

Alain set foot again in reality.

"Nothing," he said.

He began whistling softly.

Charlie and Alain met after roll call that night.

"Oscar got away last night," Charlie murmured. "One of his friends told me."

He shuffled his feet awkwardly and then added, turning away from Alain, "If he's caught, his friends will know it. The Germans always announce it."

"What do you mean by that?"

"Just that. They have always announced when they capture those who tried to escape."

"Do you mean," Alain said slowly, "that they have announced they have captured anyone who tried to escape—or that they have made an announcement whenever they captured someone who had tried to escape?"

"It seems," Charlie said, "that it's the same thing. They have always captured anyone who escaped, and the Germans have always announced it."

Alain shrugged. "That simply proves that they're telling lies."

"Do you think so?"

"It's obvious. It's inconceivable that no escape ever succeeded."

Charlie looked at Alain with the eyes of a hurt hunting dog, seeking his master's caress.

"Do you think so?" he repeated.

256

"Listen to me," Alain said. "It isn't very difficult to avoid being sent to Germany as a free worker. So it's to be expected that anyone who allows this to happen to him is not going to be the most gifted man in the world when it comes to planning an escape. If he does try it, it's probably, in the majority of cases, just the result of a momentary whim, and it's not surprising if he fails. Oscar doesn't belong in that category. He didn't get himself involved in this with his eyes closed. You told me yourself—"

Charlie interrupted him. "I remember what I told you," he said. "But the more I think about it, the more I have the feeling that it was his anxiety about his family—since he learned that Caen was in the middle of the invasion area—that caused him to make up his mind so quickly. I wonder if he really planned his escape as carefully as he claimed."

"We'll have to live through a few bad days," Alain said. "If he doesn't manage to get through, we'll know about it soon enough."

44.

IIIIIIIIIIIIIIIIIIIIIIIIIIIIIIIIIIIIIIIIIIIIIIIIIIIIIIIIIIIIIIIIIIIIIIIIIIIIIIIIIIIIIIIIIIIIIIIIII

Alain found it impossible to sleep, and he dared not move, for fear of waking Charlie. Fear was a part of him, like a pain that clutched at his bowels. He knew the feeling well; he had lived with it, night and day, during his missions in France. But then he had known how to adjust to it, even to master it. He owed this ability to the colonel who commanded his reconnaissance group at the beginning of the war. He had gone with him to inspect the sector occupied by the troops they were about to relieve.

"This antitank gun is badly placed," the colonel had observed.

Alain had jumped into the emplacement where the gun was set up, protected by an embankment of earth, just off a sharp bend in the road.

"What are you doing?" his chief had asked him.

"I was looking at what can be seen from this position. It doesn't seem bad to me. You can cover the road from it. The camouflage might be improved—"

"That's not what's wrong. Turn around. What do you see?"

Alain saw an open field, sloping gently upward.

"Suppose German tanks come," the colonel said. "Would you be happy in there? Now, I want you to find a spot for each of our guns—from which they can cover the road, obviously, but also from which the gun crew can withdraw without being shot down. And I want you to be sure the gun crews know the withdrawal route. If you do as I say, you'll have men on whom you can count. Remember that, my friend: The best antidote to fear is the certainty that you can get away from it if it becomes unbearable. For that matter, it's the same thing in civilian life. I had one hell of a fight with my wife's parents, who are very Catholic, the day I happened to mention to them that the divorce laws are the cement of households. Fifty per cent of husbands and wives tolerate marriage only because they know they can put an end to it."

Alain's withdrawal route, during his missions, had been the poison he had been given in England. He had had a tiny pocket sewn into the peak of the right lapel of his jackets and at the bottom of all his ties. He had practiced extracting a little wad of paper from these pockets, carrying it unobtrusively to his mouth, swallowing it. Once, in France, he replaced the wad of paper with a capsule of cyanide. He was certain of being able to kill himself if he should be captured.

258

He had been captured, all right—but in pajamas, while asleep in the upper berth of a railroad car. Four men had awakened him, each of them with a pistol in his hand. When his clothing was returned to him in prison, the poison had disappeared.

At his very first interrogation, he had realized that the underground network he directed had been completely infiltrated by the Gestapo. For months past, one of their men had been sleeping with his secretary. They had already learned everything they wanted to know.

His own fate had seemed certain. He would be shot.

From that moment on, he had endlessly rehearsed his role before the firing squad, just as a trapeze artist rehearses his act until he is certain of being able to perform without once ceasing to smile at the spectators. He knew by heart the words he would speak to his wife and parents if he could see them, and the letters he would leave for them if he could not. His final confession was also firm in his mind.

Having prepared himself to confront a death that refused to come, he found himself as nervous as a traveler who has packed his bags in haste, needled by the fear of not being ready on time, and then is forced to wait, in the gloom of a shuttered house, for a friend who is late in picking him up. As the days passed, the certainty of his execution was shaken, and the peace this certainty had brought him was troubled. Problems he had thought finally behind him rose up to confront him again. The future again held questions. It was still too soon to unpack the bags he had closed and locked. But he was already thinking of the clothing he had tossed into them so hastily and which now would be crushed and rumpled when he was forced to hang them again in the closets of life. Hope pressed down on his shoulders with all the weight of the anxiety with which it was mixed. Responsibilities from which he thought he had been released found a new life. The very meaning of his death could be disputed, since it was no longer certain. He discovered the virtue of action—the feeling of contentment it brings to the person accomplishing it.

Finally, the sentence of deportation had plunged Alain into the turbulent, dark, and icy waters of the camp of Neue-Breme, and then of Buchenwald.

Alain dreaded the difficult days that lay ahead. For a long time now, the dead bodies at the morning roll call had ceased to mean anything to him. They were akin to a spot on the living room wall, rendered invisible by long familiarity. Now, fear brought them back from limbo, and they became the image of what he might be tomorrow. The nauseous smoke vomited into the sky from the chimney of the crematorium again carried with it the stench of burning flesh.

45.

||||||||||||||||||||||||||||||||||||||||||||||||||||||||||||||||||||||||||||||||||||||||||||||||||||||

When Charlie returned to camp, his clothes were covered with a film of white dust. All that day his *kommando* had been digging emplacements for antiaircraft machine guns on the far side of the road bordering the factory. Two other *kommandos* were assigned to the same task, and the S.S. guards were directing the work themselves. Their impatience made it appear that they feared an imminent attack.

"Do you think that could mean something?" Charlie asked Alain.

"What are you thinking?"

"If Oscar has been captured, it might have occurred to the Germans that others had succeeded where he failed and that the secret of the factory is not as airtight as they had thought."

"You're letting your imagination run away with you. If Oscar was arrested, we would have known it long before any defense measures were taken here. You don't know the military mind. The mere fact that it might attract the attention of the Allies would certainly mean there would be weeks of discussions before the installation of antiaircraft batteries around the factory was actually undertaken."

"It would really be funny," Charlie said, "if the English already know what's being manufactured in the Mibau, and if the Germans know that they know. We would look pretty silly getting ourselves hanged for trying to send information the Allies already have."

"Are you sure it's machine guns the S.S. are installing?" Alain asked.

"Yes, ordinary machine guns, with a cylindrical radiator around the barrel. They brought some of them out, to estimate how big the emplacements should be. They want to be sure the gun crews are properly sheltered and have sufficient room to work."

"Well then, don't get so upset about it. It isn't serious. Bombers fly much too high to be reached by machine guns. If the Germans really wanted to protect the factory, they would be setting up other arms, and they wouldn't be placing them a couple of hundred yards from the target. Somewhere, some S.S. officer must have come across some ancient directive and decided to show how zealous he was."

Thursday, during the noon recess, an air raid drill was called at the Mibau. When the sirens sounded, the *kommandos* were

261

assembled and led into a little wood located between the camp and the factory.

The deportees made a holiday of the occasion, stretching out in the shade of the trees. The breeze filled the air with the scent of pine resin. Through the network of branches above their heads, the sky was blue and clear.

Lying on his stomach, propped up on his elbows, Alain tried to forget his fear by poking at a swarm of ants with a twig. Two battered galoshes containing a pair of meager ankles, covered with red and scaly flesh, planted themselves directly before his eyes. He lifted his head.

"It could be a damned sight better," Genteau said, as he squatted on the ground beside Alain.

"What could be a damned sight better?" Alain demanded.

"Our air raid shelter. We're separated from the factory only by that embankment."

Genteau nodded toward the slope of a man-made escarpment not far from where they were sitting.

"And that was built," he added, "for the railroad siding."

He paused, glanced back at Alain, and then murmured, "Did you include it in your drawings?"

"Of course."

"In that case, it will be included in the Allied objective, and since you certainly didn't report that we would be in this wood during an alert, we will not be spared."

"How on earth could I have known that we would be brought here?"

"You couldn't have," Genteau sighed. "I know that."

"On the other hand," Alain said, "I emphasized that the bombing should take place during the roll call hours, when there is no one in either the factory or the wood."

"Let's hope they'll follow your recommendations. But since I'm not certain of that, I went to see if there was possibility of getting a little further away. Unfortunately, there is a cordon of

262

Ukrainian S.S. guards less than two hundred yards from here. They have submachine guns in their hands, and they don't look as if they're there to amuse themselves. In spite of them, that's the direction in which we'll have to run if there is a raid."

"Do you think so? I would think that there is less danger at the foot of the embankment than anywhere else. Look here; the ground is soft and loose. Bombs will bury themselves in it, and if we're lucky enough not to receive a direct hit, there will be almost no danger. And all the more so because the trees will scatter the earth thrown up by the explosions and break its fall."

"Either that or the trees themselves will be uprooted and come down on our heads. I still think it would be better to get as far away from the factory as possible. The guards will take cover the minute the first bomb falls, and it should be possible to get through their line."

Genteau said nothing more, because they had both seen "Mickey Mouse" approaching. His clasped fingers held a blade of grass against his lips, drawing from it a plaintive little strain of music.

"Toss in the coins," he said when he had finished, holding out an imaginary cap.

He stretched out on the ground and added, in a tone of near-boredom, "The English radio has announced that the Allies are going to bomb the Mibau. It's too bad. What will become of us when there's no more factory?"

"Do you really think," Genteau demanded, "that they would notify the Germans in advance if they intended doing it?"

"They have issued warnings, sometimes, before dropping bombs in France. Some guys who came in just recently told me so."

"Well, even if they did," Genteau persisted, "no one here would know it."

"That's where you're wrong. I can assure you that there are people here who listen to the BBC."

"Do you know them?" Alain demanded.

"No, but the guy who told me about it knows them."

"He's just bragging," Genteau said slowly, "and you believe everything you hear. Think about it for a minute. How do you think a radio could have been brought into the camp? And how do you think anyone could hide it and use it without being seen?"

"Oh, I know it wouldn't be a simple matter," Mickey said stubbornly, "but I also know that there are people here who listen to the BBC."

Genteau had stretched out full length on the pine needles, his arms folded behind his head, his eyes closed. A little muscle in his temple was twitching to the rhythm of his heartbeat.

Alain knew that, during Dr. Ding's absences, Alstein sometimes listened to the radio in the laboratory. "Perhaps," he said, "some of the men who work in the offices, with the German civilians or the S.S., can use their radios from time to time. Aside from that, I can't think of anyone in the camp who could possibly hear a radio."

"Neither can I," Mickey confessed.

He plucked a fresh blade of grass, placed it against his lips, and walked off.

Genteau stood up and watched him go. Then he brushed off the pine needles that clung to his jacket, shrugged, and said, "It was bound to happen. In a little while the whole camp will know we're listening to the BBC. This is the third time in the past few days that someone has mentioned it."

"But it's obvious that Mickey doesn't really know anything," Alain said.

"He doesn't know anything precise, but others know; others who shouldn't know, and who talk too much. We're not going to be able to keep it up much longer. If there's an investigation, they won't have any trouble tracing the reports back to us."

Genteau began pacing back and forth, his hands in his pockets, his eyes fixed on the ground, as though he were looking for something.

264

"An indiscretion can't be called back. The best we can hope for is that the Germans won't take this seriously."

He swore briefly, and added, "I had almost forgotten that what we're doing is dangerous."

That night, Genteau came looking for Alain after roll call.

"I've considered the problem from every possible angle," he said. "What's done is done, and we can't do anything now but wait."

He went on to explain that he had considered spreading a series of confusing rumors, in the hope that the S.S. and the Gestapo would get wind of them and consider that this matter of listening to the BBC was no more than another farfetched story that did not merit an investigation. To be effective, however, the rumors would have to be sufficiently startling to insure their wide circulation. But it would also be necessary to avoid anything that might cause a break in the morale of the deportees, either now, because the news appeared too bad, or in the long run, because it raised false hopes by appearing too good. There was no way of resolving the contradiction, particularly since the operation, to be effective at all, would have to be continued for an indefinite length of time.

"Your problems will be solved before mine," Genteau sighed. "If you're still alive a week from now, you can consider that your message has arrived safely, and you will have nothing more to fear. But, as for me—"

Charlie returned to the block just before curfew and joined Alain immediately in their sleeping compartment. As he slipped beneath their shared cover, he murmured, in a voice numbed with fatigue and agony:

"I've just seen Geoffrin. Alstein was arrested this afternoon."

Alain raised to a half-sitting position and stared at his friend in the darkness.

"On what charge?"

"No one knows."

"Well, for God's sake, tell me the whole story."

"There's nothing to tell. Alstein was summoned to the gate of the camp. He didn't come back. It seems that he's in prison, and his name has been taken off the register of the block."

"And Ding, what does he say about it?"

"He wasn't there today."

"But Geoffrin certainly must have some idea."

"Yes. He thinks it's because of him that Alstein was arrested. Geoffrin is afraid the Gestapo has started an investigation, because of the rumors that have been circulating for the past few days."

"What rumors are you talking about?"

Alain was thinking of what Mickey had said that afternoon in the little wood.

"There are stories that the V-1s are being built at Dora and that they are also building huge aerial rockets there."

"Who is saying that?"

"The Germans, among themselves. That's why you didn't know about it, but there's a lot of talk about it in my *kommando*."

"That might explain Geoffrin's arrest, if he had been arrested; but it doesn't explain Alstein's."

"Yes, it does. This is Geoffrin's theory. The Gestapo starts an investigation into the leaks about what is being built at Dora. That brings them back to Geoffrin. It was Ding who insisted on his return to Buchenwald. They question him and ask for explanations of the letter and the telegram sent to the commandant of Dora. Don't forget that Ding knew nothing about what the telegram said. Alstein's insistence on having Geoffrin sent back seems suspicious—"

"And the Gestapo then arrests Alstein but leaves Geoffrin free," Alain interrupted him. "That doesn't make sense."

266

"Yes, it does make sense. Geoffrin isn't free. He's in this camp, just like you and me, available whenever they want him."

"And don't you think that if there had been an investigation, the first thing the Germans would have done would have been to arrest and interrogate Geoffrin?"

"Maybe, but that would be of no concern to Ding. He would have been very interested in Alstein's arrest, however, simply to rid himself of responsibility."

Alain turned over on his stomach, resting his head on his arms.

"There's nothing anyone can do for Alstein," Charlie murmured. "Or for Geoffrin. But he wanted me to be sure to tell you that if he's forced to admit that he did divulge information about Dora and to confess to whom he gave it, he would mention only the names of men who had died since he came back. There's no lack of choice there."

"That's exactly what I would do if I were to be asked someday where I learned the things I know. I'll tell Geoffrin that when I go to see him tomorrow."

"No, he prefers that we don't go to see him. Until we hear something to the contrary, he considers himself dangerous."

"Is he afraid?"

"Put yourself in his position. If Alstein's arrest is connected with his return from Dora, the least that can happen to him is to be sent back to Dora. And you remember the condition he was in when he came back from there."

"At the rate things are going," Alain murmured, "we stand a very good chance of seeing ourselves and our friends at the foot of the gallows. In the meantime, we might as well go to sleep."

He sighed, and then added, in a tone that was now little more than a whisper, "Tuesday, Wednesday, Thursday. Three days since Oscar left. The farther away from Weimar he gets, the less his chance of being recaptured."

"Do you really believe that?" Charlie asked.

Down deep in his heart Alain did not believe it. But he was

trying to convince himself of it, in the hope of breaking the grip of fear.

He thought of Alstein in the camp prison. Charlie was thinking of him, too.

"He was a nice guy," he said.

"Who?"

"Alstein."

Alain was dimly aware that Charlie was already speaking of him in the past tense.

Genteau was tortured by the thought of being accused of reporting the BBC news. If he were to be taken away, sabotage of the remote-control radios would stop. This was more important than maintaining the morale of the French deportees, and it should, he thought, have caused him to be more prudent. Physical fear was now coupled with the agony of having compromised his primary mission.

He decided to spread throughout the camp a rumor that the Pope had promulgated an encyclical concerning the concentration camps but that the BBC had simply announced it without revealing its contents.

This news gave rise to considerable discussion, based almost entirely on each individual's manner of thinking about the Pope and the Catholic Church; and this in itself went a long way toward neutralizing its impact. In any event, no one expected that the encyclical would have any immediate effect. Although everyone talked about it, there was little chance that it would impair the morale of the deportees, and it was so obviously false that it could distract the S.S. from any serious investigation of the rumors concerning men who listened to the English radio.

268

46.

||||||||||||||||||||||||||||||||||||||||||||||||||||||||||||||||||||||||||||||||||||||||||||||||||||||||

On Sunday morning, when he arrived at the square, Alain
saw that the gallows had been set up. There were just three
ropes. He and Charlie exchanged an agonized look. They both
expected to witness Alstein's hanging. But none of the condemned
men who were brought out, surrounded by S.S. guards, were as
tall as he. Alain breathed a sigh of relief. He resolved to pay close
attention to a scene in which, very shortly perhaps, he would be
playing a principal role. He wondered if it might be possible to
shorten the agony by leaping hard from the little bench and
substituting instantaneous rupture of the spinal column for slow
strangulation. He managed to exchange places with one of his
friends, so that he might see better.

As the guards were leading the first victim to the gallows, there
was a sudden commotion. A clamor of voices from the angle of
the square nearest the gallows swelled until it seemed to sweep
the entire camp. The running figure of a prisoner detached itself
from the confusion and was almost immediately hidden behind
the wall of the crematorium.

Some of the S.S. guards raced after him. The blocks did not
break formation, but the movement of the standing men resembled the waving of seaweed as the surf above carries it back
and forth. All of them, standing as straight as they could on
the wooden soles of their shoes, supporting themselves on the
shoulders of their neighbors, craning their necks around the heads
of the men in front, tried to see what was happening. A few

bursts of machine-gun fire broke the hubbub of thousands of voices, like the sound of a child's rattle. More S.S. guards streamed through the camp entrance and began running about in confusion. An officer waved his arm and shouted. Two stretchers were brought up. Alain could see the green uniforms on the inert bodies, and the handkerchief that covered one of the faces, as the S.S. carried them away. A detachment of S.S., with furiously barking dogs held in leash, ran by him and fanned out behind the crematorium. Near the gallows, the two other condemned men were still standing motionless, forgotten.

Alain attempted to review, in slow motion, the series of images his mind had registered too rapidly for comprehension. One of the three condemned men had killed an S.S. guard, cut up another, and then had fled. The S.S. were searching the camp with their dogs. He would be recaptured. It was a matter of minutes.

Nothing happened. Sixty thousand men had been assembled in the square since dawn, and now they simply waited. The sun climbed higher, and legs began to grow weak. The oldest and most feeble of the deportees sat down on the ground. The block chiefs and the *stubendienst* forced them to stand up again, and then finally gave up. The heat began to take its toll from the ranks of those who had remained standing. One by one they collapsed, and soon the ground was littered with their tangled bodies. Bladders overflowed. Trousers came down. The stench of defecation was added to the ever present stench of filth and carried across the field by a soft, damp breeze. From time to time, a group of S.S. guards scurried from the gate of the camp toward the barracks, or from the barracks toward the gate. Alain attempted to sleep, pulling his cap down over his eyes to shade them from the sun. His legs, imprisoned beneath the head and shoulders of another deportee, grew stiff. He was on the point of dozing off, when a few words suddenly detached themselves from the background of murmured conversations around him. Instantly, he was awake and listening.

270

"The factory is going to be bombed," a voice was saying.

"What makes you think that?" another voice demanded.

"The Germans are installing antiaircraft batteries."

"So what?"

"You'll find out."

"Why would the Allies bomb the Mibau?"

"Because they're manufacturing equipment for the V-1s there."

"You think so?"

"One of the guys who works there told me so, an engineer."

"But the English don't know it."

"That would surprise me. They're well informed."

"They can't be as well informed as you seem to think, or they wouldn't have waited until now to destroy the factory; not, at least, if it really is producing equipment for the V-1. They've been in use for six months now, and they haven't even tried to bomb the factory."

A third voice interrupted:

"It was because of the V-1s that I got arrested."

"How did that happen?"

"The chief of my Resistance group assigned me to investigate whether the Germans in my district—"

"What district?"

"The Pas de Calais. —if the Germans had started work on some equipment he described to me in detail. He called them launching ramps. I'm sure they were installations for the V-1s. I discovered three of them, and they were bombed as soon as my chief reported their position. But there were others. I would have found out exactly how many and where, if one of the guys who worked with me hadn't sold us all out."

"When were you captured?"

"April 10."

Alain sat up and looked around him, trying to locate the origin of the voices. When he had, he got up and walked toward them, moving cautiously through the maze of bodies on the ground.

271

He finally reached the deportee who had been arrested on April 10, and squatted down beside him.

"Do you really think the ramps you mentioned were intended for launching the V-1s?" he asked him.

The man turned his head and studied Alain curiously. "What else could they have been intended for?" he said.

His neighbor propped himself on an elbow. "Perhaps for rockets," he said. "It seems the Germans are building those too."

"Rockets?"

The surprise in Alain's voice was taken by the others to indicate disbelief.

"Yes, rockets."

"You mean the kind of rockets they use in fireworks?" someone asked.

"No, something like aerial torpedoes."

"Who told you that fairy tale?" Alain asked.

"A Frenchman from block 31."

"I have a feeling he was pulling your leg. Where would he get information like that?"

"He didn't have any information. He reached the conclusion that the Germans were building rockets after he learned what they were manufacturing in the Mibau. He explained to me how he had figured it out, but I didn't understand it very well."

"But," Alain said, "the Mibau's products could just as easily be intended for the V-1s, or even for something else, just as the launching ramps in the Pas de Calais were not necessarily built for the V-1s."

The deportee who had discovered the location of three of these ramps was stung to the quick, as Alain had hoped he would be. He was determined to think that his arrest was connected with the first use of the V-1. That was flattering to his vanity.

Alain took advantage of his indignation to get him to describe the installations he had located, but Alain learned nothing more except that the ramps were pointed in the direction of London. That, he thought, did not exclude the possibility that they might have been intended as bases for launching the A-4 rockets.

Finally, he asked if the details given by the chief of the man's Resistance group had indicated a weapon that would be launched like a rocket.

"He simply said that they were V-1s," the man answered.

Alain gave up all hope of extracting any reliable information from the author of so transparent a lie. He went back to his own place, bothered by the discovery that one of his comrades in the factory had made the same estimate as he himself had made of what the Mibau was producing, and had reached the same conclusion: that it was equipment for rockets. Alain was disturbed at the thought that, whoever this man might be, he was telling his story everywhere, instead of keeping it to himself; Alain also was dismayed because he still did not know whether or not the Allies were aware of the existence of the A-4 rockets.

At the foot of the square, near the barracks buildings, some of the deportees began to stand up. The murmur of their voices swelled to a steady hum. A group of S.S. guards, their dogs at their heels, came into the square from one of the streets of the camp. Two of them were dragging a limp, disjointed body at full length behind them. The head bobbed up and down, and blood dripped to the ground from the invisible face. The stomach and legs grated coarsely against the concrete walk. The letter R, in the red triangle on the right leg, could still be read. The loudspeakers blared an order, and the prisoners reformed in their blocks.

The S.S. dropped the Russian beneath the gallows like a discarded scarecrow, and the executioners were forced into a series of complicated maneuvers in order to bring the noose of one of the ropes low enough to pass it around his neck. He was beyond the point where he could be stood on his own feet. When he had been lifted by the rope, however, his knees and legs streaming blood, he found the strength to struggle for a moment before his body began slowly revolving, lifeless as a freshly skinned rabbit.

In spite of his determination to exorcise his fear and prepare himself for his own eventual ordeal, Alain did not have the courage to watch the other executions. The heat and the silence pressed down on the square, and the humming in his ears was one with the buzzing of the flies, drawn by the thousands to the excrement with which the ground was strewn. The barking of the loudspeakers informed him at last that the roll call was over. In the central street of the camp, he stepped aside to make way for prisoners too exhausted to walk, who were being carried by their friends.

The formation had lasted six hours. Back in his own block, he waited his turn at the faucet in the washroom, to hold his head beneath the trickle of water and ease the pain of thirst. It was too late to think of sleeping before distribution of the ration, so he went out again. The glare of sunlight, reflected in the crushed white stone of the walk, dizzied him. He took a few hesitant steps and then stopped. The sirens had begun to wail. He ran back into the building, his heart beating wildly, and forced his way to a window of the mess hall that looked out toward the square and, beyond that, to the factory. The strongest of the deportees, who had been out in the streets, were running back to their blocks. The *lagerschutz* were pushing the others into the nearest barracks. Alain saw Genteau and shouted to him to come into the building through a window in the sleeping quarters. As he went to join him there, Alain realized that he was trembling.

"Do you think it will be today?" Genteau asked him breathlessly as they stood side by side, searching the unbroken sky.

"I hope so," Alain said. "But it would mean that I've put in lots of effort for nothing."

"I hear planes," Genteau announced.

Alain did not move. Planes, Sunday, perfect visibility, no

274

wind. The factory was going to be demolished while it was empty. This was what he had wanted. But he had nothing to do with it.

"There they are."

The sound of voices and the scraping of galoshes drowned out the drone of the motors. Other deportees surrounded Genteau, craning their necks to see through the window. Alain turned around, and over their heads, very high, made out a formation of bombers, silvery white against the blue of the sky. The sun glittered harshly in the windows of their gun turrets. From right to left, they passed in slow and solemn procession, well beyond the Mibau. A second formation followed the first, nearer to the camp, perhaps directly above the factory. Smaller planes hovered on the flanks of this group. The powerful murmur of far-off motors could be clearly heard. And then there was a nearer roaring, swelling until the building and the air shook with it. Two shadows swept across the dazzling white of the street, thrown there by two pursuit planes with black crosses on their wings, flying very low.

When Alain looked up again toward the bombing planes, they had already passed the Mibau. He left the window and sat down on the edge of the lowest bunk. Genteau sat down beside him.

"It won't be today," Alain murmured.

"No."

The word reverberated in the sudden silence. A few heads turned toward Alain. He stood up quickly and walked off in the direction of the mess hall, followed by Genteau. He would have liked to be only disappointed, but he could not help feeling relief.

The all clear sounded, and the deportees immediately swarmed out into the streets.

Genteau and Alain sat on a bench in the deserted mess hall, their backs against the table, their legs stretched out before them. Charlie came into the mess hall and walked over to them. He threw his jacket on the table, wiped the sweat from his forehead with the sleeve of his shirt, and nonchalantly put one foot on the bench.

"Did you see that Russian this morning?" he asked. "Do you know why he was hanged?"

"No."

"You're going to get a laugh out of this. He was a butcher."

"What do you mean?" Genteau asked.

"He was a butcher in civilian life. He was arrested by the Germans for some black market deal, and his compatriots here had assigned to the crematorium *kommando*. But he found a way to take advantage of even that. He told everyone that he worked in the S.S. kitchens, and then he supplied them with meat he claimed to have stolen, in exchange for cigarettes. Obviously, it was meat from the stiffs."

After having swallowed his ration, Alain tried in vain to sleep. But his mind was too busy, the sleeping quarters too noisy. An idea he had never had before came to him quite suddenly, and he got up, put on his boots again, and walked over to the Small Camp.

After having questioned several of the Frenchmen there, he succeeded at last in finding someone who could point out Professor Verville.

"What do you want with him?" the man asked.

"I want to ask him if he knows what's happened to one of our mutual friends," Alain replied.

"It would surprise me if he could give you any information. The poor man is out of his mind."

Alain hesitated before addressing the old man seated on the ground before him. "Professor—" he began awkwardly.

276

"You may call me Master, my son," Verville said. "And, figuratively at least, you may kiss my ring."

"Master," Alain said, "I came here to ask you if you had any news of our friend Alstein."

"Alstein—our friend? Yours, perhaps, if you belong to the race of heathens. Mine, certainly not. He was an incarnation of the devil. But I conquered him. He no longer exists. Phttt—he was gone back to Hell. Don't bother me any further about him. I must meditate."

An old man who had been stretched on the ground not far away propped himself painfully on one elbow. As Alain walked by, he called to him.

"You want to know what's happened to Alstein?" he murmured. "Well, I'll tell you. He was arrested because of that poor old madman. The block chief had told us so many lies, to induce us to put down our names for a light-work *kommando,* that Verville, and some other Frenchman as senile as he, actually did volunteer for it. The day they were called, the Master's name wasn't on the list. But he went, just the same. The S.S. wouldn't have anything to do with him. His number had been struck off the list at the *Arbeitsstatistik.* He came back to the Small Camp, bellowing to everyone in sight that this was another trick Alstein had played on him, that he had been warning him for months against the light-work *kommandos* and had described them to him as extermination *kommandos.* The S.S. got wind of it and started an investigation. They summoned witnesses to the offices of the political police. Alstein was there, with handcuffs on his wrists. Would you like to talk to some of those who saw him there?"

"No," Alain replied. "What I would like to know is what became of him after that."

"I don't know. But don't you think that it's ironic?"

"What?"

"The fact that, in a camp that swarms with Germans who hate us, it should be the best friend the Frenchmen have who is lost;

277

and that he was lost because of one of us who takes himself for God Almighty."

On his way back to his own block, Alain stopped by the Institute of Hygiene and informed Geoffrin of what he had just learned.

Alstein was not hanged. He was transferred to a camp for Jewish deportees. At the time, this seemed little better than hanging. But a few weeks later, he managed to obtain a post in the camp administration which permitted him both to improve his own condition and to use what powers he had to help those who needed and deserved help.

47.

That night in the factory was torture for Alain. Lack of sleep had drawn his nerves taut, and fear now stretched them to the breaking point. On his return to camp the next morning, he fully expected to learn of Charlie's arrest and to be arrested himself. Reassured by the atmosphere of calm in the block, he devoured his bread ration and hurried to his sleeping compartment.

He did not wake until late in the afternoon. His galoshes were no longer where he had left them. He searched beneath all the neighboring bunks. He was forced at last to realize that they had been stolen. The lethargy of his animal sleep was still with him, and he felt nothing but a confused anger, directed more against himself than against the thief. He reproached himself for not having hidden the galoshes beneath his sleeping pallet and was both indignant and hurt by the betrayal of what he had come to think of as an honest society. He went down to the mess hall in his bare feet, wondering what to do.

Seated on the end of one of the tables, a deportee was thoughtfully stretching his legs, and at the ends of those legs Alain recognized his galoshes. There was no possibility of error. He walked across the room, and without speaking a word struck the man hard across the face with the flat of his hand. The man had had no time even to move to defend himself. His body rocked back and forth for an instant and then fell to the floor. He remained there, lying on his side with his knees drawn up against his stomach, shielding his face with his arms, not daring to stand up.

"My galoshes," Alain ordered.

The man twisted his head to look up at him, pushed himself to a sitting position, then hastily undid the straps and pushed the galoshes over to him.

Alain sat down on the bench and put them on, without saying another word.

The cold water in the washroom dissipated the fog of sleep and anger that still clouded his mind. Philippe had seen what happened and came over to speak to him.

"Why did you hit that guy?" he asked.

"You saw it; he had stolen my galoshes."

"That was no reason to try to kill him."

Alain was well aware of this, and the reminder served only to aggravate his ill temper.

"I know," he said angrily. "But it happened before I knew what I was doing. I've had enough!"

"Don't forget to bring a mess tin to the factory tonight," Philippe said, in an effort to change the subject.

"No, I won't," Alain groaned. "Why is it always the day of the week when the soup is its absolute worst that we're entitled to an additional ration?"

During the half-hour recess at midnight, the foremen supervised the distribution of the supplementary ration. Little half-cooked husks of rutabaga swam about in a cold and tasteless

279

liquid. Some of the deportees who received substantial packages from home claimed that they couldn't eat it, because it made them ill. Alain swallowed the rations of three of his comrades in addition to his own.

When Alain returned from the factory to his block, Charlie came up to him, smiling broadly, and said, "It's been twelve days since Oscar left. I'm beginning to breathe again."

"So am I," Alain replied, but his somber air belied his words.

"By this time, we can certainly believe that he arrived safely."

"Or that he was arrested empty-handed. He could very well have gotten rid of my papers before he even started out. In that case, let's hope he was careful about how he disposed of them. It would be the last straw if the Gestapo were to find them and arrest me for nothing."

"Don't worry, I'm sure he wouldn't have done that."

"You were worried about his escape yourself."

"That's not the same thing. I wasn't certain of his ability to get away; but from the moment he agreed to take your message, I've been sure that he would either deliver it safely or be captured while he still had it."

"Well, we'll see if your family mentions Oscar. I suppose he wouldn't have had the gall to go to see them if he had just thrown away the message."

That afternoon, Alain walked over to the Institute of Hygiene to say hello to Geoffrin. He found him in the company of a French doctor whom he had met once or twice before. He knew that he worked in the infirmary, but he was taken completely by surprise when he heard himself being asked if he wouldn't like a few days of rest.

"A few days of rest?" he repeated in bewilderment.

280

"Yes."

"But how would I get them?"

"Well, you could, for example, develop sciatica."

"Why sciatica?"

"In the first place," the doctor explained, "because I am in charge of patients with this kind of ailment, and in the second place because the diagnosis is based entirely on the patient's own statements."

"Then you really mean it—" Alain said incredulously.

His only visit to the infirmary had left him with a memory that had not made him eager to go back there in search of an excuse for avoiding work. Moreover, his job in the factory was not physically exhausting. He thanked the doctor and suggested that the favor he was offering him might be of greater benefit to some Frenchman whose health was actually in danger.

"Unfortunately," the doctor said, "that isn't possible. I have to be very careful. I can't hand out periods of rest to people who would promptly go out and tell all their friends about it."

Alain knew the truth of this all too well. "By the way," he asked, "does anyone have any news of old Verville?"

"The professor?" the doctor asked. "Did you know him?"

"I only saw him once. But a German who was a friend of ours—"

"Yes, I know that story. The professor died last week. He was at the end of his rope." The doctor sighed, and then said, "Well, do you want some rest or don't you?"

"Of course," Alain said. "With pleasure. That's something one doesn't refuse."

"On which side would you rather suffer," the doctor asked, adopting a jovial, bedside manner. "The left or the right?"

"Ah," Alain said skeptically, "so I will have to suffer!"

"No, you'll just have to pretend to be suffering."

The doctor then explained how he should walk in order to feign sciatica, and the exact spot—the only spot, he emphasized —where the physician's touch should cause him to cry out in pain.

281

"Come to the infirmary tomorrow night," he said, "without forgetting to limp, of course, and when they ask you what's wrong, say *'Ischias.'* That means sciatica in German."

"Ischias," Alain repeated.

That night, he obtained a slip authorizing him to report to the infirmary for the regular sick call the following day.

The doctor gave him ten days of rest. The S.S. doctor, who supervised his French subordinates from the far corner of the big room, did not even glance at the diagnosis. Alain was so delighted at having tricked him that he almost forgot to limp as he went out.

He spent most of Tuesday sleeping. Wednesday, he began to get bored. On Thursday, at about eleven o'clock in the morning, the sirens sounded an air raid alarm. Alain's blood became ice in his veins. His friends in the factory were scattered through the little wood. He would have liked to be able to join them immediately. He could not help thinking of himself as an officer whose troops had gone into action without him. But the lazy squadrons of bombers moved on, very high and very far away.

Alain went back to the factory the next day. In spite of his preference for night work, he was not displeased when he was told that, for the next week, he would be working on the day shift.

There was another alert that same night. The deportees who were working in the factory were kept locked up inside, under S.S. guard.

Alain learned of this the following morning. If the bombing had taken place that night, he thought, it would have been a slaughter. And now he regretted that he would be working during the day.

His thoughts seemed to have no focus. He slept badly. The heat in the sleeping quarters was intolerable and made even worse the normally suffocating odors of that vast pigsty. Hundreds of fleas swarmed constantly over his body. For a long time now he had been unaware of their bite, but the itching drove him almost mad.

"The whole thing is idiotic," he said to Charlie one night.

"What whole thing?"

"Having tried to send out information," he said at last. "Either it has been lost en route, or the Allies already knew it and weren't interested. And I'm inclined to think that the second theory is the right one. By now, everyone knows that we're producing equipment for aerial rockets, which the Germans don't seem to have used yet."

"Undoubtedly because their launching bases were bombed out before they could become operational," Charlie suggested.

Alain did not believe this. Since he had sent his message, the Germans had built two new workshops, in the northeast arc of the factory's perimeter. In these buildings, they were installing semicyclindrical cradles which could be intended only for assembling rocket hulls. And the S.S. was pushing the work with an impatience that indicated the importance they attached to these weapons.

"I'm sick at the thought that you've heard nothing from Oscar, and there's been no bombing," Alain said.

"Just wait. This is only the twelfth of July."

"I know. It was three weeks yesterday since Oscar left. What was the date of your last package from home?"

"It's been ten days since I received one. But there will certainly be another one soon."

On the fourteenth of July, the block chief summoned Charlie and gave him the package.

Every muscle of Alain's body seemed stretched to the breaking point.

"Alain! Come here."

Charlie's voice was triumphant. Alain hurried over to him. On the cover of a pasteboard box in the package, there was a name and a date: "Mercier, June 27."

"He got there fast," Charlie said.

"His name is Mercier—"

Alain was incapable of speaking another word. A hard ball obstructed his throat, tears flooded his eyes. He sniffled loudly, and then suddenly stood up and ran out of the building.

48.

|||||||||||||||||||||||||||||||||||||||||||||||||||||||||||||||||||||||||||||||||||||||||||||||||||||||||||||

Alain went back on the night shift on July 17. On the morning of the twentieth, as they were returning to camp from the factory, Philippe told him that the BBC had announced the capture of Caen by British forces. The Saint Lô bottleneck was being attacked by the Americans and would certainly be broken soon.

"It seems now," Philippe commented, "that the supplying of the bridgehead with men and matériel has been completed. So we were not sinning on the side of pessimism when we estimated that this first phase of the operation would require a month. It's been more than six weeks since the invasion, and the offensive itself is just beginning. If we figure that it will require approximately the same length of time for the Allies to reach the Rhine—"

Alain interrupted Philippe.

"It's probable," he said, "that the Germans used up their

284

best troops in the attempt to throw the Allies back into the sea. But they failed. Now things should begin to move rapidly. Perhaps we'll be liberated this year—particularly since it's not impossible that there might be an internal German collapse."

Genteau joined them after the ration distribution, and they walked through the almost deserted streets of the camp. Their hunger was momentarily stilled, but they were all conscious of the slight dizziness brought on by a sleepless night.

"Don't you think," Alain said, "that the Allies are being very slow in taking advantage of the information I sent them?"

"Don't worry about it," Genteau replied. "There hasn't been any time lost yet."

"Your sabotage is still effective?"

"Yes. Until now, there have been no radios delivered."

"But do you really think you can continue sabotaging production much longer, all by yourself?"

"Not by myself," Genteau corrected him. "Don't forget that there are nine of us in each control crew. But last night, I began the third round of the fight."

It was clear that he was in a mood to talk, and Alain was eager to listen.

"The story of the wire that vibrated because its length was inadequate had been carried just about as far as it would go," Genteau said. "We had to find something else to explain the fact that the percentage of defective sets is still abnormally high."

"And did you find it?"

"I think so."

Genteau explained that in the course of his conversations with the engineer, he had learned that the German electrical industry was suffering from a very serious shortage of high-quality insulators. That had given him an idea. He had said that the inferior performance of the radio receivers was probably due to inadequate insulation in certain of the circuits.

With great difficulty, the engineer had succeeded in obtaining some samples of dielectric and had used them, following Genteau's recommendations, to equip five sets.

"They were tested last night," Genteau said.

"And," Alain said delightedly, "of course, all five of them worked perfectly."

"All five of them," Genteau echoed. "But the best part of the whole thing is that the samples of insulating material we used come from France. By the time our engineer can notify his superiors in Berlin of my discovery and orders can be placed, Paris will be liberated and the source of the insulator will be dried up. Needless to say, no other material will be suitable. We'll see to that!"

The corners of Genteau's eyes wrinkled with pleasure.

"But certainly some of the other sets must have passed the tests," Alain said.

"About three hundred," Genteau admitted.

"Where are they?"

"They're still in the factory."

"We'll have to make sure they stay there until the bombing."

Alain spoke of the bombing as though it were a certainty.

"Unfortunately," Genteau observed, "that doesn't depend on us."

"What the hell are the English doing!" Alain exploded.

"Well," Genteau said calmly, "if we can believe the BBC, their aviation is not just sitting around. Don't forget that, for the moment, it's more important to attack the bridges and the railway lines, to prevent the Germans from bringing up reinforcements, than it is to bother with the Mibau."

"I would agree with you," Alain said, "if bombing the factory meant mobilizing a very large fleet of planes. But it would only require a few planes for a few hours, and the whole thing would be settled. It would be a profitable operation."

Philippe interrupted him.

286

"But the Allies would have to be very sure of that," he said.

"I explained all that to them!" Alain had accompanied his phrase with an irritated gesture of his fist, as if he were bringing it down on a table. He let his arm fall back against his side, and added wearily, "But it's true I'm not even certain that my message reached them."

49.

Shortly before noon on July twenty-fifth, there was another air raid alarm.

Seated at the foot of a tree in the little wood, his heart pounding against his ribs, Alain watched the sky and listened. The wind was rising, tumbling gray-black clouds across the horizon and whistling through the branches. There was a flash of lightning, followed by the rumble of thunder, and a few enormous, tepid drops of rain fell like pebbles, raising wisps of steam and scent from the mossy ground. A gust of wind swept through the wood, noisily tearing pine cones from the trees, and then the full fury of the storm burst. A gray mist clouded the air. Little rivulets of water formed and were promptly swallowed up in the dry carpeting of needles. The men stood up, clutching the collars of their jackets around their necks, and deserted the illusory shelter of the pines to gather beneath a few beech trees whose foliage, soon drenched, began to shed its burden on their already soaking garments. The eerie, yellowish gleam of the lightning lingered in the water-saturated air. Suddenly, it was very cold, and the deportees returned automatically to their winter habits, pressing close against one another in an effort to keep warm.

A fine, icy rain followed the storm; a rain that seemed as though it would never stop. The all-clear wailing of the siren seemed a reprieve from an ordeal.

In the factory, it was still warm, and Alain found himself thinking of the *kommandos* in the quarry and the fields.

The next day, the sky was clear and blue again. And the air raid alarm was sounded again, at approximately the same hour as the day before.

The drone of engines could be heard in the distance. Alain fell on his stomach on the damp earth, clenching his fists and burying his face between his outstretched arms. Then, suddenly, there was a nearby thunder of motors. Glancing up through the branches of the trees, Alain caught a glimpse of two pursuit planes, racing past just above the level of the trees. They had black crosses on their wings. He told himself that they were anticipating a formation of Allied bombers. So, it could not be far away. A French deportee lying beside him shook his head and said that the pursuit planes, judging from their altitude, were certainly not going out to attack the bombers. They had taken to the air because they were afraid of being destroyed on the ground.

Alain remembered then that, once before, two German fighter planes had flown over the camp very low. On that day, hundreds of bombers had passed overhead, in full view from the camp. But their passage had preceded that of the pursuit planes. Perhaps today the bombers had also gone by before the fighters, too far away to be seen. He rejected that idea immediately. The bombing *had* to take place today. That other time, the fighters were returning to their field. This morning, they were going in the opposite direction, they were fleeing from it. His hope revived. He was certain that, in a few seconds now, his

288

efforts would be rewarded, his agony at last be stilled. He waited, in a state of mind bordering on ecstasy, but nothing happened. At the end of half an hour or so, he heard the motors of the pursuit planes again. If they were returning to their base, it was because the bombers were gone. A moment later, the sirens confirmed this by wailing an end to the alert.

Every muscle in Alain's body ached with tension. He took his place in the column for the march back to the factory, moving stiffly, his head bowed, as though he were carrying a heavy weight.

That night, Charlie received a card from his family. In carefully guarded terms, it mentioned Oscar's visit and gave assurance that he had successfully completed his mission. When Charlie relayed this news, Alain simply nodded and thanked him.

"Is that all you can think of to say?" Charlie demanded in astonishment.

"We knew it already."

"We knew that Oscar had arrived safely, but we didn't know if—"

Alain interrupted. "It was obvious that he wouldn't have gone to see your parents just to tell them that he had swallowed the message you gave him," he said. "But something must have gone wrong. The Allied bombers promenade through the skies around here as if they were at home. What remains of the German pursuit squadrons prudently vanishes during the raids. You're not going to tell me that, if the RAF wanted to destroy the Mibau, they would have any trouble doing it. But there we are, they don't want to, and I involved you in an enormous risk for nothing. I hope you will forgive me."

He paused for a moment, and then murmured, "I'm glad you have good news from your family."

"Look," Charlie said unhappily, "it's still only the twenty-sixth of July."

"I know. It will be a month tomorrow since Oscar arrived in Paris."

When the air raid alarm sounded again the next day, Alain went out to the little wood with no feeling of emotion at all. He kicked away some pine cones, spread his jacket on the ground, stretched out on it, and went to sleep. The first passage of the pursuit planes awakened him only for an instant. When they came back, he knew that the alert was about to end.

After this, there was an alarm almost every day. The sirens no longer caused an outburst of fear. They formed a part of the routine, and when a day passed without their now-familiar wailing, the deportees had a feeling of having been deprived of their siesta in the little wood.

Those few of Alain's friends who knew of the message concerning the Mibau avoided mentioning, in front of him, their disappointment that the factory was apparently being ignored.

One day, when Philippe made some allusion to it, Alain noticed the frown that Genteau directed at him.

"Don't worry," Alain said. "The wound has healed. It doesn't hurt me any longer. It's odd, but I even derive a certain pleasure from thinking of it occasionlly. Was it because my information didn't get through? Was it because it did get through but wasn't taken seriously? Or was it because the Allies estimated that the destruction of the Mibau wasn't worth the risk of killing thousands of deportees? I don't know. All I do know is that they've done nothing. And they were apparently right, because the Germans are not using the rockets. Perhaps the English have ways of preventing their use which they preferred to bombing the factory. But it would have been idiotic if I had caused some of my friends to be hanged for nothing."

"You wouldn't have known that it wasn't worthwhile," Philippe said, smiling.

"Yes, I would have," he said, "because their hanging and mine would have meant the failure of our endeavor. We escaped that, and now I can console myself with the thought that we succeeded in doing something that was very difficult and very dangerous. Obviously, I would have preferred it to be something that was also useful. But looking at it objectively and from another viewpoint, I can't help but be relieved that the prisoners here who might have been victims of the bombing have been spared."

50.

The attempt to assassinate Hitler on July 20, 1944, had failed. Repression swept Germany like a flood, carrying off in rivers of hatred anyone who fell victim to the settlement of some ancient, sordid grudge. The Nazi executioners were willing to kill one another off, in their frantic efforts to refloat the sinking ship of the regime.

Day after day, convoys of German prisoners began arriving at the camp.* One night, a column came in during the roll call, surrounded by S.S. guards and dogs. As soon as it had passed through the gate, it veered off to the left and was brought to a halt directly in front of the assembled deportees. The men in each of the rows of five were chained to one another with handcuffs. They had come from Weimar on foot. Their faces

* Their numbers went from 66,609 at the end of July, 1944, to 82,391 at the end of the following month, and reached 84,505 in September, a figure which was only exceeded in February, 1945, when 86,232 Germans were imprisoned.

were stained with the dust of the road, and the furrows ploughed by sweat through this layer of dust revealed traces of the violence of their interrogations. They stared mutely at the hideous mass of which they were soon to be a part, and their eyes were wide with terror.

In the first row, standing out like a parrot in the midst of a flock of crows, was the tall, gray-green silhouette of a man in uniform. His black cavalry boots had once been brilliantly polished, and the collar of his tunic was stiffly braided with gold. The remnants of a red armband, with its black swastika set in a white circle, still clung to his arm.

"Hitler is sending us his generals now," Mickey remarked. "All we needed to complete the menagerie was that fine-feathered bird."

"He isn't a general," his neighbor observed.

"He is a *Gauleiter*," another voice stated.

"A *Gauleiter?*"

"Yes, a kind of regional governor."

"In that case," Mickey said firmly, "it's even worse than a general."

"Don't worry, before another hour has passed his feathers will be plucked and you won't be able to distinguish him from any of the others."

The S.S. duty officer, his mouth twisted into a scornful sneer, walked down the line, studying the new arrivals. The *Gauleiter* automatically sketched a Hitler salute, but the handcuffs that bound his arm to his neighbor's prevented him from completing the gesture. He began to talk, shaking his head like a horse attempting to shift the bit in its mouth. The S.S. officer, a small, slender man, had halted in front of him and thrust his hands into his pockets.

Almost imperceptibly, the ranks of the column drew closer together. The attention of the prisoners and of their guards was caught and held by the spectacle taking place. Had it been a performance in a circus, they could not have been more anxious

292

to know who would ultimately triumph—the great wild beast or the wiry little trainer. Some of them set down the suitcases and packages that dangled awkwardly from their manacled hands and craned their necks toward the two figures at the center of the arena.

The officer suddenly abandoned the little swaying movement of his body with which he had accompanied the *Gauleiter's* speech, withdrew his hands from his pockets, and stood rigidly erect. His lips began to move for the first time. The deportees, too far away to hear his words, followed the scene as though it were the climax of a silent film. When he had finished whatever it was he was saying, the officer took a little step backward and, very calmly, spat in the face of the *Gauleiter*. For an instant, the man stood motionless with shock, and then he hurled himself at the sneering figure in front of him. Held back by the handcuffs on his wrists, he stumbled, dragging his neighbors down with him as he fell. The S.S. officer, completely unperturbed, took his revolver from its holster and lowered the muzzle toward the man struggling at his feet. But then he seemed to change his mind and contented himself with spitting again before he turned and walked away.

The alignment of the entire column had been broken. The S.S. guards attempted to reform it by smashing the butts of their rifles against the heads and bodies of the chained prisoners, and succeeded only in increasing the disorder. More men fell. The dogs hurled themselves at the men like a hunting pack at the final kill. Their furious barking degenerated into a kind of muffled growling when they sank their teeth into the tangle of arms and legs.

The officer shouted something from the far end of the line. The dogs were dragged away, their jaws dripping blood. The handcuffs were removed, and the prisoners were allowed to gather up their baggage.

A *kapo* summoned by the loudspeakers took charge of the reformed column and led it off to the disinfection chambers.

293

As he passed, he launched a vicious kick at the *Gauleiter* and brandished his bludgeon.

The next morning the internees in the Small Camp looked on in astonishment as the death cart passed them on its daily journey to the crematorium. In the midst of the pile of fleshless corpses lay a husky, athletic body, covered with cuts and bruises, the face unrecognizable behind its mask of clotted blood. It was the *Gauleiter*. Hated by the S.S. for having betrayed their prophet and by the Communists for having served him, he had been tortured and put to death during the night, by Poles uprooted from their homeland and brought here by his order.

51.

On August 23, during the final call to attention of the evening roll call, the loudspeakers summoned some of the deportees to report to the gate of the camp. Alain listened absentmindedly as the numbers were read off, successively, in German, Russian, and French.

Then, suddenly, his mind focused on the words of the invisible speaker. He had just recognized Genteau's number. Through the rows of men in the blocks nearest him, he caught a glimpse of another member of the control group for the remote-control radio receivers, walking toward the camp entrance.

Genteau made a slight detour, so that he could pass by Alain's block. He was walking stiffly and with an unnatural jerky swing to his arms. Philippe, who was standing at the edge of the formation, whistled softly. Genteau swerved in his direction, and without turning his head, murmured something as he passed.

"What did he tell you?" Alain demanded as soon as he could reach Philippe in the street after the roll call.

"'Every member of the control crew. Good-bye.'"

"That's what I was afraid of," Alain breathed. "They've had it."

He and Philippe paced silently up and down in front of the building of block 26. The men of the control crews had been caught. They would be hanged. The evidence was too clear to require any commentary, and the bonds of fraternity that linked Philippe and Alain with Genteau were too strong to need expression.

The summer night had begun to fall when Charlie came up to them, running.

"Is it true?" he asked.

"Is what true?"

"That the men in the control crew were listening to the BBC and that they've been arrested."

"Who told you that?" Philippe demanded.

"Some guy in block 31. I don't know him."

"The son of a bitch," Alain mumured, between clenched teeth, as if he were talking to himself.

"What?"

"Nothing."

He stopped his pacing and stared hard at Charlie.

"Listen to me," he said. "It's true, the men in the control crews were listening to the BBC, and they were probably caught. But only an absolute jackass would go around shouting it from the rooftops. If they have any chance whatever of getting out of it, the only possible way we can help them is by keeping our mouths shut. Agreed? Then go back and find that character in block 31, take him by the back of the neck, and explain the facts of life to him. And tell him to instruct anyone else who knows about it to keep his big mouth shut. But only those who already know about it."

When Charlie had left, Alain turned to Philippe and said quietly, "If only the factory had been blown to bits, this would never have happened."

He had been on the point of saying something more, but he stopped suddenly, seized Philippe's arm, and dragged him toward the door.

"Paul— Paul!"

Genteau had appeared.

"What happened?" Alain demanded breathlessly.

"You look like a new man," Philippe said, surveying Genteau in astonishment.

At roll call, Genteau's hair had been a shaggy, irregular mat and he had had a two weeks' growth of beard, but now he was freshly shaven and his hair had been clipped close to his skull. He explained that he and his comrades in the control crews had been taken to the offices of the political section, just outside the camp on the Avenue of Triumph. Everyone knew what that meant—hanging or, at best, prison. However, instead of being handcuffed together and herded off for interrogation, they had been turned over to a barber.

"Then," Genteau continued, "an S.S. guard told us to take off our jackets and shirts, and one after another, we put on a thing made up of a collar, a white shirtfront, and a tie, all of it sewn into the front half of a jacket. We put our arms in the sleeves of this thing, and then it was laced up in the back, as if it were an apron."

"Carnival photographers used to use things like that," Philippe said. "You could have your picture taken in all sorts of fancy dress uniforms."

"Did they give you a wig for that bald spot?" Alain said jokingly.

"No," Genteau replied. "But they did take our photographs."

"Why?"

"That, they didn't tell us."

296

"How did they photograph you? Full face and profile?"

"Full face only. What do you think of it?"

After considering the matter for a moment, Alain said that he could think of only one possibility: the zeal of the members of the control crews was going to be rewarded. They were going to be made into free workers and sent to work elsewhere. The Germans were now preparing their identity cards.

"That would be too good to be true," Genteau said, but his tone of voice made it apparent that he had already considered this possibility.

"However," he went on, "it's also possible that they're preparing our anthropometric file before handing us over to the Gestapo."

"No," Alain said. "You are going to be freed. So, farewell to the BBC news. But what a relief. It may flatter your vanity to know that you gave us quite a scare."

"Shall we celebrate his return?" Philippe asked. He brought from his pocket half of a crumpled cigarette, lit it carefully, and they passed it around, inhaling voluptuously.

The next day was a Thursday—the twenty-fourth of August. The tar paper roofing of the factory soaked up the rays of the sun, and the various workshops were like a succession of steam rooms.

Drenched with sweat, Alain had difficulty fighting off sleep and concentrating on his little iron boxes.

"I hope the alert will come soon and that it will last a long time," his neighbor at the bench murmured.

"So do I," Alain replied. "It will do us good to get some air."

"Look," the neighbor said a moment later. "Someone is calling you."

Half-concealed behind the door to the toilets, Philippe was making frantic gestures in Alain's direction. His presence, at ten o'clock in the morning, in a building of the factory that was not

297

his own, was unusual, to say the least. Only news of great importance and urgency would have warranted running the risks involved in such a visit. His back was to the light, and Alain could not make out the expression on his face until he was standing beside him. It was an expression of delirious happiness.

Philippe seized his hand and led him into a corner of the washroom.

"Paris has been liberated," he said. "The BBC has just announced it. I couldn't wait any longer before coming to tell you."

Alain was struck dumb, his mouth hanging open, his arms dangling helplessly at his sides. Paris had been liberated! Those four words echoed and reechoed through his head.

He recovered somewhat and managed to stammer, "Was there much destruction?"

"I don't know," Philippe replied. "Genteau slipped out of his shop for just a second, to bring me the news. Oh, yes! He did say that it was General Leclerc's army that entered Paris first, and that we must be sure not to spread the information before the Germans have announced it themselves. It would be dangerous."

An S.S. guard appeared in the doorway.

As he ran for the exit, Philippe murmured to Alain, "Come and find us during the recess. We'll eat the provisions we've been saving to celebrate this—some pâté and canned peas."

As they were separated, Alain guessed at, rather than heard him add the words "cigar" and "cognac" as he zigzagged adroitly to escape the jet of the fire hose the S.S. guard was aiming directly at him.

The air raid alarm sounded, and when they went out into the little wood each of the men automatically sought out the spot that had now become his own. This had become so deeply rooted a habit that Alain did not even think of going to look for Genteau. Today, however, instead of lying down at the foot of his tree and going to sleep, he remained seated with his back propped against the trunk. The two German pursuit planes passed over his head.

Nothing has changed here, Alain thought, and yet, on this day, France's soul and image have been restored to her.

In the distance, a low, steady humming sound could be heard, swelling gradually as it drew closer. There was an unwonted stir of movement among the deportees. They left the shelter of the trees and moved out into the clearings to watch the sky.

"Look at the planes," someone shouted. "Over there!"

Dozens of heads turned to follow the direction of his pointing finger, a spot in the sky to the northwest of the camp.

In the gap between two large branches, Alain could make out a series of tiny whitish dots against the blue. His eyes followed their movement absently, as he thought about his parents in liberated Paris, of the Champs Élysées cleansed of its strollers in green uniforms, of the Arc de Triomphe, no longer standing witness to the parades of an occupying army.

The planes were approaching, but he scarcely noticed them. It had been too long a time since he had buried his hope.

They were still quite far away when a swarm of white butterflies appeared suddenly beneath their wings, seeming to fall very slowly, like a cloud of feathers cradled by the wind.

Pamphlets, Alain thought. They are announcing the news to all Germany.

All the deportees were talking at once.

Then there was a sudden silence, when the white butterflies began to fall faster, plunging in a solid mass, along parallel trajectories.

"They're bombing the camp!" someone screamed.

The little groups of deportees scattered in every direction. The air was filled with a hissing sound, swiftly transformed into a shrill whistle, which, in turn, became a deafening roar, like that of a train hurtling by at full speed. Then a gentle crackling, as slight as the snapping of dry twigs, formed a prelude to silence.

Alain had thrown himself flat on his stomach, protecting his head beneath the cushion he had formed from his jacket. His left cheek was pressed hard against the earth; the earth emitted a vast hiccup and he saw the embankment of the railroad siding, not two hundred yards from where he lay, rise silently into the air and burst. A yellow geyser sprang up from it, climbing higher and higher. It remained suspended for an instant, and then it slowly collapsed. A few stones fell on Alain's quivering body. He stood up, shook himself, and realized that he had not been hurt.

All around him, other deportees were getting to their feet and running, seeking some safer place. None of them seemed to have been hit.

A second formation of planes, and then a third, dropped their bombs from the same point in the sky. From the direction of the camp, there were scattered bursts of firing from automatic weapons.

It's inconceivable, Alain thought, that the bombardiers could have found their target from such an altitude. He wondered where all the bombs he had seen glittering in the sunlight had fallen. He had the impression that, except for the one that had exploded near him, they were scattered over some distant area. According to the English radio, Genteau had told him, the night bombing missions were carried out by the R.A.F., and the day missions by the U. S. Army Air Corps. Alain recalled the destruction of the center of Nantes by the bombs of American aviators whose objective was the port. It flashed through his mind that, if those who had just passed had not been more precise, there had really been no point in his suffering such torment to provide them with exact information. The link between the bombing and the information he had furnished had formed in his mind before he was fully conscious of it.

The earth around him had suddenly begun to sprout fountains of fire, spitting out showers of dazzling sparks, whistling and snapping as they laced the air, and leaving behind them a dense white smoke. The spot where he had been lying a moment before burst into flame. Fiery, white hot plants were flowering everywhere. For a fleeting instant, Alain had the insane idea that the Germans had circled Buchenwald with a protective belt of buried instruments that could be instantly ignited, in case of revolt or attack. Unless he fled at once, he would be asphyxiated or roasted alive. He began running in the direction of the embankment. The barbed-wire fence surrounding the railroad siding had not been broken by the explosion of the bomb, and he was forced to turn back. The flame-strewn smoke was now so thick that it was almost impossible to see or to breathe. He started out toward the road that led back to the factory and the camp. Directly in front of him, a ball of fire danced through the air for a moment, then fell back to earth and began to race through the pine needles like some demonic insect. Running as fast as he could, Alain zigzagged among the trees, sometimes hurtling against them in the almost total obscurity, sometimes forced to turn aside by a new outburst of fire. He stumbled across an outstretched body, arms and legs grotesquely twisted in an agony of dying. The back was pierced by what looked like an incandescent torch, planted deep between the shoulder bones. The dead face was Mickey's. At the same instant a little section of ordinary tubing spiraled to the ground at his feet and vomited flames. It was only then that Alain realized that the little wood had been sprayed with incendiary bombs. Suffocating, coughing, his eyes streaming tears from the smoke, he forced himself to go on. He should, he thought, have reached the edge of the wood long before this. He must have lost his way. He stumbled over a corpse, and then over another, and slammed hard against a running silhouette.

"Alain!"

"Philippe!"

Their hands automatically reached out and joined together.

301

"This way," Philippe said. "We can't be far from the road now. Hurry, this whole place is going up in flames in a minute."

They came to an area where the fireballs were more scattered and the smoke less dense, and finally emerged from the wood at the end of the Avenue of Triumph, far from the spot where they had thought they would be.

Fear still clutched at their bowels. They crossed the road, never looking up from the ground, and went on walking, aimlessly, halting only when they came to the rim of a crater. The shattered bodies of two S.S. men lay like broken dolls beside their upended machine gun.

They stood there silently for a moment, then looked around them for the first time and discovered the factory. The whole length of the Mibau was silently burning. The flames reached straight up into the sky, lazily, certain of their victory. Nothing was left of the walls but a few isolated wooden stumps.

On the other side of the road, the tower that had dominated the S.S. garages had disappeared. The buildings had collapsed, laying bare the filth concealed behind their arrogant stucco façades.

"Magnificent!" Philippe said.

For a long time they did not move but just stood at the edge of the crater, above the bodies of the two S.S., hand in hand, like schoolboys. They were all alone.

A crackling sound somewhere off to their right caused them to turn their heads at last.

On this side, too, everything was in flames. The statue of the Germanic eagle they had been forced to salute every morning and every night was now a pile of broken stones. On either side of it, the massive walls of the S.S. guardhouse and post office were still intact, but flames spiraled upward from their shattered roofs. The explosion of the bombs had blocked their heavy oaken doors. S.S. troops in the guardhouse and some women in the post office clung frantically to the bars of the

302

iron grillwork that covered the windows, screaming and dancing a frenzied jig, their eyes rolling in terror as they watched the tongues of fire and the wisps of smoke reach out toward the walls.

Almost automatically, Alain and Philippe started off again, walking straight ahead. They passed through a camp whose existence they had never suspected and of which nothing now remained. Their feet were repeatedly caught in the remains of a barbed-wire fence. The rubble of buildings was littered with corpses of well-dressed civilians.

When they reached the far side of this camp, they came out on an unpaved road. They could hear the wail of sirens signaling the all clear. A group of very young S.S. troops emerged from an underground shelter, one by one. Many of them were walking stiffly, their legs spread wide, and the trousers of their uniforms and the heels of their boots bore witness to their panic.

Alain and Philippe, purely by reflex, paused and stood at attention as they passed, but the S.S. did not even seem to see them. They moved like sleepwalkers in the direction of their barracks, where several bombs had made gaping holes.

Substituting the fear of men, to which they were accustomed, for that of elemental forces, the sight of this frightened little herd had a calming effect on Philippe and Alain. They began to take stock of what had happened and where they were. Behind them, the Mibau was fast being consumed. The glow of the dying fire was reflected in a cloud of smoke suspended above the furnace of tangled ruins. A few stubborn flames still flared up here and there, spouting trains of sparks that fell back to earth like the spent rockets of some far-off fireworks display. Beyond the broken barracks that bordered the Avenue of Triumph, the camp seemed intact. They were in an area that was unknown to them and had been completely devastated by the bombs. Alain realized that he had lost his jacket and that the sole of one of his galoshes had been split open along its entire length. His

303

legs were trembling. He sat down on the ground and forced himself to breathe regularly. Philippe sat down beside him. They were abruptly conscious of their solitude and of the silence around them.

In muted tones, as though he were afraid of disturbing the silence, Alain said, "Where are the others?"

"I don't know. I think the little wood was already empty when I picked myself up, after the third group of planes."

In the whole course of their flight together, they had seen nothing but dead bodies and destruction.

"What should we do?" Philippe murmured. "Try to get away?"

Alain smiled. "You haven't seen yourself," he said. "In the state you're in, you wouldn't go far. There's only one thing to do: go back to the camp."

"In that case," Philippe said, "there's no hurry."

Alain stretched out on his back, raised his right foot, and flexed the joint of his ankle. With every movement, the sole of the canvas boot, secured only by the stitching along one side, flapped back and forth like a swinging door. He ripped it off.

"We might perhaps," he said, "try to find what we would need in the way of equipment, and then try to get away."

He stood up, sighed, and added, "Come on, let's go and see what we can find."

Only then did he realize that he was exhausted. He put his right hand on Philippe's shoulder so that he would not have to place his full weight on his foot, and they started back down the unpaved road.

When they had walked a hundred yards or so, Philippe asked him where they were going.

"To tell you the truth, I'm not quite sure," Alain replied.

After a moment of thought, he said, "We would have to shave and find some clothing. Let's go see if there's anything left of the building the foremen lived in. I think I can find it."

He veered off to the right, across a stretch of barren ground where the bombs had dug shallow craters in the rocky soil.

304

"As a matter of fact," he said suddenly, "where did the foremen go during the alarms?"

Philippe did not answer him. He was staring fixedly at the scene before them. The pits and ridges of the earth were littered with the bodies of deportees and S.S. guards. The recumbent figure of one deportee moved its head and tried to signal them with its hand. None of the others moved. They would have to find some kind of stretcher, Alain thought.

"Let's see if we can find a plank or something to carry him," he murmured.

They turned away from the vision of this charnel house and hurried off.

Sometime before reaching the ruins of the camp they had passed through earlier, they found a single boot. Alain turned it over cautiously. It was empty. Although it was for a left foot, he used it to replace the one of his own from which the sole was missing. As he was pulling it on, he noticed a wooden door, blown off its hinges by the concussion of the bombs.

The wounded man was an elderly Russian. His face was deeply lined, and the stubble of beard on his cheeks and chin was white. His pale blue eyes followed their every movement, and his lips moved silently. He held his hands pressed against his abdomen.

Alain and Philippe lifted him carefully from the ground and set him down on the door. His features were twisted with pain. The spot where his body had been lying was covered with a little pool of blood.

"He's done for," Philippe murmured to Alain. "A wound like that, in the guts—"

Apparently, the Russian was the only survivor of his *kommando* and of the S.S. who guarded it.

"Perhaps there were others who got away," Alain said.

Philippe walked in front. At every step the door jarred against his buttocks. He started off in the direction of the Avenue of Triumph.

To the right of the path they were following, the body of an S.S. guard lay on its stomach, with arms outflung, as if he had been crucified there. Another guard was sitting up beside the body. One of his legs was a bleeding mass of flesh. When Philippe and Alain passed, he called out to them.

"What is he saying?" Alain asked.

"Comrades," Philippe replied.

"Ha! Comrades! Since when and for how long?"

They walked on without stopping.

Along the walls of the S.S. guardhouse, still-glowing embers had reached the level of the windowsills. The oak door and the iron grills were still in place.

The Avenue of Triumph resembled an anthill crushed beneath a careless foot. It was covered with the debris of the barracks that once had bordered it. A swarm of S.S. guards and deportees was coming and going in every direction.

Philippe tried to find a path through the jungle of wooden beams and planks. Each time he stumbled, the Russian groaned feebly. He had unbuttoned his pants and was holding his intestines in place with his hands. On either side of his body, blood ran down and dripped from the door.

The gate to the camp was open. Deportees were moving through it freely in either direction, and the roll call square was thronged.

What seemed to be hundreds of wounded were lying on the ground on either side of the street that led to the infirmary. More were arriving every minute, supported on the shoulders of comrades, carried in their arms, or propped on makeshift crutches and litters. A *kapo* leaned over the Russian and muttered something they did not understand.

"We'll put him down here," Philippe said.

The Russian's eyes were closed. One of his bloody hands had slipped away from his waist and was hanging down from his body. The poor old man is dead, Alain thought, and suddenly the body lying on the door seemed very heavy. Outside the crematorium, where they set down their burden, the corpses were piling up. As fast as they arrived, a work detail of deportees arranged the bodies in rows, one on top of another, like stacks of firewood.

A Frenchman who had just unloaded a body he had been carrying over his shoulders urged Alain and Philippe to go back to the quarry with him. There were others there, he said, many others. They were both completely exhausted, but they promised him that they would go as soon as they had had a drink of water.

There was no water in the washrooms of the building they went into, and the toilets gave off a putrid odor. The water mains that supplied the camp had been destroyed.

Alain abruptly remembered having noticed, in the pile of corpses outside the crematorium, one face in which the forehead had been pierced by a little round hole, very clean and neat.

"Where is Genteau?" he cried.

The man he had seen had been killed by a bullet, and Genteau had told him that, when the bombing came, he would try to get through the line of the Ukrainian S.S. guards. And they were armed with rifles.

"We must go and look for him," he said to Philippe.

They left the camp again and started back down the Avenue of Triumph. Everywhere they looked, there was an endless vista of wounded and dead being carried in by those who could still walk.

The earth in the little wood resembled a vast leopard skin. The brown carpet of dried pine needles was patterned with black spots from the fires set by the incendiary bombs. In some parts of the wood, these burned-out areas were only three or four feet apart. Philippe and Alain wondered how they had managed to get out of this rain of fire. They found no wounded or dead until they came to the bodies of six Ukrainian S.S. guards, lying in a

307

row, side by side. They were on their stomachs, with their rifles still held against their cheeks in firing position, but they seemed to be asleep. Flies were buzzing around their heads, and Philippe noticed that their cloth uniform caps were stained with blood.

"What do we do now?" he asked.

"Have you given up the idea of escape?"

Philippe shook his head, but said only that, first, they must find Genteau.

The wounded were being laid out in rows in one corner of the square. Those who were obviously dying were loaded into handcarts and pushed or pulled to the crematorium, where the pile of corpses was now almost four feet high and steadily lengthening.

None of the other deportees in his block had seen Genteau. Alain and Philippe decided to wait for him here. Overcome by the heat and fatigue, they sat down on a bench in the mess hall, resting their arms and heads on the table, and instantly fell asleep.

Genteau awakened them, tugging insistently at their shoulders.

"I've been looking for you," he said.

"And we were looking for you. Where were you?"

"I was waiting for you in your block."

Alain and Philippe simply stared at each other dumbly.

"I was afraid you had been killed by the Ukrainian S.S.," Alain said.

"That could have happened," Genteau replied. "After the first set of bombs fell, everyone began running toward the edge of the wood farthest from the factory. The Ukrainians were lying down, trying to take cover, just as I told you they would. But the bastards opened fire on us just the same. Most of the others in the group I was in were too terrified to notice it and went on running. Several of them were shot down. As for me, I threw myself on the ground, and a minute or two later I witnessed a surprising spectacle. That big S.S. noncom, the lame one who commanded the guard in the factory, came up behind the Ukrainians and took his revolver from its holster. I thought he was going to start firing at us, too. But he didn't. He went up to the first of those bastards in their black uniforms, leaned over him, and perfectly calmly, put a bullet in his brain. By that time, I could already hear the whistling of the second string of bombs. But it didn't bother him in the least. He went on to the next man and killed him, and then went right down the line, doing the same thing, until the barrel of his revolver was empty. He was standing there, emptying the shells from the barrel, when a fragment of an exploding bomb cut him in two. I got through the breech he had opened in the line of the Ukrainians without any difficulty, and came back here just as fast as I could."

Philippe gave him an account of their flight from the wood, their vague notions of escape, of finding the Russian and carrying him back to camp, and of the wounded S.S. who had addressed them as comrades.

As he listened to Philippe's words, Alain became aware that, ever since the beginning of the bombing, he had been living in a state akin to drunkenness which was beginning to fade.

He heard Genteau saying something about the buildings of the political section. Apparently, they had been completely destroyed by bombs, and he seemed to derive a lively satisfaction from the fact.

"That will teach the sons of bitches," he said, "to take photographs of me in such a ridiculous getup."

They were all silent for a moment, and then Genteau added, "It seems that the factory has been completely destroyed, too. It was high time. The radio sets were due to be sent out next week."

Philippe described the rain of incendiaries that had fallen and the sea of flames he and Alain had watched from the road. Then he made a joking remark to Genteau about the feast they had planned, to celebrate the liberation of Paris.

"Is it true," Alain asked, "that you had put aside some cigars and cognac?"

"Yes, Genteau received the cigars, and the cognac was sent to me—some very old cognac my parents had the good sense to put in a bottle labeled 'cough syrup.'" Genteau was keeping them in the drawer of his workbench in the factory.

"It's too bad we didn't take them with us to the wood. But we were so accustomed to hearing the alarm and then having nothing happen, that we never thought of it."

Alain would have given anything in the world for a glass of cognac or any form of alcohol that might have prolonged his drunkenness and retarded the moment when he would be forced to admit to himself that he was responsible for the hundreds of dead whose bodies were accumulating in the square, and for the wounded who would soon join them beneath the black smoke that would pour from the chimney of the crematorium for days and nights to come.

52.

With its water supply cut off, the camp was like a rudderless ship drifting aimlessly on a stinking ocean. There were no more roll calls, the old work *kommandos* were disbanded, there was no regular distribution of rations.

The Goethe tree had been blown to splinters by the only explosive bomb that had dropped in the camp, thereby justifying the prediction that its death would announce the collapse of the German Reich. The deportees fought over its scattered bits of wood as if they were relics of the True Cross.

Another bomb had pierced the vaulted roof of the underground shelter where the wives and children of the S.S. officers had taken refuge. There were no survivors.

The commander of the camp gathered all the deportees in the roll call square to congratulate them on their behavior during the bombing. A few of them had been found two days later, fifteen kilometers from Buchenwald, wandering in the countryside like madmen. They were not punished.

Alain learned from Geoffrin, who in turn had learned from Dr. Ding, that about five hundred deportees had been killed.* Among these was Breitscheid, the leader of the German Social Democratic party, who had been quartered in a private building, with his wife.

Thaelmann, the leader of the German Communist party, imprisoned by the Nazis for eleven years, was brought secretly to Buchenwald and strangled in the courtyard of the crematorium.†

Throughout the day, the loudspeakers in all the blocks began to relay the broadcasts of the German radio. These announced that Breitscheid and Thaelmann had been killed by Allied bombs during the raid on the Buchenwald camp which had taken place on *August 28*.

They also announced that Paris had been declared an open city and that German troops were going to evacuate it.

The deportees who had worked in the Mibau were formed into new *kommandos* to clean up the ruins of the factory.

In the chaos of the shops, a friend of Genteau's succeeded in locating his workbench. He sifted cautiously through the ashes and charred bits of wood and uncovered a photograph of his

---

* The report of Schiedlausky, the S.S. doctor of the camp, dated August 27, 1944, gives the following figures:
Internees: killed: 315; seriously wounded: 525; slightly wounded: 900; missing: undetermined.
S.S.: killed: 80; wounded: 238; missing: 65.
† Thaelmann has been arrested in 1933 after the Reichstag fire.

311

wife, holding their baby in her arms. It seemed intact, but when he picked it up it crumbled into dust.

Guided by the stench, Alain discovered the corpse of the factory foreman beneath a collapsed section of the wall.

53.

|||||||||||||||||||||||||||||||||||||||||||||||||||||||||||||||||||||||||||||||||||||||||||||||||||||||||||||

One evening, Alain could stand it no longer.

"Do you think I did the right thing?" he asked Genteau.

"You mean that you doubt it? Is that why you haven't been the same, since the bombing?"

"I'm afraid I'm going mad—all these dead—"

"A lot of them S.S."

"Do you think that that will be any consolation to the parents of the deportees who were killed, to their wives, to their orphans?"

"Try to think of all the potential victims of the rockets. You saved their lives."

The German radio announced the first employment of the V-2 rockets.

"You see," Alain said, "I accomplished nothing."*

Changing his tactics, Genteau attempted to convince Alain that

---

* The remote-control radio receivers originally intended to equip the V-2s had not been delivered. They were replaced by integrator-accelerometers, which did not provide them with the same degree of precision. (Forty-three hundred V-2s were launched in the direction of London; only 1,150 reached their objective.) Morever, the majority of the rockets constructed at Dora could never be used, for lack of electrical equipment.

the bombing might have been planned and carried out on the basis of information other than that which Alain had supplied.

This thought calmed Alain somewhat.

Geoffrin invited Alain to come to the Institute of Hygiene the following Sunday afternoon. A Norwegian deportee was going to bring a Swedish newspaper his wife had managed to insert as wrapping paper in a package she had sent. There was an article in it about the bombing of the Mibau, written by the newspaper's correspondent in London.

According to the newspaper, a completely reliable source had provided the Allies with information of the greatest importance concerning the manufacture of electrical and electronic equipment for a remote-controlled aerial rocket that the Germans had not yet employed, but whose existence was well known to Allied intelligence services.*

This equipment was being manufactured by German political internees and deportees of all nationalities, in a factory adjoining the Buchenwald concentration camp, located not far from Weimar. Allied reconnaissance had previously taken the factory for an extension of this camp. Repeated aerial reconnaissance, after receipt of this information, had revealed that the factory was occupied most of the day and night, seven days a week. In spite of the losses that were, therefore, certain to occur among the deportees if the factory were to be bombed, the Allied High Command had resolved to go ahead with it, because of the exceptional military importance of the objective. But in an attempt to reduce these losses to a minimum, and especially to

---

* On July 13, 1944, an experimental A-4 rocket, with the normal explosive charge replaced with ballast, was launched from Peenemünde and fell, almost intact, in a swamp near Kalmar, Sweden. The Swedish authorities had it brought to Stockholm and agreed to turn it over to the British, who brought it to England by plane at the beginning of the month of August. Examination of it revealed the accuracy of the information transmitted by Alain. Until that time, the Allied intelligence services had not taken this information seriously.

313

spare the camp itself, the High Command had requested all the Allied aerial forces to delegate their best crews for this mission. These crews had been assigned to a special, temporary formation. As a preliminary to the operation itself, the buildings of the camp, the factory, and their neighboring installations had been sketched, in their actual size, in whitewash on a Scottish moor. For several weeks, the aircraft crews had studied and flown over this mock-up, determining the best disposition for the formations of planes and the direction from which the objective should be attacked so that the camp would not be hit.

The raid had been carried out on Thursday, August 24, with complete success. Incendiary bombs had completed the work of the explosive bombs.

The factory and some neighboring installations of military interest had been entirely destroyed, without causing destruction to the camp.

All the aircraft had returned to their bases.

The article concluded with a panegyric to the Intelligence Service and the Allied Air Forces.

All during the reading of the translation, Alain sat motionless, his teeth tightly clenched. It was all he could do to keep from crying out.

From crying out with joy.

And also, from crying out with pain, because five hundred of his comrades were dead and others would still die. Others who would have lived if they could have continued to work in the factory. But there was no factory. There was only the quarry, and the construction *kommandos*.

There was also Dora.

The slip of paper from the *Arbeitsstatistik* that sent him to Dora seemed to Alain a form of release.

314

GLOSSARY

Arbeitsstatistik (literally, labor statistics): The *Arbeitsstatistik* was one of the principal internal bureaus of the camp. Its function involved the assignment of German internees and foreign deportees to the various work units of the camp (the *kommandos*), and the establishment of lists of personnel to be transferred from the central camp at Buchenwald to other central camps, such as Dachau or Auschwitz, or to a secondary camp administered by Buchenwald. There were more than fifty such secondary camps.

Aufstehen: German command, meaning: "On your feet; get in there."

Block chief: Each block formed an administrative unit of the camp and was placed under the authority of an S.S. *Blockführer,* to whom a German Communist internee, the block chief (*Blockälteste:* literally, dean of the block), was responsible for the complement of prisoners, maintenance of discipline, distribution of rations and clothing, and other matters of administration of the block.

Nomination to the post of block chief was made by the S.S. command of the camp, from names submitted by the *Lagerälteste* (see below).

The block chief himself selected his assistants, the *stubendienst* (literally, building wardens), from among the internees under his jurisdiction.

Effektenkammer (literally, clothing warehouse): The building of the camp in which were stored the effects and personal belongings taken from internees and deportees on arrival, as well as the articles of clothing provided for their wear in the camp.

These latter articles came from:

—shipments made by the S.S. (primarily of striped pants and jackets, made of synthetic materials),

—the wardrobes of the deportees themselves (generally, those who were already dead).

Kapo (from the Italian *il capo*, the head, the chief): Each *kommando* —each basic work unit—was placed under the jurisdiction of a *kapo*, generally a German Communist internee, who was responsible to the S.S. command for his unit's work and discipline.

Kommando: A basic work unit made up of a variable number of internees and deportees, assigned to a specific job and placed under the authority of a *kapo*.

Lagerälteste (literally, dean of the camp): The *Lagerälteste* was responsible for the administration of the camp to the S.S. command, which, in turn, was headed by a *Lagerführer*. The *Lagerälteste* had several assistants.

In his book, *Der S.S. Staat*, Eugen Kogon wrote this about the *Lagerälteste:*

"On the prisoners' side, the internal organization of the camp, based on the principal of administration of the camp by the internees themselves, was pieced together from the cogwheels listed below:

"At the top was the dean of the camp—the *Lagerälteste*—who was selected by the S.S. In many camps, it was possible for the internees to propose, and win nomination for the man who was to exercise these important functions. At first, there was only one *Lagerälteste;* but subsequently, because of the extension of the camps, there were as many as three. Their respective titles were LA 1, LA 2 and LA 3. The primary function of the *Lagerälteste* was to represent the camp in all matters concerning the S.S. com-

316

mand, which communicated all of its orders through him. It was an extremely delicate and dangerous task. Acceptance of it required both courage and a high sense of responsibility. An unworthy occupant of this post signified catastrophe for the entire camp.

"At first, the S.S. sought to appoint as *Lagerälteste* a man who was devoted to its own aims and could be utilized against the camp. It is characteristic that the first of this type, at Buchenwald, was a professional criminal named Hubert Richter who, before being interned in a camp in Northwest Germany, had belonged to the infamous "SA 33 Murder Battalion" in Berlin. He was a blind instrument of the S.S., and was himself a man of unbelievable brutality. The phrase which reads: 'We are no longer in a country of poets and thinkers, but in a country of judges and executioners'* could certainly be applied to him—he acted in more than complete compliance with it. At the end of 1937, following an investigation of the escape of two 'green' internees, which he had hushed up because of his fear of its consequences, he was relieved of his functions as *Lagerälteste,* beaten and tossed into prison, and later released. About six months later, he was again named *Lagerälteste* for the 'blacks' who had been brought to the camp in the intervening period, and continued in his course of indescribable tyranny. In the spring of 1939, following a story of corruption in the S.S., he was again thrown into prison, where the S.S. executed him in a horrible manner. His successor, Paul Henning, was also a criminal and little different from Richter. After having been relieved of his post, he was himself sent to Mauthausen. The first 'political' *Lagerälteste* was Paul Mohr, of Wiesbaden, who certainly attempted to modify the customs installed in the camp by these criminals, but had too many links with the criminals to impose his own views with sufficient energy. He, too, was later executed by the S.S., in connection with another story of corruption. After him, the post of *Lagerälteste* at Buchenwald always remained—contrary to what happened in many other camps—in the hands of political internees.

Lagerschutz (literally, camp security): A kind of auxiliary police corps recruited among the internees and deportees and functioning primarily within the limits of the camp.

Meister (literally, master): The name by which the German foremen in the factory were addressed.

* In the original German, this phrase is a play on words: Dichter, R'
Denker, and Henker—respectively; poet, judge, thinker, and exe'

Mützen . . . ab (literally, hats off): Command to the deportees to salute by taking off their hats. The following command, to replace their hats, is *Mützen . . . auf*.

S.S.: Abbreviation of *Schutzstaffel,* which means, guard troop. It was first formed on November 9, 1925, the second anniversary of the abortive Munich *putsch*. The mission of the S.S., initially, was to assure the personal protection of Hitler. Himmler, its commander in chief after 1934, gradually transformed it into the Black Order; a kind of order of knighthood, corrupted by Nazi doctrine, in which he saw, in his own words: ". . . the superior class which will dominate the Europe of tomorrow."

Stubendienst: Assistant to a block chief.

"Blueprint of Buchenwald"